Student Resource Book

ELEMENTS OF LITERATURE

THIRD COURSE

Vocabulary Activity Worksheets
and
Workbook

HOLT, RINEHART AND WINSTON, INC.

AUSTIN   NEW YORK   SAN DIEGO   CHICAGO   TORONTO   MONTREAL

Printed in the United States of America

ISBN 0-03-031607-3

901234567 063 987654321

Vocabulary Activity Worksheets

ELEMENTS OF LITERATURE

THIRD COURSE

USING THE VOCABULARY ACTIVITY WORKSHEETS

This resource book contains 64 Vocabulary Activity Worksheets in blackline master form. The Worksheets accompany ELEMENTS OF LITERATURE, Third Course, and can be used in conjunction with the literature program or as a stand-alone vocabulary supplement.

The Worksheets offer a practical, flexible, and effective way to enhance one's command of useful English words. They are both a supplement and an alternative to the developmental vocabulary feature, "Analyzing Language and Vocabulary," that follows selections in ELEMENTS OF LITERATURE. Whereas the exercises in the anthology emphasize language concepts, the Worksheets target a limited number of specific words from each literature selection. Words taught in the Worksheets are also covered in the "Developing Vocabulary" sections of the Test Book selection tests.

WHAT IS TAUGHT ABOUT EACH WORD

For each of the six to ten words introduced in a Worksheet, complete information is given, as a school dictionary might provide. Below is a sample entry with each of the elements labeled.

VOCABULARY WORD   PART OF SPEECH

PRONUNCIATION   DEFINITION

vexation (vek•sā′shən) *n.* annoyance.
► This word is derived from a Latin word meaning "to shake." ■ Mosquitoes can be

POINT OF INTEREST   EXAMPLE SENTENCE

a great <u>vexation</u> on a camping trip.
Page 219

PAGE REFERENCE TO THE LITERATURE SELECTION

ORIGINAL SENTENCE: _____

The symbols used to indicate **pronunciation** follow the system used in *Webster's New World Dictionary* and in the Glossary of the literature anthology and are explained in the accompanying key (page vii). This Guide to Pronunciation can be consulted frequently as Worksheets are used.

The abbreviations used to signify **parts of speech** also follow the system used in *Webster's New World Dictionary* and in the Glossary of the literature anthology. The part of speech of a vocabulary word reflects its use in the literary selection and is demonstrated by the example sentence.

The **definition** explains the meaning of the word as it is used in the literary selection, and the **example sentence** provides a clear illustration of the word in context. The location of the word in the selection is indicated by the boldfaced **page reference**.

The words "**Original Sentence**" followed by two blank lines provide for immediate application of new knowledge. The resulting original sentence may also serve as a memory jogger for those who turn to the worksheet at a later date for a quick review.

A special feature of each entry is the "**point of interest**," which provides additional information about the word or its usage. Here are some examples of the types of information contained in this feature:

Etymology—The origin and history of a word are explained, particularly when they give insight into the word's meaning or may help one to remember the word.

Example: ► *Mukluk* is the Eskimo name for a large seal, and because Eskimos make boots from sealskin, *mukluk* came to refer to boots.

Structural Analysis—Prefixes, suffixes, and roots are pointed out and defined, especially when they may serve as keys to other words that may occur throughout the anthology and in independent reading.

Example: ▶ The Latin root of *tumult*, also found in *tumor*, means "to swell."

Words Frequently Confused—When the entry word is similar in appearance or sound to another word, the difference is explained.

Example: ▶ Do not confuse this word [broach] with the word *brooch*, which refers to a type of jewelry that attaches with a pin.

Multiple Meanings—Other uses, including more familiar ones, are given to help clarify the specific meaning being taught.

Example: ▶ Another meaning of *acute* [defined here as "severe; intense"] is "keen or shrewd," as in "an acute mind."

Related Words—When the entry word and other useful words are derived from the same source, the relationship is explained.

Example: ▶ This word [crypt] shares a common Greek ancestor with the English word *cryptic*, which means "having a hidden meaning."

Precise Usage—Fine distinctions between synonyms and shadings of connotation are explained.

Example: ▶ *Skirmish* differs from *battle* in that a skirmish is lighter and shorter, and involves fewer soldiers.

Points of interest may also include additional and noteworthy information about the entry word, hints for remembering meanings, pointers on pronunciation, and other enrichment material.

Following a comprehensive introduction to the words, provided by the "Developing Vocabulary" section of the Worksheets, knowledge is tested and applied in the "Practice Tests." The format of these exercises varies, running the gamut from multiple choice, true-false, and sentence completion to matching, word analogies, and word searches.

GUIDE TO PRONUNCIATION

Knowing how to pronounce a new word that you encounter in your reading is helpful in two ways. First, if you know how the word is pronounced, you may realize that you already know its meaning, even though it looked unfamiliar at first glance. Second, if you know how to pronounce a new word, you are more likely to begin to use the word in your own speech.

To show you how words in the Vocabulary Activity Worksheets are pronounced, each entry word is respelled using symbols as well as letters of the alphabet. Here is a sample entry, as an example of the way the pronunciation is given:

PRONUNCIATION

canopy (kan′ə•pē) *n.* a covering, often over a bed, doorway, or airplane cockpit. ▶ This word is derived from a Greek word meaning "gnat," and originally meant a couch with curtains to keep out insects. ■ Judy stood under the canopy of the huge doorway, trying to avoid the rain. **Page 380**

ORIGINAL SENTENCE: _____

_____

KEY TO PRONUNCIATION

Because the English language is made up of at least 43 different sounds but only 26 letters, some letters have more than one sound. Thus, symbols must be used to indicate which sound a letter represents. The chart below lists the symbols used in the Worksheets, along with sample words in which each sound appears:

PRONUNCIATION KEY

Symbol	Sample Words	Symbol	Sample Words
a	mad, patch, fat	ou	out, crowd, plow
ā	date, fade, ape	u	up, cut, color
ä	cart, heart, cot	ʉ	urn, fur, deter
e	ten, bet, get	g	get, go, big
ē	even, easy, feet	j	job, gem, edge
i	is, festive, tip	y	yet, yard, onion
ī	side, buy, try	ch	chin, arch, catcher
ō	go, bone, know	sh	she, dash, cushion
ô	horn, all, law	th	thin, truth, nothing
o͞o	tool, ooze, crew	*th*	then, father, lathe
oo	look, pull, moor	zh	azure, leisure, pleasure
oi	coin, point, toy	ŋ	ring, anger, ink

TWO SPECIAL SYMBOLS

The schwa (ə) is used for the neutral vowel sound that often occurs in the unstressed syllables of words with two or more syllables. It can be spelled with any of the vowels, depending on the word: banana, agent, sanity, collect, focus.

The apostrophe (′) is used in syllables that have no noticeable vowel sound in them, as in apple (ap′l). Some people, however, pronounce the schwa sound in place of the missing vowel (ap′əl).

SYLLABLE DIVISION AND STRESS

A center dot (•) or an accent mark (′ or ′) in the respelling indicates how the word is divided into parts when it is spoken. Almost always this division is the same when a word must be hyphenated at the end of a line. But in some cases, the division is different. For example, *vision* is divided between the *i* and the *s* at the end of a line in writing (vi-sion). Yet, it is between the *s* and the *i* when speaking (vizh′ən).

In most words not all syllables are pronounced with the same amount of stress, or loudness. In the Worksheets, three relative degrees of stress are shown in the pronunciations:
1) Strongest stress is indicated by a heavy accent mark (′) at the end of the syllable.
2) Medium stress is indicated by a lighter accent mark (′) at the end of the syllable.
3) Weak stress is shown by no mark at all.
For example: the stresses in *constellation* would be shown thus: (kän′stə•lā′shən).

PRACTICE A

Directions: In the blank, write the word for each pronunciation shown. (*6 points each*)

  1. mezh′ər

  2. deth

  3. in•joi′

  4. biz′nis

  5. kood

  6. ʉr′jənt

  7. trī′əl

  8. mōn

  9. plät

  10. di•lā′

  11. gôŋ

  12. brē*th*

1. _____

2. _____

3. _____

4. _____

5. _____

6. _____

7. _____

8. _____

9. _____

10. _____

11. _____

12. _____

PRACTICE B

Directions: In the blank, write the word for each pronunciation shown. Then, over each syllable, write the number **1**, **2**, or **3** to indicate the amount of stress the syllable is given (**1** = strong, **2** = medium, **3** = weak). (*7 points each*)

  1. bag′pīp′

  2. səg•jest′

  3. nach′ər•əl

  4. kan′sə•lā′shən

1. _____

2. _____

3. _____

4. _____

TABLE OF CONTENTS

VOCABULARY ACTIVITY WORKSHEETS

POISON   Roald Dahl   (Textbook page 6)

DEVELOPING VOCABULARY

Directions: Read carefully the explanation of each word. Then write a sentence of your own using that word. Include in your sentence clues to the meaning of the word.

malaria (mə•ler′ē•ə) *n.* a disease, carried by mosquitoes, causing chills and fever. ▶ Once people thought this disease was caused by poisonous air, and so they based its name on two Italian words, *mala,* meaning "bad," and *aria,* meaning "air." ■ On our trip to Central America, we took medicine to prevent malaria.   **Page 6**

ORIGINAL SENTENCE: _____

_____

sarcasm (sär′kaz″m) *n.* the use of cutting remarks to hurt or criticize. ▶ An earlier form of this word meant "tearing flesh, the way dogs or wolves attack." ■ Randy's sarcasm is sometimes funny, but often it makes me feel sorry for the person he is criticizing.   **Page 11**

ORIGINAL SENTENCE: _____

_____

serum (sir′əm) *n.* a medicine used as an antitoxin (against poison or disease). ▶ This word also refers to the thin, watery part of blood. ■ The explorers carried rattlesnake serum in their first-aid kit.   **Page 9**

ORIGINAL SENTENCE: _____

_____

intravenously (in′trə•vē′nəs•lē) *adv.* placed directly into a vein. ▶ The prefix of this word, *intra-,* means "within" or "inside." The root word *venous* refers to veins. ■ When Liza was in the hospital, she had to receive medicine intravenously.   **Page 9**

ORIGINAL SENTENCE: _____

_____

to administer (əd•min′ə•stər) *v.* to give or apply. ▶ This word can also mean "to manage or direct," as in "to administer a government agency." ■ Dr. Lowe told the nurse to administer the medication every 12 hours.   **Page 9**

ORIGINAL SENTENCE: _____

_____

chloroform (klôr′ə•fôrm′) *n.* a liquid medicine used as an anesthetic (preventing pain or bringing on sleep). ▶ When used as a verb, this word means "to kill by administering chloroform." ■ Chloroform was one of the first drugs used to put patients to sleep for surgery.   **Page 10**

ORIGINAL SENTENCE: _____

_____

tourniquet (toor'nə•kit) *n.* a rubber or cloth device used to stop bleeding or raise veins for an injection. ▶ Since this word comes from French, some people pronounce it toor'nə•kā'. ■ Before taking a blood sample, Dr. Sullivan tied a <u>tourniquet</u> above my elbow.   **Page 9**

ORIGINAL SENTENCE: _____

_____

to discern (di•surn') *v.* to detect something with the senses. ▶ The prefix *dis-* means "apart." ■ We were barely able to <u>discern</u> the shape of a house through the fog.   **Page 10**

ORIGINAL SENTENCE: _____

_____

oppressive (ə•pres'iv) *adj.* weighing heavily on the mind; distressing. ▶ The root of this word, *-press-*, means "to press against." ■ The students complained that the workload had become <u>oppressive</u>.   **Page 11**

ORIGINAL SENTENCE: _____

_____

scalpel (skal'pəl) *n.* a knife used by surgeons. ▶ *Scalpel* is based on a Latin word meaning "to cut." ■ Holding the scalpel in his hand, Dr. Chan prepared to begin the operation.   **Page 11**

ORIGINAL SENTENCE: _____

_____

PRACTICE TEST

Directions: Fill in the blank with the vocabulary word that best fits the meaning of the sentence. *(10 points each)*

malaria	serum	to administer	tourniquet	oppressive
sarcasm	intravenously	chloroform	to discern	scalpel

1. You may need to apply a _____ in order to stop the bleeding.

2. _____ is often used by people who do not know how to criticize others in a helpful way.

3. Before stitching a cut, most doctors need _____ an anesthetic.

4. The surgeon used a(n) _____ to make a crescent-shaped cut.

5. Fluids are administered _____ if a patient is too sick to swallow.

6. Standing on the porch, I was able _____ the smell of chicken.

7. When high temperatures are combined with high humidity, the weather can become extremely _____.

8. Ether and _____ were used to put patients to sleep for surgery.

9. As soon as he saw the fever, the doctor diagnosed _____.

10. The scientists worked for years to develop a(n) _____ to protect against the bite of a brown spider.

THE ADVENTURE OF THE SPECKLED BAND
Arthur Conan Doyle   (Textbook page 14)

DEVELOPING VOCABULARY

Directions: Read carefully the explanation of each word. Then write a sentence of your own using that word. Include in your sentence clues to the meaning of the word.

metropolis (mə•träp′′l•is) *n.* a large city. ► The root word *polis* means "city," and was borrowed from Greek. ▪ Although

Albany is the capital city of New York State, it is certainly not the metropolis that New York City is.   **Page 14**

ORIGINAL SENTENCE: _____

_____

deductions (di•duk′shənz) *n. pl.* logical conclusions. ► *Deduction* can also refer to the process of reducing or subtracting.

▪ After reviewing the evidence, the detectives arrived at the deduction that the death was accidental, not murder.   **Page 14**

ORIGINAL SENTENCE: _____

_____

premature (prē′mə•toor′) *adj.* taking place before the proper time. ► The prefix *pre-* means "before." ▪ The baby's birth was

premature, so he was placed in a newborn intensive care unit for a few weeks. **Page 15**

ORIGINAL SENTENCE: _____

_____

dense (dens) *adj.* thick; packed together. ► *Dense* also can mean "slow to

understand." ▪ Dense traffic caused many people to be delayed.   **Page 16**

ORIGINAL SENTENCE: _____

_____

tiara (tē•er′ə) *n.* a jeweled headdress for a woman. ► A tiara is similar to a crown, but is usually smaller and simpler. ▪ After her

death, the duchess's diamond tiara was sold for over $100,000.   **Page 16**

ORIGINAL SENTENCE: _____

_____

manifold (man′ə•fōld′) *adj.* many and varied. ► *Manifold* usually is used with a plural noun. ▪ The manifold duties of a

police officer make the job appealing to a person who likes stimulation and change. **Page 16**

ORIGINAL SENTENCE: _____

_____

pauper (pô'pər) *n.* a poor person. ▶ This word, in exactly the same form, means the same in Latin. ■ "I'm afraid if I lose my job," said Mr. Cravens, "that I will soon become a pauper." **Page 16**

ORIGINAL SENTENCE: _____

_____

morose (mə•rōs') *adj.* gloomy; sullen. ▶ *Morose* is used to refer to people's moods, not to the appearance of things. ■ Everyone enjoyed the party except Tony, who sat in morose silence at the end of the couch and spoke to no one. **Page 16**

ORIGINAL SENTENCE: _____

_____

hubbub (hub'ub') *n.* noise; uproar. ▶ Hubbub is created by the sound of many voices, while noise is any loud or disturbing sound. ■ We could hardly hear the speaker over the hubbub of the audience. **Page 18**

ORIGINAL SENTENCE: _____

_____

blanched (blancht) *adj.* a form of *to blanch*, meaning "to make white" or "to bleach." ▶ This word, from the Old French word for white (*blanc*), can also mean "scalded." ■ Carl's face was blanched with fear. **Page 18**

ORIGINAL SENTENCE: _____

_____

PRACTICE TEST

Directions: Circle the letter of the best meaning for each word. *(10 points each)*

1. dense: **a.** heavy **b.** deep **c.** tightly packed **d.** sad

2. premature: **a.** weak **b.** sick **c.** wrong **d.** early

3. blanched: **a.** hot **b.** white **c.** stiff **d.** stale

4. hubbub: **a.** center **b.** noise **c.** activity **d.** circle

5. metropolis: **a.** large city **b.** quaint village **c.** Greek landscape **d.** group of people

6. tiara: **a.** gem **b.** crown **c.** dress with long train **d.** glove

7. deductions: **a.** logical conclusions **b.** products of multiplication **c.** prayers **d.** examinations

8. pauper: **a.** wall covering **b.** stupid person **c.** poor person **d.** invalid

9. morose: **a.** gloomy **b.** happy **c.** tightly packed **d.** tiny

10. manifold: **a.** occurring too soon **b.** worn on the head **c.** scattered around **d.** many and varied

VOCABULARY ACTIVITY WORKSHEET

THE BIRDS Daphne du Maurier (Textbook page 32)

DEVELOPING VOCABULARY

Directions: Read carefully the explanation of each word. Then write a sentence of your own using that word. Include in your sentence clues to the meaning of the word.

disposition (dis′pə•zish′ən) *n.* a person's nature or temperament. ▶ *Disposition* can also mean "selling, giving away, or otherwise getting rid of," as in "the disposition of one's wealth." ■ Myra has a very pleasant <u>disposition</u>. **Page 33**

ORIGINAL SENTENCE: _____

_____

clamor (klam′ər) *n.* a loud outcry; an uproar. ▶ This word was borrowed from a Latin verb meaning "to cry out." ■ Over the walls of the castle, the king heard the <u>clamor</u> of his angry people demanding food. **Page 33**

ORIGINAL SENTENCE: _____

_____

misgiving (mis•giv′iŋ) *n.* a feeling of doubt or fear; qualm. ▶ Often this word is used in the plural: *misgivings*. ■ Toni did not have a single <u>misgiving</u> about the wisdom of her choice. **Page 34**

ORIGINAL SENTENCE: _____

_____

crested (kres′tid) *adj.* having a plume or other decoration on one's head. ▶ This word is based on the noun *crest*, which can also mean "the highest point." ■ The colorful plumage of the <u>crested</u> birds of paradise makes them one of the most beautiful types of birds in the world. **Page 37**

ORIGINAL SENTENCE: _____

_____

trough (trôf) *n.* a long, narrow container or low place. ▶ *Trough* is probably derived from a Greek word meaning "hollowed wooden object." ■ The surfer soon capsized when she hit the <u>trough</u> of the waves. **Page 38**

ORIGINAL SENTENCE: _____

_____

jostling (jäs′′liŋ) *n.* bumping; coming in close contact with. ▶ This word may remind you of *joust*, which refers to a form of combat between knights on horseback. ■ The <u>jostling</u> of the crowd entering the stadium caused me to drop my ticket. **Page 44**

ORIGINAL SENTENCE: _____

_____

larder (lär′dər) *n.* a pantry or other place where food is stored. ▶ *Larder* is related to the Latin word for lard and probably originally referred to a place where bacon was stored. ■ The hungry orphan could hardly believe the abundance of the couple's larder. **Page 39**

ORIGINAL SENTENCE: _____

_____

furtively (fur′tiv•lē) *adj.* secretly; sneakily. ▶ This word is based on the Latin word *fur*, which means "thief." ■ Looking furtively around the corner, Don sneaked past the guard and into the corridor. **Page 43**

ORIGINAL SENTENCE: _____

_____

ruthless (rooth′lis) *adj.* without pity; cruel. ▶ The suffix *-less* means "without." ■ When it comes to video games, Christine is a ruthless competitor. **Page 46**

ORIGINAL SENTENCE: _____

_____

PRACTICE TEST

Directions: In front of each number, write the letter of the definition that best matches each vocabulary word. For one of the words, there are two similar definitions. Be sure to use both. *(10 points each)*

_____ 1. clamor

_____ 2. jostling

_____ 3. trough

_____ 4. furtively

_____ 5. larder

_____ 6. misgiving

_____ 7. disposition

_____ 8. ruthless

_____ 9. clamor

_____ 10. crested

a. pitiless

b. feeling of doubt or fear

c. a person's nature; temperament

d. with decorations on one's head

e. to jump

f. an uproar

g. previous disappointment

h. lacking skill

i. a storage place for food

j. sneakily

k. a loud outcry

l. a long, narrow, hollow place

m. bumping

A CHRISTMAS MEMORY   Truman Capote   (Textbook page 62)

DEVELOPING VOCABULARY

Directions: Read carefully the explanation of each word. Then write a sentence of your own using that word. Include in your sentence clues to the meaning of the word.

dilapidated (di•lap′ə•dāt′•id) *adj.* broken down; neglected; shabby. ▶ The prefix *di-* is a variation of *dis-,* which means "apart." ■ Mr. Rosen's car is a dilapidated 1958 Buick that looks like it is ready for the junk heap. **Page 62**

ORIGINAL SENTENCE: _____

_____

paraphernalia (par′ə•fər•nāl′yə) *n. pl.* a collection of things, often equipment used in some activity. ▶ This word is also properly pronounced with the second *r* silent; it is technically plural, but most speakers use it with singular verbs. ■ Chip arrived with his arms filled with cleaning paraphernalia. **Page 62**

ORIGINAL SENTENCE: _____

_____

to accumulate (ə•kyoom′yə•lāt′) *v.* to pile up; to gather together over time. ▶ This word is built on a Latin root word that means "pile." ■ Standing near the smoldering ruins of their home, Mr. and Mrs. Santiago grieved over the loss of the belongings they had accumulated during a lifetime together. **Page 63**

ORIGINAL SENTENCE: _____

_____

conspiracy (kən•spir′ə•sē) *n.* the act of planning secretly, especially for something illegal or harmful. ▶ The prefix *con-* means "together." ■ Two people in my father's company were arrested for conspiracy to steal office equipment. **Page 63**

ORIGINAL SENTENCE: _____

_____

carnage (kär′nij) *n.* widespread slaughter. ▶ This word sometimes refers to the bodies left after a battle or massacre. ■ The Battle of the Bulge resulted in some of the worst carnage of the entire Second World War. **Page 64**

ORIGINAL SENTENCE: _____

_____

festooned (fes•toond′) *adj.* a form of *to festoon,* which means "to decorate in curves or loops." ▶ *Festooned* is based on an Italian word meaning "feast" or "celebration." ■ The Christmas tree was festooned with bright paper chains. **Page 64**

ORIGINAL SENTENCE: _____

_____

*Vocabulary Activity Worksheet: **Elements of Literature,** Third Course*   7

simultaneously (sī′m′l•tā′nē•əs•lē) *adv.* at the same time. ▶ This word is closely related to two familiar words: *similar* and *same*. ■ My mother and my Aunt Priscilla simultaneously warned me to drive carefully. **Page 66**

ORIGINAL SENTENCE: _____

_____

potent (pōt′′nt) *adj.* powerful. ▶ The Latin root of this word is also the basis for the English word *potential*. ■ Sulfuric acid is a potent chemical. **Page 66**

ORIGINAL SENTENCE: _____

_____

burnishes (bur′nish•iz) *v.* polishes. ▶ An earlier form of this word meant "to make brown," as in *brunette*. ■ When my grandfather makes a piece of furniture, he burnishes the wood by rubbing it with a cloth. **Page 66**

ORIGINAL SENTENCE: _____

_____

PRACTICE TEST

Directions: In front of each number, write **T** if the statement is true or **F** if the statement is false. One vocabulary word appears twice.

_____ **1.** *Conspiracy* requires planning in secret.

_____ **2.** Air tanks, flippers, and face mask are scuba-diving *paraphernalia*.

_____ **3.** If a house is *dilapidated,* it has been neglected for many years.

_____ **4.** Something that *burnishes* brass trim makes it dull or dirty.

_____ **5.** Explosions that happen *simultaneously* occur at the same time.

_____ **6.** If an accident results in *carnage,* many people are dead or injured.

_____ **7.** To *accumulate* photographs means to throw them away.

_____ **8.** For a medicine to be *potent,* it must have little or no effect.

_____ **9.** A room that is *festooned* with garlands of flowers is probably used for storage.

_____ **10.** If two events take place *simultaneously,* one happens first and then the other.

MARÍA TEPACHE   Amado Muro   (Textbook page 72)

DEVELOPING VOCABULARY

Directions: Read carefully the explanation of each word. Then write a sentence of your
own using that word. Include in your sentence clues to the meaning of the word.

warped (wôrpt) *adj.* a form of *to warp*,
which means "to bend, twist, or distort."
▶ In Old English the word *weorpan* meant
"to throw." You can remember the meaning
of *warped* by thinking of something "thrown
out of shape." ■ The piece of plywood was
warped from lying for months in the rain.
Page 72

ORIGINAL SENTENCE: _____

_____

gilt (gilt) *n.* a gold-like substance. ▶ *Gilt*
comes from an earlier form of the word *gold*.
■ It must have taken much skill and patience
to apply gilt to the many ornate carvings that
decorate the palace.   **Page 73**

ORIGINAL SENTENCE: _____

_____

reflective (ri•flek′tiv) *adj.* thoughtful;
pensive. ▶ This word is composed of two
Latin parts: *re-*, which here means "back,"
and *-flect-*, meaning "to bend." ■ Jerry
seemed to be in a reflective mood, staring
silently into the distance for what seemed like
hours.   **Page 74**

ORIGINAL SENTENCE: _____

_____

stumpy (stum′pē) *adj.* short and thick, like a
stump. ▶ Although they are easy to
confuse, *stumpy* and its synonym *stubby* are
two different words. ■ The water fountain
in the park is stumpy, and therefore children
can easily help themselves to a drink.
Page 74

ORIGINAL SENTENCE: _____

_____

pall (pôl) *n.* a dark, gloomy covering.
▶ Another related but more specific meaning
of *pall* is "the cloth used to cover a coffin
during a funeral." ■ Every day the factories
of Manchester cast a pall of black smoke over
the city.   **Page 72**

ORIGINAL SENTENCE: _____

_____

burdened (bʉrd′′nd) *adj.* a form of *to
burden*, which means "to load, weigh down,
or oppress." ▶ *Burdened* is closely related
to the verb *to bear*, meaning "to carry."
■ Tanya was so burdened by the heavy
backpack that she could hardly haul herself
up the rope.   **Page 72**

ORIGINAL SENTENCE: _____

bonbons (bän'bänz') *n. pl.* small pieces of candy. ▶ This word is from the French word *bon*, which means "good." ■ Ms. Divine laid down her novel long enough to open another box of <u>bonbons</u>. **Page 72**

ORIGINAL SENTENCE: _____

_____

humble (hum'b'l) *adj.* low in rank; not proud. ▶ This word can also be used as a verb, meaning "to reduce someone's pride," similar to the word *humiliate*. ■ Chuck continues to be a <u>humble</u> person, even after being elected class president. **Page 72**

ORIGINAL SENTENCE: _____

_____

burlap (bur'lap) *n.* a coarse cloth. ▶ The first part of this word comes from the Old French word *burel*, which referred to "coarse cloth used as a table cover." ■ In the corner of the warehouse were stacked dozens of <u>burlap</u> bags filled with coffee beans. **Page 73**

ORIGINAL SENTENCE: _____

_____

ambition (am•bi'shən) *n.* the drive to succeed. ▶ The prefix *ambi-* means either "both" or "around"; *ambition* is based on a word that meant "going around soliciting votes." ■ Will's goal of attending medical school is only one example of his <u>ambition</u>. **Page 74**

ORIGINAL SENTENCE: _____

_____

PRACTICE TEST

Directions: In front of each number, write **A** if the words are antonyms or **S** if the words are synonyms. *(10 points each)*

_____ **1.** humble—proud

_____ **2.** bonbons—candies

_____ **3.** burdened—oppressed

_____ **4.** warped—straight

_____ **5.** gilt—tarnish

_____ **6.** ambition—drive

_____ **7.** stumpy—tall

_____ **8.** reflective—thoughtful

_____ **9.** pall—covering

_____ **10.** burlap—satin

DEVELOPING VOCABULARY

Directions: Read carefully the explanation of each word. Then write a sentence of your own using that word. Include in your sentence clues to the meaning of the word.

frail (frāl) *adj.* weak; easily broken.
▶ *Frail* and *fragile* are both derived from the same Latin word meaning "delicate."

■ Tiny Tim in Dickens's *A Christmas Carol* was a frail child whom everyone loved.
Page 78

ORIGINAL SENTENCE: _____

_____

contact (kän′takt) *n.* communication; touch.
▶ The prefix *con-* means "together."
■ Get in contact with me when you arrive in

Dallas, and I'll send someone to pick you up.
Page 78

ORIGINAL SENTENCE: _____

_____

furnished (fʉr′nisht) *adj.* a form of *to furnish*, which means "to supply or outfit with everything necessary." ▶ The oldest known ancestor of this word and the closely related word *furniture* is the Greek word

frommen, which means "to benefit."
■ Gerry looked for a furnished apartment because he owned nothing but a few lamps.
Page 78

ORIGINAL SENTENCE: _____

_____

suede (swād) *n.* soft leather with a velvet-like surface. ▶ This word is derived from the French word for Sweden. ■ Maria smiled as

she tried on the new pair of suede gloves and touched them to her face.   **Page 79**

ORIGINAL SENTENCE: _____

_____

dash (dash) *n.* a sudden, swift movement; a rush. ▶ This word comes from a Danish word meaning "slap." ■ The commuter

had to make a wild dash to catch the subway.
Page 79

ORIGINAL SENTENCE: _____

_____

icebox (īs′bäks′) *n.* a refrigerator or cabinet with ice in it for keeping foods cold.
▶ This compound word easily reveals its meaning when divided into its parts.

■ When my grandmother was a child, ice was delivered to her home each day and placed in the icebox.   **Page 79**

ORIGINAL SENTENCE: _____

_____

presentable (pri•zen′tə•b'l) *adj.* suitably dressed; fit to be seen. ▶ The Latin word *praesentare* (to place before) is the origin of this word. ■ Carol rushed to make the living room presentable before the company arrived. **Page 79**

ORIGINAL SENTENCE: _____

_____

barren (bar′ən) *adj.* empty; boring. ▶ *Barren* can also mean "not able to bear children or grow vegetation." ■ The explorer surveyed the barren landscape, hoping to catch sight of even a single rock or tree. **Page 79**

ORIGINAL SENTENCE: _____

_____

stoop (stoōp) *n.* a small porch with steps. ▶ *Stoop* is related to the Dutch and German words for step. ■ On warm summer evenings we like to sit on the front stoop and talk late into the night. **Page 79**

ORIGINAL SENTENCE: _____

_____

combined (kəm•bīnd′) *adj.* a form of *to combine*, which means "to join together." ▶ Like the prefix *con-*, the prefix *com-* here means "together." ■ When rice is combined with beans, the result is a meal high in protein. **Page 78**

ORIGINAL SENTENCE: _____

_____

PRACTICE TEST

Directions: In the blank at the right, write the vocabulary word that fits the definition at the left. *(10 points each)*

| frail | furnished | dash | icebox | stoop |
| contact | suede | presentable | barren | combined |

1. weak   1. _____

2. fit to be seen   2. _____

3. equipped   3. _____

4. a small porch   4. _____

5. a rush   5. _____

6. empty; boring   6. _____

7. a refrigerator   7. _____

8. communication   8. _____

9. soft leather   9. _____

10. joined together   10. _____

VOCABULARY ACTIVITY WORKSHEET

BLUES AIN'T NO MOCKIN BIRD   Toni Cade Bambara
(Textbook page 81)

DEVELOPING VOCABULARY

Directions: Read carefully the explanation of each word. Then write a sentence of your
own using that word. Include in your sentence clues to the meaning of the word.

weird (wird) *adj.* strange; fantastic. ▶ This
word is commonly misspelled as ''wierd,''
but remember that in this case the *e* comes
before the *i*. ■ Hearing a weird noise, the
two boys hid behind the tree and waited.
Page 81

ORIGINAL SENTENCE: _____

_____

crystal (kris′t'l) *adj.* made of a type of fine,
clear glass. ▶ *Crystal* is derived from a
Latin word meaning ''ice.'' ■ In the third
act of the play, a crystal chandelier crashes to
the floor and breaks into pieces.   **Page 81**

ORIGINAL SENTENCE: _____

_____

ladle (lā′d'l) *n.* a long-handled spoon.
▶ The verbs *to ladle* and *to lade* mean ''to
scoop out with a ladle.'' ■ My mother
inherited an expensive soup tureen and
matching ladle.   **Page 81**

ORIGINAL SENTENCE: _____

_____

dairy (der′ē) *n.* a farm that raises milk-
producing cows. ▶ An earlier, Old English
form of this word meant ''breadmaker.''
■ Mr. McAllister uses a pickup truck
to transport the milk from his dairy to the
processing plant in town.   **Page 81**

ORIGINAL SENTENCE: _____

_____

vats (vats) *n. pl.* large containers for holding
liquids. ▶ In Middle English, an earlier
form of our langauge, the word *vat* was
spelled *fat* and meant ''cask.'' ■ At the
processing plant, the milk is poured into large
vats to be pasteurized.   **Page 81**

ORIGINAL SENTENCE: _____

_____

lassoed (las′ōd) *adj.* a form of *to lasso,*
which means ''to catch with a long rope that
has a sliding loop at the end.'' ▶ This word
is sometimes pronounced las′ōōd. ■ Once
the rodeo event was over, the lassoed calf
was let loose.   **Page 81**

ORIGINAL SENTENCE: _____

_____

Vocabulary Activity Worksheet: Elements of Literature, Third Course   13

original (ə•rij′ə•n'l) *adj.* fresh; new; not copied. ▶ *Original* implies being the first; don't confuse it with *unique*, which implies being the only one. ■ I think Estella's way of dressing is <u>original</u>; soon we all may be copying her style.   **Page 81**

ORIGINAL SENTENCE: _____

_____

pecan (pi•kan′) *n.* a thin-shelled nut. ▶ *Pecan* is an Algonquian Indian word. ■ A large <u>pecan</u> tree litters our backyard with nuts every fall.   **Page 81**

ORIGINAL SENTENCE: _____

_____

campaign (kam•pān′) *n.* a series of organized actions for a particular purpose. ▶ *Campaign* comes from a French word meaning "military expedition."   ■ The <u>campaign</u> took more energy and money than I had expected.   **Page 83**

ORIGINAL SENTENCE: _____

_____

reckless (rek′lis) *adj.* careless; irresponsible. ▶ This word is based on the verb *to reck*, which means "to have concern for," plus the suffix *-less*, which means "without."   ■ The <u>reckless</u> criminal did not care who got hurt during the crime.   **Page 84**

ORIGINAL SENTENCE: _____

_____

PRACTICE TEST

Directions: Fill in the blank with the vocabulary word that best fits the meaning of the sentence. *(10 points each)*

weird	ladle	vats	original	campaign
crystal	dairy	lassoed	pecan	reckless

1. As a wedding gift, we gave my cousin a _____ punch bowl.

2. Tanya, who has always loved cows, hopes to operate a _____ .

3. When the soup was ready, Mother used an aluminum _____ to fill each bowl.

4. The science fiction movie depicted a number of _____ events.

5. At the bottling company we saw the huge, plastic _____ in which juice is stored.

6. The _____ plan was much more complex than this later one.

7. My mother makes a hickory pie that is similar to _____ pie.

8. The _____ way in which Mike waved a knife around in his cooking class frightened the other students.

9. The _____ for student council officers begins in a month.

10. In the movie the _____ calf pulls the cowboy off his horse.

TOP MAN   James Ramsey Ullman   (Textbook page 96)

DEVELOPING VOCABULARY

Directions: Read carefully the explanation of each word. Then write a sentence of your own using that word. Include in your sentence clues to the meaning of the word.

gorge (gôrj) *n.* a deep, narrow valley. ▶ *Gorge* is derived from an Old French word for "throat." ■ The river had cut a <u>gorge</u> through the sandstone mountain range. **Page 97**

ORIGINAL SENTENCE: _____

_____

taciturn (tas′ə•tʉrn′) *adj.* silent; not liking to talk. ▶ A related word is *tacit,* which means "unspoken," as in "a tacit agreement." ■ Janet is a <u>taciturn</u> person who rarely expresses an opinion. **Page 98**

ORIGINAL SENTENCE: _____

_____

ominous (äm′ə•nəs) *adj.* threatening; sinister. ▶ This word is related to *omen,* a sign of some future event. ■ In an <u>ominous</u> tone of voice, the principal told us that by the end of the week he would make a very important announcement. **Page 104**

ORIGINAL SENTENCE: _____

_____

desolation (des′ə•lā′shun) *n.* the condition or state of being deserted or uninhabited. ▶ *Desolation* is based on a Latin word meaning "to leave alone." ■ Survivors were stunned by the extent of <u>desolation</u> caused by the first atomic bomb explosion over Hiroshima, Japan. **Page 100**

ORIGINAL SENTENCE: _____

_____

spasm (spaz′′m) *n.* a sudden contraction of muscles. ▶ *Spasm* can refer to any sudden, temporary burst of activity or feeling. ■ The spasm in my leg muscle was probably caused by my failure to stretch and warm up before running. **Page 104**

ORIGINAL SENTENCE: _____

_____

laboriously (lə•bôr′ē•əs•lē) *adv.* difficultly; in a manner requiring hard work. ▶ This word is based on the familiar word *labor,* meaning "work." ■ Getting to the top of Mt. LeConte required that we climb <u>laboriously</u> for five hours. **Page 102**

ORIGINAL SENTENCE: _____

_____

summit (sum′it) *n.* the highest point; peak. ► *Summit* usually refers to the top of a hill or mountain, but sometimes it refers to the highest level of achievement. ■ The summit of Mt. Whitney is the highest point in the continental United States. **Page 97**

ORIGINAL SENTENCE: _____

_____

imminent (im′ə•nənt) *adj.* approaching; likely to happen soon. ► Do not confuse *imminent* with *eminent*, which means "famous." ■ Moviemakers often use background music to signal imminent danger. **Page 97**

ORIGINAL SENTENCE: _____

_____

simultaneously (sī′m′l•tā′nē•əs•lē) *adv.* at the same time. ► The suffix *-eous*, like *-ious*, signals an adjective. The second suffix, *-ly*, turns the adjective into an adverb. ■ The two explosions occurred simultaneously and combined to create a deafening roar. **Page 107**

ORIGINAL SENTENCE: _____

_____

taut (tôt) *adj.* tightly stretched. ► *Taut* probably comes from an Old English verb meaning "to pull." ■ Hold the canvas taut while I pound this stake into the ground. **Page 104**

ORIGINAL SENTENCE: _____

_____

PRACTICE TEST

Directions: Circle the letter of the best meaning for each word. *(10 points each)*

1. taciturn: **a.** silent   **b.** lucky   **c.** hopeful   **d.** careless

2. ominous: **a.** recent   **b.** threatening   **c.** dark   **d.** bright

3. simultaneously: **a.** previously   **b.** leaving nothing behind   **c.** without any reason   **d.** at the same time

4. taut: **a.** tight   **b.** woven   **c.** not likely to talk   **d.** waterproof

5. laboriously: **a.** excitedly   **b.** steeply   **c.** difficultly   **d.** in a shy manner

6. desolation: **a.** pain   **b.** deserted state   **c.** coarse fabric   **d.** overpopulation

7. spasm: **a.** event   **b.** muscle contraction   **c.** length of time   **d.** place for resting

8. imminent: **a.** famous   **b.** tight   **c.** young   **d.** approaching

9. summit: **a.** sides   **b.** back   **c.** top   **d.** prevention

10. gorge: **a.** narrow valley   **b.** grassy plain   **c.** highest point   **d.** place where two rivers meet

ANTAEUS   **Borden Deal**   (Textbook page 111)

DEVELOPING VOCABULARY

Directions: Read carefully the explanation of each word. Then write a sentence of your own using that word. Include in your sentence clues to the meaning of the word.

parapet (par′ə•pit) *n.* a low wall or railing. ▶ This word comes from a Latin word meaning "to prepare," and sometimes refers to a wall put up to protect soldiers from the enemy. ■ The bride leaned over the <u>parapet</u> to toss her bouquet of flowers to the well-wishers below. **Page 111**

ORIGINAL SENTENCE: _____

_____

obscure (əb•skyoor′) *adj.* not easily seen or understood. ▶ *Obscure* comes from a Latin word meaning "covered over." ■ The teacher helped us to interpret the meaning of the <u>obscure</u> poem. **Page 113**

ORIGINAL SENTENCE: _____

_____

stolid (stäl′id) *adj.* showing little emotion; unexcitable. ▶ Do not confuse this word with *solid*. ■ Danny's father is a <u>stolid</u> man, who rarely raises his voice or cracks a smile. **Page 113**

ORIGINAL SENTENCE: _____

_____

domain (dō•mān′) *n.* an estate; the land belonging to one owner or ruler. ▶ *Domain* is based on the same Latin word as *dominate*, which means "to rule or control." ■ The <u>domain</u> of the British Empire has shrunk considerably since the beginning of the twentieth century. **Page 113**

ORIGINAL SENTENCE: _____

_____

to contemplate (kan′təm•plāt′) *v.* to think about intently; to consider. ▶ Do not confuse this word with *to concentrate*, which means "to focus one's attention." ■ The astronomer was able to <u>contemplate</u> the stars for hours without becoming bored. **Page 114**

ORIGINAL SENTENCE: _____

_____

dilating (dī•lāt′iŋ) *adj.* a form of *to dilate*, which means "to make wider; to stretch; to cause to open." ▶ The first part of this word is a variation of the prefix *dis-*, which here means "apart." ■ The doctor put drops in my eyes, <u>dilating</u> them for the eye examination. **Page 114**

ORIGINAL SENTENCE: _____

_____

*Vocabulary Activity Worksheet: **Elements of Literature**, Third Course*   17

desecrated (des′ə•krāt′id) *v.* past participle of *to desecrate,* which means "to treat without reverence." ▶ Compare this word with *consecrated,* which means "made sacred"; the prefix *de-* means "away." ■ The altar of the temple was desecrated by the vandals the previous night when it was smeared with mud. **Page 115**

ORIGINAL SENTENCE: _____

_____

esoteric (es′ə•ter′ik) *adj.* understood by only a certain group of people. ▶ This word is somewhat similar to *exotic,* which means "strange or foreign." ■ The scriptures of that religious sect contain many esoteric ideas. **Page 115**

ORIGINAL SENTENCE: _____

_____

resolute (rez′ə•loot) *adj.* determined; fixed. ▶ This word is based on one meaning of the word *to resolve:* "to reach a firm decision." ■ The healthcare workers were resolute in their commitment to bring medical supplies to the people in the flooded areas. **Page 113**

ORIGINAL SENTENCE: _____

_____

inert (in•ʉrt′) *adj.* without power to move; lifeless. ▶ Do not confuse this word with *inept,* which means "clumsy or bungling." ■ A rock is an inert object. **Page 114**

ORIGINAL SENTENCE: _____

_____

PRACTICE TEST

Directions: In front of each number, write the letter of the definition that best matches each vocabulary word. *(10 points each)*

_____ 1. parapet

_____ 2. obscure

_____ 3. inert

_____ 4. stolid

_____ 5. resolute

_____ 6. esoteric

_____ 7. desecrated

_____ 8. dilating

_____ 9. domain

_____ 10. to contemplate

a. understood by only a certain group of people

b. sorry for a mistake

c. treated without reverence

d. poor

e. causing to get wider

f. to consider

g. lonely

h. a low wall

i. determined

j. unclear

k. unexcitable

l. the land of a ruler or owner

m. lifeless

A MAN CALLED HORSE Dorothy M. Johnson (Textbook page 119)

DEVELOPING VOCABULARY

Directions: Read carefully the explanation of each word. Then write a sentence of your own using that word. Include in your sentence clues to the meaning of the word.

forestalled (fôr•stôld′) *v.* past tense of *to forestall*, which means "to prevent or slow down by taking action ahead of time." ▶ In Middle English this word meant "to ambush." ■ Kathryn <u>forestalled</u> disaster by warning the villagers that a flash flood was approaching. **Page 119**

ORIGINAL SENTENCE: _____

_____

regalia (ri•gāl′yə) *n.* fancy clothing; ceremonial costume. ▶ This word is always plural. It is based on the word *regal,* which means something associated with royalty. ■ At my brother's college graduation, the faculty wore brightly colored <u>regalia</u>. **Page 121**

ORIGINAL SENTENCE: _____

_____

brandishing (bran′dish•iŋ) *adj.* a form of *to brandish,* which means "to wave in a triumphant or threatening way." ▶ The word on which *brandishing* is based once meant "sword" or "torch." Most of the time *brandishing* is used in connection with weapons. ■ The actor appeared on stage <u>brandishing</u> a sword. **Page 121**

ORIGINAL SENTENCE: _____

_____

prosperous (präs′pər•əs) *adj.* successful; well-off. ▶ The prefix *pro-* can mean before or ahead of, and the root *-sper-* means "hope." ■ On our drive through the Ohio countryside, we saw many <u>prosperous</u> farms. **Page 122**

ORIGINAL SENTENCE: _____

_____

rancid (ran′sid) *adj.* smelling or tasting like spoiled grease or oil. ▶ This word is similar to *rank,* which can also mean smelling or tasting bad. ■ All that was left in the broken refrigerator were three sticks of <u>rancid</u> butter. **Page 121**

ORIGINAL SENTENCE: _____

_____

docile (däs′′l) *adj.* easily taught or managed. ▶ British and Canadian speakers usually pronounce this word dō′sīl. ■ In five weeks Allison's training had turned the wild mustang into a <u>docile</u> horse that she could easily ride. **Page 122**

ORIGINAL SENTENCE: _____

_____

detractor (di•trakt′ər) *n.* a person who criticizes or makes fun of someone. ▶ Do not confuse this word with *distraction,* which means something that draws your attention away. ■ Hearing the jeers and catcalls, José turned to face his detractors. **Page 123**

ORIGINAL SENTENCE: _____

_____

deviation (dē′vē•ā′shun) *n.* a turning away from. ▶ This word is a combination of the prefix *de-* (away from) and the Latin word *via* (road). You can remember its meaning by thinking about turning off a road. ■ The governor gave the speech without any deviation from his prepared text. **Page 126**

ORIGINAL SENTENCE: _____

_____

piteously (pit′ē•əs•lē) *adv.* in a way that arouses or deserves pity. ▶ *Piteously* and *pitifully* are synonyms and can be used interchangeably. ■ All night long we heard the trapped kitten crying piteously. **Page 127**

ORIGINAL SENTENCE: _____

_____

querulous (kwer′ə•ləs) *adj.* whining; finding fault. ▶ This word looks similar to *query* (question) but is not related in meaning. ■ Because of her constant querulous comments, I vowed never to take Keesha camping with me again. **Page 128**

ORIGINAL SENTENCE: _____

_____

PRACTICE TEST

Directions: Circle the letter of the best meaning for each word. *(10 points each)*

1. prosperous: **a.** reasonable   **b.** successful   **c.** slow   **d.** complaining

2. regalia: **a.** tools   **b.** stars   **c.** ceremonial costume   **d.** discussion

3. rancid: **a.** spoiled   **b.** devoted   **c.** exciting   **d.** late

4. deviation: **a.** destruction   **b.** investigation   **c.** a moving away from   **d.** attempt

5. detractor: **a.** something that distracts   **b.** someone who criticizes   **c.** farm equipment   **d.** something to forget

6. piteously: **a.** in a hurried manner   **b.** in a careless way   **c.** in a way that deserves pity   **d.** silently

7. forestalled: **a.** caused   **b.** prevented   **c.** aroused   **d.** created

8. brandishing: **a.** watering   **b.** wearing   **c.** waving   **d.** withering

9. docile: **a.** obedient   **b.** dumb   **c.** insane   **d.** hopeful

10. querulous: **a.** incorrect   **b.** different   **c.** constant   **d.** complaining

CORRESPONDENCE $\qquad$ **Carson McCullers** $\qquad$ **(Textbook page 138)**

DEVELOPING VOCABULARY

Directions: Read carefully the explanation of each word. Then write a sentence of your own using that word. Include in your sentence clues to the meaning of the word.

correspondence (kôr′ə•spänd′dəns) *n.* communication through letters. ▶ This word is made up of two parts borrowed from Latin: *cor-*, which means "together," and *-respond-*, which means "to answer." ■ For fifteen years the two friends maintained regular correspondence. **Page 138**

ORIGINAL SENTENCE: _____

_____

pondered (pän′dərd) *v.* past participle of *to ponder*, which means "to think deeply about; to consider carefully." ▶ The Latin root of this word means "to weigh"; it is also found in *ponderous*, which means "very heavy." ■ Before answering, Stefan had pondered the question for several minutes. **Page 138**

ORIGINAL SENTENCE: _____

_____

diligently (dil′ə•jənt•lē) *adv.* in a hardworking manner. ▶ Do not confuse the base word *diligent* with *dilettante*, a noun that means "an amateur." ■ Ms. Cortez worked diligently on her income tax return and finished it in only one evening. **Page 139**

ORIGINAL SENTENCE: _____

_____

exceedingly (ik•sēd′iŋ•lē) *adv.* extremely; to a great degree. ▶ The Latin prefix *ex-* here means "out" or "beyond." ■ News of the approaching hurricane made me exceedingly anxious. **Page 139**

ORIGINAL SENTENCE: _____

_____

reincarnation (rē′in•kär•nā′shən) *n.* the rebirth of the soul in a different body. ▶ The prefix *re-* means "again." ■ Many Eastern religions include a belief in reincarnation. **Page 139**

ORIGINAL SENTENCE: _____

_____

hunch (hunch) *n.* a feeling about something not based on facts. ▶ This meaning of the word *hunch* (which also means "hump") resulted from a belief that touching a hunchback brought good luck. ■ I had a hunch that Rusty would find his way home, even though he had never been lost for this long before. **Page 140**

ORIGINAL SENTENCE: _____

_____

in vain (vān) without results. ► *In vain* can also be used to mean "profanely," or without respect, as in "taking the Lord's name in vain." ■ The attempts made by the rescue squad to save the life of the trapped boy were not <u>in vain</u>. **Page 138**

ORIGINAL SENTENCE: _____

_____

astray (ə•strā′) *adv.* off the right path. ► This word is based on the familiar word *to stray,* which means "to wander." ■ The mother feared that her son would go <u>astray</u> if he left the family farm to take a job in the city. **Page 140**

ORIGINAL SENTENCE: _____

_____

raffle (raf′l) *n.* a lottery; a game of chance. ► This word derives from a Middle French word that meant, literally, "a raking in (of money)." ■ In some cities, laws forbid holding a <u>raffle</u>, even if the proceeds go to charity. **Page 140**

ORIGINAL SENTENCE: _____

_____

to fulfill (fool•fil′) *v.* to carry something out as promised. ► The Old English form of this word contained two words meaning "full," and thus was an example of a pleonasm, or the use of more words than necessary to express an idea. ■ The rock star was sued by the concert organizers because he did not <u>fulfill</u> the terms of his contract. **Page 141**

ORIGINAL SENTENCE: _____

_____

PRACTICE TEST

Directions: In the blank at the right, write the vocabulary word that fits each definition at the left. *(10 points each)*

| correspondence | exceedingly | raffle | in vain | hunch |
| pondered | reincarnation | to fulfill | diligently | astray |

1. on the wrong path

1. _____

2. game of chance

2. _____

3. to carry out as promised

3. _____

4. extremely

4. _____

5. in a hardworking manner

5. _____

6. exchange of letters

6. _____

7. thought carefully about

7. _____

8. a feeling not based on facts

8. _____

9. rebirth in a new body

9. _____

10. without results

10. _____

THE HAT   **Jessamyn West**   (Textbook page 143)

DEVELOPING VOCABULARY

Directions: Read carefully the explanation of each word. Then write a sentence of your own using that word. Include in your sentence clues to the meaning of the word.

becoming (bi•kum′iŋ) *adj.* having an attractive effect; appropriate. ▶ This is a somewhat unusual use of *becoming,* which can also be a verbal meaning "changing to be," as in "weather becoming colder." ■ For the beauty pageant, Kristine wore a becoming floor-length dress of white taffeta. **Page 143**

ORIGINAL SENTENCE: _____

_____

instinctive (in•stiŋk′tiv) *adj.* naturally acquired; inborn. ▶ This is an adjective form of *instinct,* which means "an inborn tendency to behave in a certain way." ■ Craig's knowledge of sailing seems almost *instinctive;* he has never been on a boat before. **Page 143**

ORIGINAL SENTENCE: _____

_____

languorous (laŋ′gə•rəs) *adj.* tired; listless. ▶ *Languorous* comes from a Latin word meaning "to be weary." ■ Even a jog around the block couldn't shake Paul from his languorous mood. **Page 144**

ORIGINAL SENTENCE: _____

_____

gait (gāt) *n.* a way of walking or running. ▶ The earliest form of this word meant "path." ■ Rachel had to wear a brace on her leg for three months to correct a problem with her gait. **Page 146**

ORIGINAL SENTENCE: _____

_____

malicious (mə•lish′əs) *adj.* intentionally harmful; showing ill will. ▶ The basis for this word is the Latin root *-mal-,* which means "bad." ■ According to a malicious rumor, Brenda is planning to break up with Jerome so that she can date his best friend. **Page 149**

ORIGINAL SENTENCE: _____

_____

crux (kruks) *n.* the essential or deciding point. ▶ *Crux* means "cross" in Latin. You can remember the meaning of this word by thinking of the deciding point as the place where all other points cross. ■ The crux of Andy's argument was that we should pay for his gas because he has been exceedingly generous to us in the past. **Page 149**

ORIGINAL SENTENCE: _____

_____

PRACTICE TEST A

Directions: Fill in the blank with the vocabulary word that best fits the meaning of the sentence. *(10 points each)*

> instinctive   malicious   gait
> languorous   crux

1. The _____ of the matter is that I simply do not want to go with you.

2. I know that you did not mean to be _____, but your actions hurt me badly.

3. The horse's awkward _____ made me wonder if perhaps he had injured himself in the last race.

4. Since Marlene has never taken music lessons, I can assume that her appreciation of music is _____.

5. The movements of the cat were _____, as she slowly stood and moved to a warmer spot.

PRACTICE TEST B

Directions: Complete each analogy by writing in the vocabulary word that fits. For example, black: (is to) white :: (as) brave : (is to) afraid. *(10 points each)*

> becoming   gait   languorous
> instinctive   malicious

1. tight : loose :: learned : _____

2. docile : obedient :: mean : _____

3. resolute : determined :: tired : _____

4. uninhabited : desolated :: suitable : _____

5. swimmer : stroke :: runner : _____

VOCABULARY ACTIVITY WORKSHEET

THE OLD DEMON   Pearl S. Buck   (Textbook page 153)

DEVELOPING VOCABULARY

Directions: Read carefully the explanation of each word. Then write a sentence of your
own using that word. Include in your sentence clues to the meaning of the word.

hearsay (hir′sā′) *n.* rumor; gossip. ▶ This word is from the phrase *to hear say*. ■ Your dislike for Louise is based more on hearsay than on any personal knowledge of what she is like.   **Page 153**

ORIGINAL SENTENCE: _____

_____

disconcerting (dis′kən•sʉrt′iŋ) *adj.* a form of *to disconcert*, which means "to embarrass; to confuse." ▶ It is easy to remember the meaning of this word if you think of its two parts: *dis-* (cause to be the opposite of) and *concert* (harmony). ■ Her disconcerting comments about my appearance left me with nothing to say.   **Page 153**

ORIGINAL SENTENCE: _____

_____

deprecatingly (dep′rə•kāt′iŋ•lē) *adv.* in a way that belittles or makes something seem less valuable. ▶ The base *to deprecate* is similar to the word *to depreciate*, which is usually used to mean "to lessen the price of." ■ I left the room because I could not stand to hear Cheryl speak deprecatingly of our efforts to decorate the gym for the dance. **Page 154**

ORIGINAL SENTENCE: _____

_____

to wheedle (hwē′d′l) *v.* to coax; to persuade by flattery. ▶ Note the slight difference in pronunciation between this word and *to whittle* (hwit′′l), which means "to cut wood with a knife." ■ Cassandra tried to wheedle an extra five dollars from her father by telling him how handsome he looked in his new jogging suit.   **Page 156**

ORIGINAL SENTENCE: _____

_____

quavering (kwā′vər•iŋ) *adj.* a form of *to quaver*, which means "to shake or tremble." ▶ This word probably comes from a word meaning "tadpole," perhaps because of the wobbly motion a tadpole makes when it swims. ■ Terry's quavering voice was a sure sign that he was scared.   **Page 153**

ORIGINAL SENTENCE: _____

_____

resolutely (rez′ə•lōōt′lē) *adv.* determinedly; faithfully. ▶ A related noun, *resolution*, refers to a promise that one is determined to keep. ■ My parents held resolutely to their intention that we should all finish college. **Page 160**

ORIGINAL SENTENCE: _____

_____

dike (dīk) *n.* a protective wall or dam, particularly one to hold back water. ▶ The spelling *dyke* is also proper. ■ By building one <u>dike</u> after another, the Dutch people have managed through the centuries to increase the amount of land they have to live on. **Page 153**

ORIGINAL SENTENCE: _____

_____

demon (dē′mən) *n.* a devil; an evil spirit. ▶ This word, also spelled *daemon*, can be found in both Latin and Greek with much the same meaning. ■ The story told of an esoteric ritual to rid the house of a <u>demon</u>. **Page 159**

ORIGINAL SENTENCE: _____

_____

somberly (säm′bər•lē) *adv.* in a gloomy or solemn manner. ▶ This word is a combination of the Latin prefix *sub-*, which means "under," and the Latin root *-umbra-*, which means "shade." ■ The Red Cross coordinator reported <u>somberly</u> that over two hundred people had been left homeless by the earthquake. **Page 157**

ORIGINAL SENTENCE: _____

_____

acutely (ə•kyōōt′lē) *adv.* sharply; seriously. ▶ *Acutely* comes from a Latin word meaning "sharp." ■ Within a few weeks, farmers began to feel the drought <u>acutely</u>. **Page 159**

ORIGINAL SENTENCE: _____

_____

PRACTICE TEST

Directions: In the blank at the right, write the vocabulary word that is a synonym for the word at the left.

hearsay	deprecatingly	quavering	demon	acutely
disconcerting	to wheedle	dike	somberly	resolutely

1. belittlingly   1. _____

2. devil   2. _____

3. determinedly   3. _____

4. sharply   4. _____

5. gloomily   5. _____

6. dam   6. _____

7. shaking   7. _____

8. gossip   8. _____

9. embarrassing   9. _____

10. coax   10. _____

THE SCARLET IBIS   James Hurst   (Textbook page 168)

DEVELOPING VOCABULARY

Directions: Read carefully the explanation of each word. Then write a sentence of your own using that word. Include in your sentence clues to the meaning of the word.

rank (raŋk) *adj.* growing vigorously.
▶ The Old English form of *rank* meant "strong or proud."   ■ Weeds were rank throughout the abandoned garden.
Page 169

ORIGINAL SENTENCE: _____

_____

billowed (bil′ōd) *v.* past tense of *to billow,* which means "to swell or surge like a wave."   ▶ *To billow* and *belly* share a common language ancestor that meant "bag."   ■ Every time Grandfather tried to start his old jalopy, smoke billowed from the exhaust pipe and made us cough.
Page 169

ORIGINAL SENTENCE: _____

_____

vortex (vôr′teks) *n.* a whirl of air or water.
▶ Don't confuse *vortex* with *vertex,* which means "highest point or summit."   ■ Tornados and dust devils are both examples of a vortex.   **Page 173**

ORIGINAL SENTENCE: _____

_____

infallibility (in•fal′ə•bil′ə•tē) *n.* inability to do wrong; dependability.   ▶ This word is based on a prefix meaning "not," a root meaning "fail," and a suffix meaning "ability."   ■ Most young children have faith in their parents' infallibility.   **Page 173**

ORIGINAL SENTENCE: _____

_____

reiterated (rē•it′ə•rāt′id) *v.* past tense of *to reiterate,* which means "to repeat."   ▶ The prefix *re-* means "again."   ■ The second paragraph of your essay merely reiterates the content of the first paragraph.   **Page 174**

ORIGINAL SENTENCE: _____

_____

uncoordinated (un•kō•ôr′də•nāt′id) *adj.* not functioning harmoniously; not working together.   ▶ The word part *un-* means "not," and *co-* means "together."   ■ The work of the various committees planning the horse show was uncoordinated until Sheila stepped in to organize everyone's efforts.
Page 175

ORIGINAL SENTENCE: _____

_____

armada (är•mä′də) *n.* a fleet of warships. ► This word comes from the same Latin root as *arms*, meaning "weapons." ■ The Spanish king sent an <u>armada</u> north to engage the British navy. **Page 176**

ORIGINAL SENTENCE: _____

_____

to solder (säd′ər) *v.* to join or patch with melted metal. ► Note that the letter *l* is silent in this word. ■ Uncle Dan attempted to <u>solder</u> the broken fender on my bike. **Page 176**

ORIGINAL SENTENCE: _____

_____

evanesced (ev′ə•nest′) *v.* past tense of *to evanesce,* which means "to fade from sight; to disappear; to vanish." ► The prefix *e-* means "out," and the root word *-van-* means "vanish." ■ By noon in Aruba, any fog and mist that may have gathered overnight <u>evanesced</u> in the hot sun. **Page 176**

ORIGINAL SENTENCE: _____

_____

vermilion (vər•mil′yən) *adj.* bright red. ► This word developed from an Old French word that described the same color. ■ Scott created a sensation when he arrived at the party wearing a black tuxedo and a floor-length <u>vermilion</u> cape. **Page 176**

ORIGINAL SENTENCE: _____

_____

PRACTICE TEST

Directions: In front of each number, write **T** if the statement is true or **F** if the statement is false. *(10 points each)*

_____ **1.** To look at an *armada,* you would have to be near water.

_____ **2.** *Infallibility* is something many people strive for, but few attain.

_____ **3.** A wall covered with a *rank* growth of ivy would not have many vines on it.

_____ **4.** A room with *vermilion* walls is probably very restful.

_____ **5.** Persons with *uncoordinated* movements are usually good athletes.

_____ **6.** If a speaker *reiterated* his ideas, he repeated them.

_____ **7.** If the sea *billowed,* its surface remained as smooth as glass.

_____ **8.** A whirlpool is a *vortex.*

_____ **9.** If the mist *evanesced,* it is no longer there.

_____**10.** Someone repairing an object made of metal may *solder* two pieces together.

THE BRIDGE   **Nicolai Chukovski**   (Textbook page 178)

DEVELOPING VOCABULARY

Directions: Read carefully the explanation of each word. Then write a sentence of your own using that word. Include in your sentence clues to the meaning of the word.

hoisting (hoist′iŋ) *adj.* a form of *to hoist,* which means "to lift." ▶ *Hoisting* usually implies raising something by means of a pulley or other device. ■ Hoisting the heavy sail, the sailors were soon tired and thirsty. **Page 178**

ORIGINAL SENTENCE: _____

_____

translucent (trans•l$\overline{oo}$′s'nt) *adj.* allowing light through but preventing objects on the other side from being seen clearly. ▶ Compare this word to *transparent,* which means "completely clear." ■ The large panels of etched glass in the restaurant made attractive, translucent room dividers. **Page 178**

ORIGINAL SENTENCE: _____

_____

compounded (käm•pound′id) *v.* past participle of *to compound,* which means "to increase by adding new elements." ▶ This word is a combination of the Latin prefix and root *com-* (together) and *-pon-* (to put). ■ The jeep's flat tire had compounded the problem we faced of getting to the beach by noon.   **Page 179**

ORIGINAL SENTENCE: _____

_____

tributaries (trib′yoo•ter′ēz) *n. pl.* small streams that flow into a larger one. ▶ This word can also mean "nations under another's control." ■ The Cumberland River is a large tributary of the Tennessee River. **Page 179**

ORIGINAL SENTENCE: _____

_____

crest (krest) *n.* the highest point; the top. ▶ The earliest form of this word meant "to shake," evident in the fact that *crest* can also mean "a plume or other waving decoration attached to the head." ■ The swollen river reached its crest soon after midnight and then slowly began to go down.   **Page 180**

ORIGINAL SENTENCE: _____

_____

scaffolding (skaf′′l•diŋ) *n.* the poles, boards, and other materials used to form a temporary framework for workers. ▶ A scaffold can also be the platform on which criminals are hanged. ■ Because extensive repairs were being made to its outer walls, the church was almost completely covered with scaffolding. **Page 181**

ORIGINAL SENTENCE: _____

_____

*Vocabulary Activity Worksheet: **Elements of Literature**, Third Course*   29

remnants (rem′nəntz) **n. pl.** small remaining parts. ▶ Both *remnants* and *remain* evolved from the same Old French word. ■ Today, only remnants of the great buffalo herds remain in the western United States. **Page 179**

ORIGINAL SENTENCE: _____

_____

impetus (im′pə•təs) **n.** a driving force; anything that stimulates activity. ▶ Do not confuse this word with *impetuous*, which means "acting suddenly with little thought." ■ My eagerness to win the magazine sales contest was the impetus for my spending Saturday knocking on every door in our neighborhood. **Page 180**

ORIGINAL SENTENCE: _____

_____

hampered (ham′pərd) **v.** past tense of *to hamper,* which means "to hinder; to keep from acting or moving freely." ▶ As a noun, this word can also mean "a large covered basket, such as a picnic hamper or clothes hamper." ■ The other group's refusal to share their materials hampered our efforts to complete the work. **Page 182**

ORIGINAL SENTENCE: _____

_____

grandiose (gran′dē•ōs′) **adj.** impressive; showy. ▶ Note the similarity between this word and the familiar word *grand.* ■ The movie star staged a grandiose celebration to attract attention to his recent accomplishments. **Page 184**

ORIGINAL SENTENCE: _____

_____

PRACTICE TEST

Directions: Circle the letter of the best meaning for each word. *(10 points each)*

1. scaffolding: **a.** rope ladder   **b.** unusual event   **c.** interesting costume   **d.** temporary framework

2. crest: **a.** wave   **b.** river bank   **c.** highest point   **d.** part that remains

3. remnants: **a.** remainders   **b.** adventures   **c.** criminal activities   **d.** powerful forces

4. compounded: **a.** pushed down   **b.** solved   **c.** added to   **d.** prevented

5. hoisting: **a.** raising   **b.** chasing   **c.** examining   **d.** building a framework

6. translucent: **a.** totally clear   **b.** letting only light through   **c.** gloomy   **d.** encouraging

7. tributaries: **a.** highest points   **b.** picnic baskets   **c.** pulleys used to raise sails   **d.** smaller streams flowing into a larger one

8. impetus: **a.** reason   **b.** driving force   **c.** careless behavior   **d.** whirlpool

9. hampered: **a.** held back   **b.** pushed   **c.** encouraged   **d.** thought through carefully

10. grandiose: **a.** over quickly   **b.** impressive   **c.** hardworking   **d.** shaking

VOCABULARY ACTIVITY WORKSHEET

RED DRESS **Alice Munro** **(Textbook page 187)**

DEVELOPING VOCABULARY

Directions: Read carefully the explanation of each word. Then write a sentence of your own using that word. Include in your sentence clues to the meaning of the word.

stubble (stub´'l) *n.* the short stumps of growth left after something is cut off. ▶ *Stubble* is based on a Latin word meaning "stem." ■ Once the mowing machine had completed its work, all that was left in the field was stubble. **Page 187**

ORIGINAL SENTENCE: _____

_____

ferocious (fə•rō´shəs) *adj.* fierce; violently cruel. ▶ This word comes from a Latin word meaning "wild"; note the similarity to *fierce*. ■ The lions and tigers we saw at the zoo hardly looked ferocious because they were happy living in the open area designed for them. **Page 187**

ORIGINAL SENTENCE: _____

_____

to accentuate (ak•sen´choo•wāt´) *v.* to emphasize. ▶ This word is a synonym of *accent*, and is derived from the same Latin root. ■ The pale green dress and brown eye shadow accentuate the color of Rita's eyes. **Page 189**

ORIGINAL SENTENCE: _____

_____

inflicting (in•flikt´iŋ) *n.* causing pain; imposing on. ▶ The prefix *in-* means "against," and the root *-flict-* means "to strike." ■ Our basketball coach seems to delight in inflicting additional workouts on us when she thinks we are getting out of shape. **Page 189**

ORIGINAL SENTENCE: _____

_____

rapt (rapt) *adj.* completely absorbed; carried away. ▶ *Rapt* is based on a Latin word meaning "to seize." ■ The young child listened with rapt attention as I read him a story. **Page 189**

ORIGINAL SENTENCE: _____

_____

premonitions (prē´mə•nish´ənz) *n. pl.* warnings in advance; feelings that something bad will happen. ▶ The prefix *pre-* means "before," and the root *-mon-* means "to warn." ■ Mrs. Parker claims she had a premonition that her car would be stolen. **Page 189**

ORIGINAL SENTENCE: _____

_____

Vocabulary Activity Worksheet: Elements of Literature, Third Course 31

delirium (di•lir′ē•əm) **n.** a temporary state of confusion, agitation, or excitement. ▶ *De-* means "away"; hence, *delirium* means away from one's normal state of mind. ■ The high fever accompanying diseases such as malaria can sometimes cause <u>delirium</u>. **Page 190**

ORIGINAL SENTENCE: _____

_____

inanimate (in•an′ə•mit) **adj.** lifeless; dull. ▶ The prefix *in-* means "not." The English word *to animate* means "to bring to life." ■ Before starting to paint, the artist arranged a group of <u>inanimate</u> objects, including a bowl, a pitcher, and a loaf of bread. **Page 190**

ORIGINAL SENTENCE: _____

_____

languidly (laŋ′gwid•lē) **adj.** weakly; listlessly; slowly. ▶ Note that *languidly* and *languorously* are synonymous. ■ Weak from the flu, Ramon moved <u>languidly</u> about the house looking for something to relieve his boredom. **Page 190**

ORIGINAL SENTENCE: _____

_____

barbaric (bär•ber′ik) **adj.** uncivilized; primitive; wild; crude. ▶ It is interesting to note that this word originally meant "foreign," implying that most people perceive foreigners to be uncivilized compared to themselves. ■ Most civilized people consider cannibalism a <u>barbaric</u> practice. **Page 191**

ORIGINAL SENTENCE: _____

_____

PRACTICE TEST

Directions: In front of each number, write **A** if the words are antonyms or **S** if the words are synonyms. *(10 points each)*

_____ **1.** stubble—smoothness

_____ **2.** to accentuate—to emphasize

_____ **3.** delirium—confusion

_____ **4.** premonitions—warnings

_____ **5.** barbaric—civilized

_____ **6.** languidly—energetically

_____ **7.** inanimate—lively

_____ **8.** inflicting—imposing

_____ **9.** rapt—absorbed

_____ **10.** ferocious—tame

THE LITTLE GIRL AND THE WOLF/THE PRINCESS AND THE TIN BOX   James Thurber   (Textbook page 203)

DEVELOPING VOCABULARY

Directions: Read carefully the explanation of each word. Then write a sentence of your own using that word. Include in your sentence clues to the meaning of the word.

lyre (līr) *n.* a small harp. ▶ The lyrebird, an Australian songbird, is so named because it has long tail feathers that resemble the curved sides of a lyre. ■ The Persian king relaxed by listening to one of his servants softly play the <u>lyre</u>. **Page 204**

ORIGINAL SENTENCE: _____

_____

revelry (rev′′l•rē) *n.* noisy merrymaking. ▶ This word is derived from the same Latin word as *rebel*. ■ Bourbon Street in New Orleans is the scene of <u>revelry</u> lasting far into the night. **Page 205**

ORIGINAL SENTENCE: _____

_____

ebony (eb′ən•ē) *n.* a hard, black wood found in the tropics. ▶ Ebony was once used for the black keys of pianos. ■ My sister, a Peace Corps volunteer, sent us a large <u>ebony</u> carving from Sri Lanka. **Page 204**

ORIGINAL SENTENCE: _____

_____

disdainful (dis•dān′fəl) *adj.* proud; scornful; aloof. ▶ This word is related to the English words *to deign* (to condescend) and *dignity* (worthiness, honor). ■ I feel it is wrong to be <u>disdainful</u> toward people simply because they do not have college degrees. **Page 204**

ORIGINAL SENTENCE: _____

_____

tawdry (tô′drē) *adj.* cheap and showy; gaudy; sleazy. ▶ This word emerged from running together the syllables of *St. Audrey's,* the name of a fair in Norwich, England, where showy articles were sold. ■ Andrea turned away from the <u>tawdry</u> souvenirs and looked for some well-made handicrafts to buy for her mother. **Page 204**

ORIGINAL SENTENCE: _____

_____

glutted (glud′id) *v.* past participle of *to glut,* which means "to supply more than can be used." ▶ *Glutted* is based on an Old French word meaning "to swallow," and is related to *glutton,* which means "a person who overeats." ■ The trade bill was designed to penalize any nation that had <u>glutted</u> the American market with inexpensive goods. **Page 204**

ORIGINAL SENTENCE: _____

_____

*Vocabulary Activity Worksheet: **Elements of Literature**, Third Course*   33

realm (relm) *n.* a kingdom; a domain.
▶ *Realm* and *regimen* both come from a Latin word meaning "rule." ■ The queen's decree applied to all adults living within her realm. **Page 204**

ORIGINAL SENTENCE: _____

_____

mica (mī′kə) *n.* a mineral that can be separated into thin, translucent layers.
▶ The Latin form of this word means "crumb" or "grain." ■ Before plexiglass was created, a transparent material made from mica was used. **Page 204**

ORIGINAL SENTENCE: _____

_____

nightingale (nīt′′n•gāl′) *n.* a reddish-brown and off-white bird noted for its sweet singing.
▶ The Old English word part -*galan*- means "to sing." ■ Many people believe that the nightingale sings only at night, but it sings both day and night during the weeks following its return from migration to the south. **Page 204**

ORIGINAL SENTENCE: _____

_____

topaz (tō′paz) *n.* a yellow gemstone.
▶ Most topaz is mined in Brazil ■ On our trip to South America, I bought a bracelet set with topaz. **Page 204**

ORIGINAL SENTENCE: _____

_____

PRACTICE TEST

Directions: Fill in the blank with the vocabulary word that best fits the meaning of the sentence. *(10 points each)*

lyre	realm	glutted	topaz	disdainful
nightingale	mica	revelry	ebony	tawdry

1. If you were born in November, is _____ your birthstone?

2. The mineral _____ does not readily conduct electricity.

3. An ancient _____, its strings missing for centuries, was on display.

4. Rio de Janeiro is the scene of much _____ during Carnival.

5. The once elegant part of town is now filled with _____ nightclubs, pool halls, and hangouts for petty criminals.

6. Messengers took the king's announcement to all corners of the _____.

7. Although poets frequently use "she" to refer to the _____, only the male bird of this species sings.

8. Once pocket calculators _____ the market, the price dropped.

9. The student was _____ of the suggestion to cheat, preferring to pass the test honestly or not at all.

10. The surface of some _____ furniture is so hard and shiny that many people think it has been painted.

THE SNIPER Liam O'Flaherty (Textbook page 206)

DEVELOPING VOCABULARY

Directions: Read carefully the explanation of each word. Then write a sentence of your own using that word. Include in your sentence clues to the meaning of the word.

enveloped (in•vel′əpt) *adj.* a form of *to envelop,* which means "to wrap; to cover; to hide." ▶ The prefix *en-* means "in" and the Latin root *-vel-* means "to wrap."

■ Frequently the road was <u>enveloped</u> in fog so that it could not be seen at all. **Page 206**

ORIGINAL SENTENCE: _____

_____

fleecy (flēs′ē) *adj.* soft; light; like wool. ▶ Adding the suffix *-y* to a word can change it from a noun (*fleece*) to an adjective

(*fleecy*). ■ <u>Fleecy</u> snow covered the branches of the trees. **Page 206**

ORIGINAL SENTENCE: _____

beleaguered (bi•lē′gərd) *adj.* a form of *to beleaguer,* which means "to harass; to besiege." ▶ This word derives from a Dutch word meaning "to encircle with an

army." ■ <u>Beleaguered</u> by personal problems, Cary sought help from a counselor. **Page 206**

ORIGINAL SENTENCE: _____

_____

spasmodically (spaz•mäd′ik•lē) *adv.* suddenly, violently, and temporarily. ▶ This word is the adverb form of *spasm,* which means "an involuntary muscle

contraction or any sudden activity." ■ Sean worked on his project only <u>spasmodically</u>. **Page 206**

ORIGINAL SENTENCE: _____

_____

ascetic (ə•set′ik) *adj.* self-denying; extremely self-disciplined; severe. ▶ *Ascetic* is based on a Greek word that means "to train the body." ■ When soccer season starts, Duane

becomes <u>ascetic</u>—eating carefully, sleeping regularly, and running three miles a day. **Page 206**

ORIGINAL SENTENCE: _____

_____

tattered (tat′ərd) *adj.* torn and ragged. ▶ The less frequently used noun form of this word is *tatter,* which means "a torn and

hanging shred or piece." ■ If Katie shows up in those <u>tattered</u> jeans she wears, the headwaiter may not let her in. **Page 206**

ORIGINAL SENTENCE: _____

_____

fractured (frak′chərd) *v.* past participle of *to fracture,* which means "to break or crack." ▶ This word connotes the breaking of a hard substance, such as rock or bone. ■ The fall must have fractured Jeff's femur, the large bone in his thigh. **Page 207**

ORIGINAL SENTENCE: _____

_____

paroxysm (par′ək•siz'm) *n.* a sudden attack; a spasm. ▶ *Paroxysm* evolved from a Greek word meaning "to excite." ■ Watching the antics of the Three Stooges always put Theresa into a paroxysm of laughter. **Page 207**

ORIGINAL SENTENCE: _____

_____

remorse (ri•môrs′) *n.* a deep sense of guilt; painful regret. ▶ The Latin words on which *remorse* is based mean "to bite again." ■ I always feel *remorse* when I remember how I hurt her with my sarcastic comments. **Page 208**

ORIGINAL SENTENCE: _____

_____

fasting (fast′iŋ) *n.* going without food, usually intentionally. ▶ The word *breakfast* is based on the idea of breaking a fast. ■ Joel observed the holiday by fasting and was especially hungry the next day. **Page 208**

ORIGINAL SENTENCE: _____

_____

PRACTICE TEST

Directions: In front of each number, write the letter of the definition that best matches each vocabulary word. *(10 points each)*

_____ **1.** ascetic		**a.** wrapped; hidden; covered
_____ **2.** enveloped		**b.** soft; light; like wool
_____ **3.** beleaguered		**c.** harassed; besieged
_____ **4.** fasting		**d.** suddenly, violently, and temporarily
_____ **5.** paroxysm		**e.** delay
_____ **6.** fractured		**f.** self-disciplined; severe
_____ **7.** spasmodically		**g.** torn; ragged
_____ **8.** fleecy		**h.** broken; cracked
_____ **9.** remorse		**i.** a noun meaning a sudden, severe attack
_____ **10.** tattered		**j.** frightening
		k. painful regret
		l. going without food

THE CASK OF AMONTILLADO   Edgar Allan Poe
(Textbook page 210)

DEVELOPING VOCABULARY

Directions: Read carefully the explanation of each word. Then write a sentence of your own using that word. Include in your sentence clues to the meaning of the word.

precluded (pri•klōōd′id) *v.* past tense of *to preclude,* which means "to prevent; to make impossible." ▶ This word is based on the prefix *pre-,* which means "ahead of time," plus the root *-clud-,* which mean "to close." ■ Making poor grades in high school will probably preclude your getting into an Ivy League college.   **Page 210**

ORIGINAL SENTENCE: _____

_____

redresser (ri•dres′ur) *n.* a person who sets something right. ▶ The prefix *re-* means "again" or "back," and the root word *-dress-* means "to make straight." ■ The redresser of a mistake usually experiences great satisfaction over having made up for the error.   **Page 210**

ORIGINAL SENTENCE: _____

_____

imposture (im•päs′chər) *n.* fraud; deception. ▶ An imposture is the act of an impostor, a person who pretends to be someone or something he or she is not. ■ Only through imposture were Mal and Maryann able to gain admittance to the Inaugural Ball, since they were not eligible for invitations.   **Page 210**

ORIGINAL SENTENCE: _____

_____

accosted (ə•kôst′id) *v.* past tense of *to accost,* which means "to approach and speak to, especially in a rude way." ▶ The Italian word on which this word is based means "to bring side by side." ■ It irritates me when a salesperson accosts me the minute I enter the store.   **Page 210**

ORIGINAL SENTENCE: _____

_____

absconded (əb•skänd′id) *v.* past participle of *to abscond,* which means "to run away and hide." ▶ The prefix *ab-* means "from," and the root *-cond-* means "to hide." ■ The thief had absconded with the diamond before the museum opened the next morning.   **Page 211**

ORIGINAL SENTENCE: _____

_____

obstinate (äb′stə•nit) *adj.* stubborn. ▶ The Latin parts of this word mean "to stand against." ■ Although Marcella thought she was standing up for what she believed, her friends considered her merely obstinate.   **Page 214**

ORIGINAL SENTENCE: _____

_____

gesticulation (jes•tik´yə•lā´shən) *n.* a motion made with the hands to add force or meaning to one's speech. ▶ *Gesticulation* and *gesture* are synonyms. ■ ''Your gesticulations are distracting,'' the speech teacher told Robin as she rehearsed her speech. **Page 213**

ORIGINAL SENTENCE: _____

_____

crypt (kript) *n.* a burial chamber, usually under the floor of a church. ▶ This word shares a common Greek ancestor with the English word *cryptic,* which means ''having a hidden meaning.'' ■ For a small fee, tourists in Munich can visit the crypt where many of the Bavarian kings are buried. **Page 213**

ORIGINAL SENTENCE: _____

_____

circumscribing (sʉr´kəm•skrīb´iŋ) *adj.* a form of *to circumscribe,* which means ''to limit; to restrict the action of.'' ▶ The prefix *circum-* means ''around,'' and the base word *-scribe-* means ''to write or draw.'' You can remember the meaning of this word by thinking of drawing a line around something as a way to restrict it. ■ The dog ran around the yard of his new home sniffing at the circumscribing chain-link fence. **Page 213**

ORIGINAL SENTENCE: _____

_____

endeavored (in•dev´ərd) *v.* past tense of *to endeavor,* which means ''to make a serious attempt; to try.'' ▶ This word is based on a French word meaning ''duty.'' ■ Although he will be busy with work, Jorge says he will endeavor to read one book each week this summer. **Page 213**

ORIGINAL SENTENCE: _____

_____

PRACTICE TEST

Directions: In the blank at the right, write the vocabulary word that fits each definition at the left. *(10 points each)*

| precluded | absconded | endeavored | imposture | crypt |
| redresser | gesticulation | obstinate | accosted | circumscribing |

1. hand motion   1. _____

2. prevented   2. _____

3. stubborn   3. _____

4. made a serious attempt   4. _____

5. deception; fraud   5. _____

6. restricting or limiting   6. _____

7. an underground burial place   7. _____

8. ran away and hid   8. _____

9. approached and greeted rudely   9. _____

10. a person who makes something right 10. _____

THE NECKLACE   Guy de Maupassant   (Textbook page 218)

DEVELOPING VOCABULARY

Directions: Read carefully the explanation of each word. Then write a sentence of your own using that word. Include in your sentence clues to the meaning of the word.

dowry (dou′rē) ***n.*** property brought to her husband by a woman at the time of marriage. ▶ This word is related to *endow,* which means "to give or provide." ■ It is rare nowadays that a woman is required to give her husband a <u>dowry</u> in order to get married. **Page 218**

ORIGINAL SENTENCE: _____

_____

dinginess (din′jē•nis) ***n.*** dirtiness; shabbiness. ▶ This word is closely related to *dung,* which means "manure." ■ Thad's father used bleach to wash out the <u>dinginess</u> of his son's gym clothes. **Page 218**

ORIGINAL SENTENCE: _____

_____

instinctive (in•stiŋk′tiv) ***adj.*** natural; not learned. ▶ This word derives from *instinct,* which is an inborn skill or drive, rather than one developed after birth. ■ Lucy seems to have an <u>instinctive</u> ability to make money with almost no effort. **Page 218**

ORIGINAL SENTENCE: _____

_____

incessantly (in•ses′′nt•lē) ***adv.*** continually. ▶ The prefix *in-* means "not," and the root *-cess-* means "to stop." Thus *incessantly* means "without stopping." ■ The small child chattered <u>incessantly</u>. **Page 218**

ORIGINAL SENTENCE: _____

_____

disconsolate (dis•kän′sə•lit) ***adj.*** so unhappy that nothing will provide comfort. ▶ The prefix *dis-* here means "not," and the root *-consol-* means "to give comfort." ■ Timmy was <u>disconsolate</u> following the death of Max, his puppy. **Page 218**

ORIGINAL SENTENCE: _____

_____

vexation (vek•sā′shən) ***n.*** annoyance. ▶ This word is derived from a Latin word meaning "to shake." ■ Mosquitoes can be a great <u>vexation</u> on a camping trip. **Page 219**

ORIGINAL SENTENCE: _____

_____

pauper (pô′pər) *n.* an extremely poor person. ▶ *Pauper* and *poor* are derived from the same Latin word. ■ At one time, if you were a <u>pauper</u>, you had to live on a farm run by the county government, which provided support for the poor. **Page 219**

ORIGINAL SENTENCE: _____

_____

predicament (pri•dik′ə•mənt) *n.* a difficult, embarrassing, or unpleasant situation. ▶ Two everyday words with the same meaning as *predicament* are *fix* and *pickle*. ■ When the check for dinner arrived, Geraldo discovered that he had forgotten his wallet, and he wondered how he could possibly get out of this *predicament*. **Page 219**

ORIGINAL SENTENCE: _____

_____

scanty (skan′tē) *adj.* not enough; insufficient. ▶ The Old Norse word on which this word was built meant "short." ■ The city council had forbidden the wearing of <u>scanty</u> swimsuits at the public beach. **Page 222**

ORIGINAL SENTENCE: _____

_____

exorbitant (ig•zôr′bə•tənt) *adj.* beyond what is usual or proper. ▶ This word derives from a Latin prefix meaning "out" and a base word meaning "orbit." ■ My parents consider that $100 is an <u>exorbitant</u> price to pay for a blouse. **Page 222**

ORIGINAL SENTENCE: _____

_____

PRACTICE TEST

Directions: Circle the letter of the best meaning for each word. *(10 points each)*

1. exorbitant: **a.** very tired **b.** easy to doubt **c.** going beyond what is usual **d.** lacking human qualities

2. scanty: **a.** complicted **b.** not enough **c.** happening continuously **d.** very sad

3. predicament: **a.** large payment **b.** undeserved success **c.** pretty picture **d.** difficult situation

4. pauper: **a.** poor person **b.** short walk **c.** annoying situation **d.** country ruled by one person

5. vexation: **a.** uncivilized action **b.** annoyance **c.** burial place **d.** vacation

6. disconsolate: **a.** unable to be comforted **b.** without pity **c.** stubborn **d.** larger than expected

7. incessantly: **a.** courteously **b.** slowly **c.** continually **d.** rudely

8. instinctive: **a.** angry **b.** natural **c.** offensive **d.** new

9. dinginess: **a.** price **b.** original thought **c.** energy **d.** dirtiness

10. dowry: **a.** bride's offering **b.** woman's marriage clothes **c.** groom's friend **d.** husband's father

THE GIANT WATER BUG   Annie Dillard   (Textbook page 377)

DEVELOPING VOCABULARY

Directions: Read carefully the explanation of each word. Then write a sentence of your own using that word. Include in your sentence clues to the meaning of the word.

dire (dīr) *adj.* causing extreme distress; dreadful; terrible.   ▶ *Dire* is based on a Latin word meaning "fearful."   ■ When he lost his job, my uncle soon found himself in dire financial need.   **Page 377**

ORIGINAL SENTENCE: _____

_____

schematic (skē•mat′ik) *adj.* having the nature of a plan.   ▶ This word is related to the word *scheme*, a carefully arranged plan of action, particularly one that is secret. *Schematic*, however, does not suggest secrecy; it suggests the abstract quality of a blueprint or diagram.   ■ The engineer used a schematic drawing to plan the new subway system.   **Page 377**

ORIGINAL SENTENCE: _____

_____

to rumple (rum′p′l) *v.* to crumple; to make or become disheveled.   ▶ Do not confuse this word with *rumble*, which means "to make a deep rolling sound like thunder."   ■ The travel consultant explained how poor packing can rumple clothing in a suitcase. **Page 378**

ORIGINAL SENTENCE: _____

_____

scum (skum) *n.* a layer of material that forms on the top of a liquid.   ▶ *Scum* can also mean "trash."   ■ I can't stand the scum that coats the top of some ponds.   **Page 378**

ORIGINAL SENTENCE: _____

_____

appalled (ə•pôld′) *adj.* a form of *to appall*, which means "to shock or horrify."   ▶ This word comes from an Old French word meaning "to grow pale." You can remember its meaning by thinking about someone turning pale with horror.   ■ Donna was appalled by the report of the parents' cruelty to their young child.   **Page 378**

ORIGINAL SENTENCE: _____

_____

tadpoles (tad′pōlz′) *n. pl.* young frogs or toads.   ▶ This word comes from Middle English words meaning "toad" and "head," since a tadpole is a young toad that seems to be all head.   ■ One fond memory from my childhood is catching tadpoles in the pond of my grandfather's farm.   **Page 378**

ORIGINAL SENTENCE: _____

_____

taut (tôt) *adj.* stretched tightly. ► *Taut* is related to the word *tow*, which means "to pull." ■ Pegs are driven around a tent in order to pull the sides <u>taut</u>. **Page 378**

ORIGINAL SENTENCE: _____

_____

paralyzes (par′ə•līz′iz) *v.* produces a state of inactivity in. ► The noun form of this word, *paralysis*, was borrowed from Latin. Then the verb form was created out of the noun by the process known as back-formation. ■ Curare, used on arrows by South American Indians to <u>paralyze</u> small animals, is now the basis of useful medicines. **Page 378**

ORIGINAL SENTENCE: _____

_____

enzymes (en′zīmz) *n. pl.* substances that speed up a chemical process in the body. ► Many Greek words, such as the one that *enzymes* is based on, use *y* rather than *i* to indicate the long *i* sound. ■ Saliva contains an <u>enzyme</u> that makes food easier to digest. **Page 378**

ORIGINAL SENTENCE: _____

_____

amphibian (am•fib′ē•ən) *n.* a type of animal that first breathes through gills like a fish, then develops lungs. ► The Greek root of this word means "living a double life." You can remember this word's meaning by thinking of the double life amphibians lead, in water and on land. ■ The frog is a good example of an <u>amphibian</u>. **Page 377**

ORIGINAL SENTENCE: _____

_____

PRACTICE TEST

Directions: In front of each number, write **T** if the statement is true and **F** if the statement is false. *(10 points each)*

_____ **1.** A *dire* situation is likely to make a person happy.

_____ **2.** *Tadpoles* can be thought of as adult frogs.

_____ **3.** A raccoon is a common type of *amphibian*.

_____ **4.** *Scum* can be found mixed evenly throughout a liquid.

_____ **5.** If children bounce on a bed, they will probably *rumple* the bedspread.

_____ **6.** If all *enzymes* were removed from the human body, the body would not function very efficiently.

_____ **7.** A *schematic* plan lays out a clear diagram.

_____ **8.** A *taut* rope gives a lot of slack.

_____ **9.** Living conditions that *appalled* you probably made you smile.

_____ **10.** A broken neck sometimes *paralyzes* a person.

VOCABULARY ACTIVITY WORKSHEET

22

THE NIGHT THE BED FELL   James Thurber   (Textbook page 379)

DEVELOPING VOCABULARY

Directions: Read carefully the explanation of each word. Then write a sentence of your own using that word. Include in your sentence clues to the meaning of the word.

passel (pas′′l) *n.* a fairly large group or collection. ▶ This word is considered to be colloquial; that is, it is used in informal situations. ■ "There was quite a passel of kinfolks at the family reunion," Grandmother told me. **Page 379**

ORIGINAL SENTENCE: _____

_____

premonition (prē′mə•nish′ən) *n.* a feeling that something is going to happen. ▶ This word is based on a Latin word that means "to warn before," so you can think of a premonition as a feeling that warns you about something before it happens. ■ Mrs. Garcia says she's had a premonition that she will soon get an important telephone call from her niece. **Page 379**

ORIGINAL SENTENCE: _____

_____

calamity (kə•lam′ə•tē) *n.* disaster. ▶ A legendary character of the Old West was called *Calamity Jane* because she brought disaster to the people she robbed and to the sheriffs who tried to catch her. ■ It is hard to know which was the greater calamity—the earthquake that hit San Francisco in 1906 or the huge fire that followed it. **Page 380**

ORIGINAL SENTENCE: _____

_____

fortitude (fôr′tə•tōōd′) *n.* strength; courage. ▶ This word is derived from the same Latin word as *fort*. An everyday slang word that means the same is *guts*. ■ Only great fortitude made it possible for Mrs. Raines to rush into the burning building three times in order to rescue the children. **Page 380**

ORIGINAL SENTENCE: _____

_____

canopy (kan′ə•pē) *n.* a covering, often over a bed, doorway, or airplane cockpit. ▶ This word is derived from a Greek word meaning "gnat," and originally meant a couch with curtains to keep out insects. ■ Judy stood under the canopy of the huge doorway, trying to avoid the rain. **Page 380**

ORIGINAL SENTENCE: _____

_____

deluge (del′yōōj) *n.* a flood. ▶ This word is based on a Latin word that means "to wash away." Think of a deluge as a flood that washes everything away. ■ As soon as school was out, a deluge began, and I was drenched on the way to the car. **Page 380**

ORIGINAL SENTENCE: _____

_____

pungent (pun′jənt) *adj.* smelling or tasting sharp; spicy. ▶ *Puncture* and *pungent* come from the same Latin word, meaning ''to pierce.'' Think of pungent food as piercing or puncturing your taste buds or your sense of smell. ■ As we walked past the food vendor's cart, we smelled the <u>pungent</u> aroma of garlic. **Page 380**

ORIGINAL SENTENCE: _____

_____

culprit (kul′prit) *n.* a criminal; a guilty person. ▶ A useful related word is *culpable*, which means ''deserving blame.'' ■ The last page of a mystery novel usually reveals who the <u>culprit</u> is. **Page 381**

ORIGINAL SENTENCE: _____

_____

ominous (äm′ə•nəs) *adj.* threatening. ▶ The base word *omen*, from which *ominous* derives, means ''a thing or event that warns about the future.'' ■ An <u>ominous</u> rumble in the southwest announced an impending thunderstorm. **Page 379**

ORIGINAL SENTENCE: _____

_____

uncanny (un•kan′ē) *adj.* weird; mysterious. ▶ This word is a combination of the familiar prefix *un-,* meaning ''not,'' plus the base word *-can-,* meaning ''know.'' You can think of something uncanny as something that is unknown and mysterious. ■ Latoya has the <u>uncanny</u> ability to predict who's calling when the telephone rings. **Page 381**

ORIGINAL SENTENCE: _____

_____

PRACTICE TEST

Directions: In the blank at the right, write the vocabulary word that is an approximate synonym for the word at the left. *(10 points each)*

passel	canopy	ominous	calamity	pungent
premonition	deluge	uncanny	fortitude	culprit

1. warning   1. _____

2. disaster   2. _____

3. covering   3. _____

4. strength   4. _____

5. collection   5. _____

6. weird   6. _____

7. threatening   7. _____

8. sharp   8. _____

9. criminal   9. _____

10. flood   10. _____

23

THE WASHWOMAN   Isaac Bashevis Singer   (Textbook page 384)

DEVELOPING VOCABULARY

Directions: Read carefully the explanation of each word. Then write a sentence of your own using that word. Include in your sentence clues to the meaning of the word.

rancor (raŋ′kər) *n.* hatred; ill will.   ▶ Both *rancor* and *rancid* come from the same Latin root, which means "to stink."   ■ The <u>rancor</u> between the two teams threatened to turn into violence as the game got more and more tense.   **Page 386**

ORIGINAL SENTENCE: _____

_____

affront (ə•frunt′) *n.* an open insult.   ▶ The Latin word from which *affront* derives means "to encounter face to face."   ■ I considered Sarah's suggestion that I go home and change before we went out a real <u>affront</u>.   **Page 386**

ORIGINAL SENTENCE: _____

_____

institution (in′stə•tōō′shən) *n.* an established custom, system, or way of doing things.   ▶ The base word *-stitu-* means "to set up."   ■ Having breakfast at Andy's Restaurant on Saturday has become practically an <u>institution</u> for me and my friends.   **Page 386**

ORIGINAL SENTENCE: _____

_____

atonement (ə•tōn′mənt) *n.* amends made for doing something wrong.   ▶ In Middle English, *at-onen* meant "at one"; therefore, *atonement* means "becoming 'at one' with another person again."   ■ I brought flowers home to my mother as <u>atonement</u> for shouting at her last night.   **Page 386**

ORIGINAL SENTENCE: _____

_____

parasitic (par′ə•sit′ik) *adj.* living at the expense of another.   ▶ This word comes from a Greek word that means "a person who eats at the table of another." A person can be parasitic; so can an animal that lives off another living animal, such as a tick.   ■ My father finally confronted his <u>parasitic</u> brother, the one who always borrows money and never pays it back.   **Page 386**

ORIGINAL SENTENCE: _____

_____

dear (dir) *adj.* high-priced; costly; expensive.   ▶ The more familiar meaning of this word is "beloved" or "much loved." You can imagine that if something is well loved, it might be sold at a high price.   ■ Because coffee became so <u>dear</u> during World War II, most people turned to coffee substitutes made from grain.   **Page 386**

ORIGINAL SENTENCE: _____

_____

vagrants (vā′grənts) *n. pl.* wanderers, especially those with no regular homes or jobs. ▶ The oldest form of this word meant "to walk," so a vagrant is someone who is always wandering or walking. ■ A vagrant came to our door asking for work. **Page 387**

ORIGINAL SENTENCE: _____

_____

catastrophe (kə•tas′trə•fē) *n.* a great and sudden disaster or misfortune. ▶ The Greek root of this word meant "to overturn," suggesting that a catastrophe turns someone's world upside down. ■ Losing my bike was a catastrophe for me, because I depend on it for my paper route. **Page 387**

ORIGINAL SENTENCE: _____

_____

benediction (ben′ə•dik′shən) *n.* a blessing. ▶ This word is based on the Latin prefix *bene-*, meaning "well," and the root *-dicere-*, meaning "to speak." ■ The minister ended the service with a short benediction. **Page 387**

ORIGINAL SENTENCE: _____

_____

recompense (rek′əm•pens′) *n.* payment made for services. ▶ This word has the same root as *to compensate*, which means "to make up for." ■ I believed the Baezes deserved recompense for all the trouble I'd caused them. **Page 387**

ORIGINAL SENTENCE: _____

_____

PRACTICE TEST

Directions: In front of each number, write **A** if the words are antonyms and **S** if they are synonyms. *(10 points each)*

_____ **1.** vagrants—wanderers

_____ **2.** benediction—blessing

_____ **3.** affront—compliment

_____ **4.** rancor—affection

_____ **5.** parasitic—generous

_____ **6.** institution—custom

_____ **7.** recompense—repayment

_____ **8.** dear—cheap

_____ **9.** atonement—amends

_____**10.** catastrophe—disaster

CHARLEY IN YELLOWSTONE   John Steinbeck
(Textbook page 389)

DEVELOPING VOCABULARY

Directions: Read carefully the explanation of each word. Then write a sentence of your
own using that word. Include in your sentence clues to the meaning of the word.

tranquility (traŋ•kwil′ə•tē) *n.* quiet; calm;
serenity. ▶ This word can also be properly
spelled with two *l*'s. ■ The <u>tranquility</u> of a
mountain meadow can soothe even the most
tense person. **Page 389**

ORIGINAL SENTENCE: _____

ambled (am′bəld) *v.* past tense of *to amble,*
which means "to walk leisurely." ▶ The
Latin root of this word means "to walk,"
and forms the basis of other English words
like *ambulatory* and *ambulance.* ■ The old
dog <u>ambled</u> over to his food bowl, sniffed
halfheartedly, and turned away. **Page 391**

ORIGINAL SENTENCE: _____

cuff (kuf) *n.* a slap or blow. ▶ This
meaning is less familiar than using *cuff* to
mean "the fold at the end of a sleeve or
trouser leg." ■ Every time I see my little
brother start to suck his thumb, I give his
hand a playful <u>cuff</u> to remind him to stop.
Page 391

ORIGINAL SENTENCE: _____

palpable (pal′pə•b′l) *adj.* able to be touched,
felt, or handled; easy to perceive. ▶ The
verb *palpate* means "to examine by
touching," the way a doctor presses on the
abdomen to check for a swollen liver.
■ When Liz entered the locker room, she was
met with an angry silence that was almost
<u>palpable</u>. **Page 391**

ORIGINAL SENTENCE: _____

ranted (rant′id) *v.* past tense of *to rant,*
which means "to talk loudly and wildly."
▶ *To rant* is probably derived from a Greek
word meaning "to be noisy." ■ Unhappy
with his seating assignment, the passenger
<u>ranted</u> about the poor service he was getting.
Page 391

ORIGINAL SENTENCE: _____

maniac (mā′nē•ak′) *n.* a person with a wild
or violent mental disorder. ▶ This word is
related to *mania,* which can also mean "an
excessive liking for something," as in
Beatlemania. ■ She ran from one locked
door to another like a <u>maniac</u>, trying to
escape the small room. **Page 391**

ORIGINAL SENTENCE: _____

scuttled (skut′′ld) *v.* past tense of *to scuttle*, which means "to run quickly; to scurry." ▶ Another meaning of *to scuttle* is "to sink a ship deliberately by making holes in its bottom." ■ The cat watched the cockroach scuttle across the floor and disappear under the refrigerator. **Page 391**

ORIGINAL SENTENCE: _____

_____

depleted (di•plēt′id) *adj.* a form of *to deplete,* which means "to use up gradually; to empty or exhaust." ▶ The Latin prefix *de-* means "from," and the root *plere* means "to fill." ■ I'm afraid that if I stay on vacation more than three days, I will be totally depleted of cash. **Page 391**

ORIGINAL SENTENCE: _____

_____

pandemonium (pan′də•mō′nē•əm) *n.* a wild uproar. ▶ This word is derived from Greek words meaning "all devils," referring to the place where all demons live, or hell. ■ Michael created pandemonium in his biology class when he opened a cage of white mice. **Page 391**

ORIGINAL SENTENCE: _____

_____

belching (belch′iŋ) *adj.* a form of *to belch,* which means "to gush or spurt spasmodically." ▶ The most familiar meaning of this word is "expelling gas from the stomach through the mouth with a burping sound." However, a furnace may belch fire, a smokestack may belch smoke, and so on. ■ The television program on science showed footage of smoke and lava belching from the center of an active volcano. **Page 391**

ORIGINAL SENTENCE: _____

_____

PRACTICE TEST

Directions: In front of each number, write the letter of the definition that best matches each vocabulary word. *(10 points each)*

_____ 1. maniac

_____ 2. belching

_____ 3. tranquility

_____ 4. pandemonium

_____ 5. depleted

_____ 6. ranted

_____ 7. cuff

_____ 8. ambled

_____ 9. palpable

_____ 10. scuttled

a. quiet; calm

b. slap

c. spoke wildly

d. moved quickly

e. to sleep soundly

f. disorder and uproar

g. spurting

h. emptied or exhausted

i. a person with a violent mental disorder

j. a penniless person

k. able to be touched

l. capable of anger

m. walked leisurely away

FROM COMING INTO THE COUNTRY   John McPhee
(Textbook page 398)

DEVELOPING VOCABULARY

Directions: Read carefully the explanation of each word. Then write a sentence of your own using that word. Include in your sentence clues to the meaning of the word.

sarcophagus (sär•käf′ə•gəs) *n.* a stone coffin. ▶ This word comes from a Greek word that meant "to eat flesh," because the limestone used for this kind of coffin caused the contents to decay quickly. ■ Instead of burying the emperor in the ground, the adoring citizens erected a grand sarcophagus to hold his remains. **Page 399**

ORIGINAL SENTENCE: _____

_____

promontory (präm′ən•tôr′ē) *n.* a peak of high land sticking out into a body of water. ▶ This word is closely related to *prominent,* which means "sticking out" or "widely known." ■ Barbara's parents built their house on a wind-swept *promontory* overlooking Puget Sound. **Page 399**

ORIGINAL SENTENCE: _____

_____

exodus (ek′sə•dəs) *n.* a departure, especially of a group of people. ▶ The prefix *ex-* means "out." You can think of an exodus as the act of leaving or going *out.* ■ Rumors of an impending hurricane caused an exodus of tourists from the resort towns along the coast. **Page 399**

ORIGINAL SENTENCE: _____

_____

tundra (tun′drə) *n.* a vast treeless plain in the Arctic. ▶ This word was borrowed from Russian, not surprisingly, since the Soviet Union includes many acres of tundra. ■ We thought we saw a woman staggering toward us across the frozen tundra. **Page 401**

ORIGINAL SENTENCE: _____

_____

williwaws (wil′i•wôz′) *n. pl.* sudden, violent cold winds. ▶ This word may be a variation of *willy-willy,* which means "a cyclone" or "whirlwind." ■ The williwaw blew the snow almost horizontally, making it impossible to locate the trail. **Page 402**

ORIGINAL SENTENCE: _____

_____

abraded (ə•brād′id) *adj.* a form of *to abrade,* which means "to scrape or rub off." ▶ Related English words are *abrasive*— "grating"—and *abrasion*—"a scrape." ■ Horseback riders often use a blanket so that the skin on the horse's back will not become abraded. **Page 400**

ORIGINAL SENTENCE: _____

_____

oblique (ə•blēk′) *adj.* slanting; at an angle; not straight. ▶ This word can be used in a literal sense to mean ''slanting'' or to refer to actions that are not straightforward. ■ The car veered off the track on an oblique course that took it crashing into the grandstand. **Page 401**

ORIGINAL SENTENCE: _____

_____

refurbishment (ri•fur′bish•mənt) *n.* renovation; brightening; polishing up to make bright again. ▶ The prefix *re-* means ''again''; *furbish* (usually followed by *up*) is a rarely used English word meaning ''to polish'' or ''to make attractive again.'' ■ Following its refurbishment, the hotel was able to attract as many guests as in the old days. **Page 401**

ORIGINAL SENTENCE: _____

_____

oblivion (ə•bliv′ē•ən) *n.* the state of being forgotten. ▶ *Oblivion* is probably based on a Latin word meaning ''smooth.'' A related word, *oblivious,* means ''not noticing.'' ■ Although I memorized the Spanish vocabulary thoroughly, by the time of the test, my knowledge of it had disappeared into oblivion. **Page 401**

ORIGINAL SENTENCE: _____

_____

mukluks (muk′luks′) *n. pl.* waterproof boots. ▶ *Mukluk* is the Eskimo name for a large seal, and because Eskimos make boots from sealskin, *mukluk* came to refer to boots. ■ Without a pair of mukluks you can be sure that your feet will get soaking wet in weather like this. **Page 400**

ORIGINAL SENTENCE: _____

_____

PRACTICE TEST

Directions: In front of each number, write **T** if the statement is true or **F** if the statement is false. *(10 points each)*

_____ **1.** An interior decorator could be helpful in the *refurbishment* of a person's apartment.

_____ **2.** If you plan to stay long on the *tundra,* it is best to wear light clothing and stay out of the sun.

_____ **3.** *Oblivion* is a place full of conflict and suffering.

_____ **4.** A pair of *mukluks* is very useful in the winter.

_____ **5.** A *sarcophagus* is a stone coffin.

_____ **6.** If you leap from a *promontory,* it is likely you will land in water.

_____ **7.** The book of the Bible called *Exodus* probably deals with a group of people leaving one place on their way to another.

_____ **8.** When a sailboat is steered at an *oblique* angle, it is headed directly for its destination.

_____ **9.** *Williwaws* are warm breezes.

_____**10.** A tight leather strap will probably result in *abraded* skin unless something cushions it.

EVERYTHING IN ITS PATH Kai Erickson (Textbook page 407)

DEVELOPING VOCABULARY

Directions: Read carefully the explanation of each word. Then write a sentence of your own using that word. Include in your sentence clues to the meaning of the word.

affluent (af'loo•wənt) *adj.* wealthy; rich. ► The Latin word on which *affluent* is based means "to flow." You can remember this word's meaning by thinking of wealth as flowing toward affluent people. ■ <u>Affluent</u> people, such as Andrew Carnegie, may sometimes be generous in using their wealth to improve the lives of others. **Page 407**

ORIGINAL SENTENCE: _____

_____

impoverished (im•pav'ər•isht) *adj.* a form of *to impoverish,* which means "to make poor or penniless." ► *Impoverished* comes from the same root as *poverty,* which means "the state of being poor." Someone who is impoverished has been reduced to poverty. ■ The <u>impoverished</u> man thought of the days when he had had more money. **Page 407**

ORIGINAL SENTENCE: _____

_____

impoundment (im•pound'mənt) *n.* an enclosure that gathers water for irrigation. ► This word has two other useful meanings: "shutting up an animal in a pound" and "taking and holding in legal custody." ■ Upstream from his farm, Mr. Rodriguez built an <u>impoundment</u> to store water for the long, dry summers. **Page 407**

ORIGINAL SENTENCE: _____

_____

slag (slag) *n.* impure materials separated from useful minerals during mining or smelting. ► Do not confuse *slag* with *slake,* a verb meaning "to satisfy a desire such as thirst." ■ The ugly hills of brown <u>slag</u> ruined the landscape until the companies were required to restore the land to its original condition. **Page 408**

ORIGINAL SENTENCE: _____

_____

viscous (vis'kəs) *adj.* having the consistency of a sticky fluid. ► Do not confuse this word with *vicious,* which means "evil, harmful, or mean." ■ The <u>viscous</u> paint dried slowly. **Page 408**

ORIGINAL SENTENCE: _____

_____

to clamber (klam'bər) *v.* to climb using both hands and feet, especially in a somewhat clumsy way. ► This word is derived from an Old Norse word meaning "to climb." ■ In order to return to the car, we had to <u>clamber</u> over large boulders at the river's edge. **Page 412**

ORIGINAL SENTENCE: _____

_____

to accentuate (ak•sen′choo•wāt′) *v.* to emphasize or stress. ▶ This word is closely related to *accent* in both origin and meaning. ■ His energetic gestures helped to <u>accentuate</u> his enthusiasm as he described his project to the eager audience. **Page 415**

ORIGINAL SENTENCE: _____

_____

precarious (pri•ker′ē•əs) *adj.* risky; insecure; uncertain. ▶ *Precarious* and *prayer* are both derived from a Latin word meaning "obtained by begging." *Precarious* does not suggest begging, however; rather, it suggests something shaky. ■ From a <u>precarious</u> perch in the top of a tall tree, Luisa watched for the approach of the other group of scouts. **Page 419**

ORIGINAL SENTENCE: _____

_____

carnage (kär′nij) *n.* slaughter; massacre; bloodshed; dead bodies. ▶ The Latin root of this word means "flesh," from which is also derived the English word *carnivore,* a meat-eating animal. ■ The battlefield was strewn with the <u>carnage</u> of war. **Page 409**

ORIGINAL SENTENCE: _____

_____

disconsolately (dis•kän′sə•lit•lē) *adv.* cheerlessly; sadly; so unhappily that nothing will comfort. ▶ The prefix *dis-* has several meanings, including "away" and "not." ■ Mrs. Rayburne stared <u>disconsolately</u> at her home that had been destroyed by the tornado. **Page 416**

ORIGINAL SENTENCE: _____

_____

PRACTICE TEST

Directions: Circle the letter of the best meaning for each word. *(10 points each)*

1. carnage:　　**a.** bloodshed　　**b.** promises　　**c.** food supplies　　**d.** directions

2. to accentuate:　　**a.** to reject　　**b.** to decrease　　**c.** to emphasize　　**d.** to make poor

3. viscous:　　**a.** having the consistency of a sticky liquid　　**b.** characterized by anger and hatred　　**c.** lacking feelings of pity　　**d.** similar to a frog or toad

4. to clamber:　　**a.** to make a loud noise　　**b.** to climb　　**c.** to ring a bell　　**d.** to save a drowning person

5. slag:　　**a.** liquid drunk when thirsty　　**b.** brief speech　　**c.** male deer　　**d.** impurities left from mining

6. impoverished:　　**a.** made guilty　　**b.** made poor　　**c.** turned into something completely different　　**d.** related to music

7. affluent:　　**a.** rich　　**b.** costly　　**c.** powerful　　**d.** famous

8. impoundment:　　**a.** heavy weight　　**b.** stray dog　　**c.** enclosure for water　　**d.** unit for measuring weight

9. disconsolately:　　**a.** in a bored manner　　**b.** eagerly　　**c.** in a confident way　　**d.** very sadly

10. precarious:　　**a.** wealthy　　**b.** unnatural　　**c.** restful　　**d.** risky

ANNAPURNA   **Maurice Herzog**   **(Textbook page 423)**

DEVELOPING VOCABULARY

Directions: Read carefully the explanation of each word. Then write a sentence of your own using that word. Include in your sentence clues to the meaning of the word.

sapped (sapt) *v.* past tense of *to sap,* which means "to weaken or to drain." ▶ This is a verb form of *sap.* The noun form has three meanings: "the juice that nourishes a plant," "any fluid necessary for life," and "energy" or "vigor." ■ The heat and humidity of New Orleans in summer <u>sapped</u> our energy. **Page 427**

ORIGINAL SENTENCE: _____

_____

diminished (də•min′isht) *adj.* a form of *to diminish,* which means "to make smaller; to lessen, reduce, or decrease." ▶ The root of *to diminish* is related to the English word *minus.* ■ John Donne, the poet, said that our lives are <u>diminished</u> when others die because we are all in some way connected to every other human being. **Page 424**

ORIGINAL SENTENCE: _____

_____

hurtling (hurt′′liŋ) *adj.* a form of *to hurtle,* which means "to move with great speed." ▶ A second meaning of *to hurtle* is "to throw." You can think of something moving at great speed—hurtling—as though it were throwing itself forward. ■ The failure of its brakes sent the truck <u>hurtling</u> down the mountain road out of control. **Page 424**

ORIGINAL SENTENCE: _____

_____

chaos (kā′äs) *n.* confusion; disorder. ▶ The Greek word that *chaos* was borrowed from referred to the disorder that existed in space before the universe was created. ■ The first day of school is always marked by <u>chaos</u>, as students try to locate new classes and teachers cope with extra tasks. **Page 425**

ORIGINAL SENTENCE: _____

_____

wrenched (rencht) *v.* past tense of *to wrench,* which means "to twist, pull, or jerk suddenly or violently." ▶ *To wrench* is similar in meaning to *to wrest,* but the latter term has the connotation of taking away, whereas *to wrench* suggests a twisting motion. ■ Mrs. Ming was careful not to <u>wrench</u> her back as she moved the typewriter. **Page 426**

ORIGINAL SENTENCE: _____

_____

instinctively (in•stiŋk′tiv•lē) *adv.* in a natural, inborn way. ▶ This word is based on a Latin word meaning "to drive" or "to cause to happen." ■ Sheila seemed to know instinctively what colors to wear together. **Page 425**

ORIGINAL SENTENCE: _____

_____

frenzied (fren′zēd) *adj.* a form of *to frenzy*, which means "to make frantic or to drive mad." ▶ *To frenzy* comes from a Greek word meaning "inflammation of the brain." ■ The hotel staff engaged in <u>frenzied</u> preparation for the arrival of the Duchess of York. **Page 424**

ORIGINAL SENTENCE: _____

_____

couloir (kōōl•wär′) *n.* a deep valley with steep sides; a gorge. ▶ *Couloir* is related to the French word *coulee* (gorge). ■ The hikers decided to rest before attempting to scale the sides of the <u>couloir</u>. **Page 424**

ORIGINAL SENTENCE: _____

_____

to rouse (rouz) *v.* to stir up or awaken. ▶ *To rouse* was originally used in hunting, meaning "to cause game to come out of hiding." ■ I shook Todd violently to <u>rouse</u> him from his deep sleep. **Page 427**

ORIGINAL SENTENCE: _____

_____

to linger (liŋ′gər) *v.* to stay as though reluctant to leave. ▶ Both *linger* and *long* are derived from the same source. ■ Although the party was clearly over, Lindsey wanted to <u>linger</u> awhile, since she was hoping for a chance to talk with Walter. **Page 425**

ORIGINAL SENTENCE: _____

_____

PRACTICE TEST

Directions: Fill in the blank with the vocabulary word that best fits the meaning of the sentence. *(10 points each)*

sapped	to linger	wrenched	instinctively	diminished
to rouse	chaos	frenzied	couloir	hurtling

1. The woman used a stick _____ the sleeping animal.

2. The car was about to be hit by the boulder that was _____ onto the mountain highway.

3. Without a chairperson, the meeting quickly fell into _____.

4. A flimsy bridge was the only way we had to cross the _____.

5. With guests in the house, our supply of coffee _____ daily.

6. Having left her project until the last minute, Carolyn had to spend the weekend in _____ work.

7. It _____ my heart to see the child so sick.

8. We wanted _____ after dinner, but Dad said we had to hurry.

9. His illness had _____ his strength.

10. When most people hear a loud noise, they jump _____.

DEVELOPING VOCABULARY

Directions: Read carefully the explanation of each word. Then write a sentence of your own using that word. Include in your sentence clues to the meaning of the word.

destitution (des′tə•tōō′shən) **n.** poverty. ► This word comes from a Latin word meaning "to desert." ■ When the stock market crash occurred, many millionaires went from affluence to <u>destitution</u> almost overnight.   **Page 437**

ORIGINAL SENTENCE: _____

_____

desolate (des′ə•lit) **adj.** lonely; joyless; sorrowful.   ► This word also can mean "uninhabited" or "deserted."   ■ Without her faithful dog Trixie, Anita was <u>desolate</u>. **Page 437**

ORIGINAL SENTENCE: _____

_____

illiterate (i•lit′ər•it) **adj.** uneducated; especially, unable to read and write.   ► The prefix *il-*, like *in-* and *un-*, means "not." ■ Try to imagine how difficult it must be for an <u>illiterate</u> person to get along in today's world.   **Page 437**

ORIGINAL SENTENCE: _____

_____

to defray (di•frā′) **v.** to furnish the money for; pay for.   ► Do not confuse *defray* with *defy*, which means "to resist" or "to dare." ■ The Pep Club held a bake sale and other fund-raising events to <u>defray</u> the expenses of our fall dance.   **Page 438**

ORIGINAL SENTENCE: _____

_____

dilapidated (di•lap′ə•dāt′id) **adj.** falling to pieces; neglected; broken down.   ► This word is based on a Latin word meaning "to demolish."   ■ The lot was empty except for a <u>dilapidated</u> shack with broken windows and a sagging door.   **Page 438**

ORIGINAL SENTENCE: _____

_____

manic (man′ik) **adj.** afflicted with the emotional disorder known as mania, in which the person is highly active and excited. ► *Manic* is a technical term in psychiatry; do not confuse it with *maniac*, which means simply "an insane person."   ■ Elizabeth told us that during the <u>manic</u> phase of her illness, she felt full of energy and capable of doing anything she wanted.   **Page 439**

ORIGINAL SENTENCE: _____

_____

to relent (ri•lent′) *v.* to give in; to become less stern or harsh. ▶ The Middle English form of this word meant "to melt."

■ Chandra begged her mother to <u>relent</u> and allow her to spend the weekend at the lake. **Page 439**

ORIGINAL SENTENCE: _____

_____

penances (pen′əns•iz) *n. pl.* punishments accepted to show sorrow for doing something wrong. ▶ This word is related to *penitentiary* (a place where people are put for

punishment), but a penance is undertaken voluntarily, out of remorse. ■ As <u>penance</u> for breaking Mom's tennis racket, I agreed to wax her car. **Page 441**

ORIGINAL SENTENCE: _____

_____

melancholy (mel′ən•käl′ē) *adj.* sad; gloomy; depressed. ▶ In the Middle Ages, people thought sadness resulted from a body fluid called bile, and they used the Greek words

for *black bile* to label this mood. ■ Rainy days make me <u>melancholy</u>, although I know there is no reason to feel sad. **Page 442**

ORIGINAL SENTENCE: _____

_____

mortality (môr•tal′ə•tē) *n.* the state of being subject to death. ▶ The Latin root word *mors* means "death." ■ Most people have

no sense of their own <u>mortality</u> until someone close to them gets sick or dies. **Page 439**

ORIGINAL SENTENCE: _____

_____

PRACTICE TEST

Directions: In front of each number, write **A** if the words are antonyms and **S** if they are synonyms. *(10 points each)*

_____ **1.** desolate—lonely

_____ **2.** mortality—life

_____ **3.** destitution—prosperity

_____ **4.** melancholy—happy

_____ **5.** illiterate—educated

_____ **6.** penances—punishments

_____ **7.** to defray—to pay

_____ **8.** manic—depressed

_____ **9.** dilapidated—broken down

_____ **10.** to relent—to give in

BARRIO BOY   Ernesto Galarza   (Textbook page 446)

DEVELOPING VOCABULARY

Directions: Read carefully the explanation of each word. Then write a sentence of your own using that word. Include in your sentence clues to the meaning of the word.

contraption (kən•trap′shən) *n.* a gadget; a device one does not particularly understand. ▶ This word is generally used in informal speech. ■ Josh had rigged up an elaborate contraption to bring his clothes over to him while he was still in bed. **Page 446**

ORIGINAL SENTENCE: _____

_____

barrio (bär′ē•ō) *n.* a suburb, district, or city neighborhood. ▶ Since this is a Spanish word, it is used mostly to denote neighborhoods where Spanish-speaking people live. ■ Asked where they live, most residents of Guatemala City answer by naming their barrio, rather than by giving their street address. **Page 446**

ORIGINAL SENTENCE: _____

_____

flanked (flaŋkt) *adj.* a form of *to flank,* which means "to be at the side of." ▶ This word is derived from a word meaning "hip"; its noun form means the outer side of the upper part of the thigh. ■ The bowl of flowers at the center of the table was flanked by two candlesticks. **Page 446**

ORIGINAL SENTENCE: _____

_____

benchmark (bench′märk′) *n.* a reference point used in measuring; a significant point. ▶ This word originally referred to a surveyor's mark on a landmark whose position was already known, from which other points were measured. ■ The classic film *Casablanca* became a benchmark in Humphrey Bogart's career; it was his first romantic role. **Page 450**

ORIGINAL SENTENCE: _____

_____

gringo (griŋ′gō) *n.* a foreigner, especially a North American. ▶ This term is used by Latin Americans, most often in a critical way. ■ The couple complained that their favorite beach resort was being overrun by vacationers from the United States, with one especially rude gringo playing his radio very loudly at all hours. **Page 448**

ORIGINAL SENTENCE: _____

_____

to survey (sər•vā′) *v.* to look over; to examine. ▶ The Latin root of this word means "to see." ■ Gustin stopped a moment to survey the crowd. **Page 448**

ORIGINAL SENTENCE: _____

_____

buxom (buk′səm) *adj.* plump, especially referring to having a large bosom. ▶ The Middle English form of this word meant "humble" or "obedient." ■ Ms. Dodd was a <u>buxom</u> woman, with big arms and an ample bosom. **Page 448**

ORIGINAL SENTENCE: _____

_____

runty (runt′ē) *adj.* undersized; small. ▶ The noun form of this word, *runt,* means "the smallest animal in a litter." ■ Josh was always rather <u>runty</u> until he reached age twelve and began to grow tall very quickly. **Page 448**

ORIGINAL SENTENCE: _____

_____

withering (with′ər•iŋ) *adj.* a form of *to wither,* which means "to cause someone to feel small by a scornful look." ▶ The most common meaning of this word is "drying up from lack of water," the way a plant does. To wither someone with a look means to look so scornful that the other person "withers" or "dries up" with shame. ■ The senator was well known for the <u>withering</u> glances she gave her opponents. **Page 448**

ORIGINAL SENTENCE: _____

_____

resonant (rez′ə•nənt) *adj.* having a full, deep sound. ▶ The Latin word from which *resonant* comes means "echo." ■ Burt's <u>resonant</u> voice makes me think he'd be a successful newscaster. **Page 450**

ORIGINAL SENTENCE: _____

_____

PRACTICE TEST

Directions: In the blank at the right, write the vocabulary word that fits each definition at the left. *(10 points each)*

contraption	flanked	gringo	to survey	withering
barrio	benchmark	buxom	runty	resonant

1. Spanish for "neighborhood"   1. _____

2. foreigner or North American   2. _____

3. device or gadget   3. _____

4. reference point   4. _____

5. with something at the side of   5. _____

6. having a full, deep sound   6. _____

7. causing to feel small   7. _____

8. undersized   8. _____

9. to look over   9. _____

10. plump   10. _____

THE PHANTOM OF YAZOO   Willie Morris   (Textbook page 452)

DEVELOPING VOCABULARY

Directions: Read carefully the explanation of each word. Then write a sentence of your own using that word. Include in your sentence clues to the meaning of the word.

seer (sir) *n.* a person who can foretell the future; a prophet; a fortuneteller. ▶ This word combines the English word *see* with the suffix *-er* to yield "one who sees." ■ The seer spoke to the man for several minutes, describing the man's past, present, and future in uncanny detail.   **Page 459**

ORIGINAL SENTENCE: _____

_____

acute (ə•kyo͞ot′) *adj.* sharp and severe. ▶ *Acute* is related to the noun *acumen*, which means "mental sharpness." ■ <u>Acute</u> pain is sharp, but ends quickly; chronic pain is dull and lasting.   **Page 453**

ORIGINAL SENTENCE: _____

_____

tortuous (tôr′cho͞o•wəs) *adj.* crooked; full of twists and turns. ▶ This word derives from the same Latin word as *torture*, which originally meant "a twisting." ■ The road across Independence Pass from Denver to Aspen is long and <u>tortuous</u>.   **Page 453**

ORIGINAL SENTENCE: _____

_____

gyrations (jī•rā′shənz) *n. pl.* circular or whirling motions. ▶ A well-known Greek food is *gyro* (pronounced yir′ō), made by rotating lamb or beef on a spit over a fire, so named because of the circular motion of the meat. ■ It made me dizzy just to watch the <u>gyrations</u> of the dancers.   **Page 453**

ORIGINAL SENTENCE: _____

_____

cryptic (krip′tik) *adj.* having a hidden meaning; mysterious. ▶ The related noun, *crypt*, means "a burial place." Both words derive from a Greek word meaning "to hide." ■ The woman left a <u>cryptic</u> note about needing a change of scenery, and disappeared without a trace.   **Page 455**

ORIGINAL SENTENCE: _____

_____

somnolence (säm′nə•lənce) *n.* sleepiness. ▶ The familiar word *insomnia* contains the prefix *in-*, meaning "not." Both words contain the root *somn*, which means "sleep." ■ The droning voice of the boring speaker lulled the audience into <u>somnolence</u>. **Page 455**

ORIGINAL SENTENCE: _____

_____

PRACTICE TEST A

Directions: Complete each analogy by writing in the vocabulary word that fits. For example, black : (is to) white : : (as) brave : (is to) <u>afraid</u>. *(10 points each)*

seer   tortuous   cryptic
acute   gyrations   somnolence

1. rocking chair : rocking :: spinning top : _____

2. past : future :: reporter : _____

3. joy : sorrow :: wakefulness : _____

4. ominous : threatening :: mysterious : _____

5. terrible : dire :: sharp : _____

6. inadequate : sufficient :: straightforward : _____

PRACTICE TEST B

Directions: Fill in the blank with the vocabulary word that best fits the meaning of the sentence. *(10 points each)*

acute   cryptic
tortuous   somnolence

1. Lying in the hammock on a warm summer afternoon, Kurt was soon overcome by _____ .

2. Most daytime TV dramas have such _____ plots that I can never keep up with the many turns they take.

3. Dogs seem to have more _____ hearing than humans.

4. Earline made a _____ comment about her new boyfriend, then refused to say any more.

I KNOW WHY THE CAGED BIRD SINGS   Maya Angelou
(Textbook page 462)

DEVELOPING VOCABULARY

Directions: Read carefully the explanation of each word. Then write a sentence of your own using that word. Include in your sentence clues to the meaning of the word.

segregated (seg′rə•gāt′id) *adj.* separated; set apart; including a system that separates the races. ▶ The Latin root of this word is also found in *secede,* which means "to withdraw." ■ South Africa is one of the few countries that legally maintains facilities that keep the races segregated.   **Page 462**

ORIGINAL SENTENCE: _____

_____

paranoia (par′ə•noi′ə) *n.* a mental disorder often characterized by being overly suspicious and feeling victimized. ▶ This is a technical term used in psychiatry, but it is also used in a general way to describe extreme suspicion in normal persons. ■ "I know you feel that all our competitors are out to get us," said Jeffrey's business partner, "but don't let the feeling turn into paranoia."   **Page 464**

ORIGINAL SENTENCE: _____

_____

reneged (ri•nigd′) *v.* past tense of *to renege,* which means "to go back on a promise." ▶ The prefix *re-* means "again," and the Latin word *negare* means "to deny." The word *negate,* "to cancel out," has a related root. ■ Doug was upset that his father reneged on his promise to drive him to the game.   **Page 462**

ORIGINAL SENTENCE: _____

_____

staples (stā′p′lz) *n. pl.* chief items of trade, such as sugar, flour, or salt. ▶ This word is based on a Middle Dutch word meaning "trading post." ■ In addition to the usual staples, the little food store carried a small quantity of gourmet foods and exotic spices.   **Page 463**

ORIGINAL SENTENCE: _____

_____

inordinate (in•ōr′d′n•it) *adj.* too much; excessive; lacking moderation. ▶ The root of this word is related to *ordinary,* and the prefix *in-* means "not." ■ Don't you think Ms. Garcia assigns an inordinate amount of homework?   **Page 464**

ORIGINAL SENTENCE: _____

_____

winced (winst) *v.* past tense of *to wince,* which means "to draw back; to flinch, as if in pain or embarrassment." ▶ Do not confuse this word with *winch,* which refers to a machine for lifting. ■ The Senator winced at the reporter's question about his dishonest financial dealings.   **Page 464**

ORIGINAL SENTENCE: _____

_____

vittles (vit′′lz) *n. pl.* provisions; supplies of food. ▶ This is a variant form of the English word *victuals;* both forms are used only informally or by speakers of particular dialects. ■ The grizzled old cook stocked the chuck wagon with <u>vittles</u> in preparation for the long trail ride. **Page 464**

ORIGINAL SENTENCE: _____

_____

thwarted (thwôrt′id) *adj.* a form of *to thwart,* which means "to frustrate, hinder, or obstruct." ▶ The original meaning of this word relates to something lying crosswise across something else, hence forming a barrier or obstacle. ■ The young man's efforts to get a better job were <u>thwarted</u> by his lack of education. **Page 464**

ORIGINAL SENTENCE: _____

capacity (kə•pas′ə•tē) *n.* ability. ▶ A more frequent use of this word is to mean "the amount that can be held by a container." This word is based on the Latin verb *capere,* "to hold," which is also found in *capable.* ■ Most people have the <u>capacity</u> to show great compassion for their fellow human beings. **Page 464**

ORIGINAL SENTENCE: _____

_____

rancor (raŋ′kər) *n.* hatred; ill will. ▶ A related verb, *to rankle,* means "to cause long-lasting anger or resentment." ■ For decades smoldering <u>rancor</u> existed between the two feuding families, until no one in either family would speak to any member of the other. **Page 467**

ORIGINAL SENTENCE: _____

_____

PRACTICE TEST

Directions: Circle the letter of the best meaning for each word. *(10 points each)*

1. paranoia: **a.** interest **b.** extreme suspiciousness **c.** embarrassment **d.** humor

2. rancor: **a.** sharp odor **b.** hatred **c.** provisions of food **d.** poison

3. vittles: **a.** small animals **b.** ammunition **c.** food supplies **d.** articles of clothing

4. staples: **a.** seasonings **b.** unforeseen disasters **c.** exaggerations or deceptions **d.** principal items of trade

5. segregated: **a.** separated or set apart **b.** proven guilty **c.** made victims of **d.** showed hatred

6. reneged: **a.** arranged for transportation **b.** hired for a job **c.** failed to honor a promise **d.** examined one's own motives

7. inordinate: **a.** lacking moderation **b.** restrained **c.** strong **d.** unclear

8. winced: **a.** hoisted with a rope **b.** drew back as if in pain **c.** fought back **d.** beat an opponent

9. thwarted: **a.** built a bridge **b.** threw a rope to **c.** hindered **d.** felt strong dislike for

10. capacity: **a.** eagerness **b.** willingness to stop **c.** ability **d.** purpose

LIFE ON THE MISSISSIPPI   Mark Twain   (Textbook page 471)

DEVELOPING VOCABULARY

Directions: Read carefully the explanation of each word. Then write a sentence of your own using that word. Include in your sentence clues to the meaning of the word.

malicious (mə•lish′əs) *adj.* showing hatred or spite. ▶ The Latin root on which this word is based means "bad" or "evil," and can be found in numerous English words, such as *malefactor,* which means "wrongdoer." ■ Some of George's friends circulated a malicious rumor about Tony's actions at the party.   **Page 472**

ORIGINAL SENTENCE: _____

_____

obliterating (ə•blit′ə•rāt′iŋ) *adj.* a form of *to obliterate,* which means "to erase, destroy, or wipe out." ▶ The Latin word on which *obliterate* is based means "to blot out." ■ The nuclear explosion was incredibly destructive, obliterating all structures for as far as three miles in every direction. **Page 479**

ORIGINAL SENTENCE: _____

_____

contemptuously (kən•temp′chōō•wəs•lē) *adv.* in a manner that indicates a feeling that something is low or worthless; scornfully. ▶ The prefix *con-* means "with," and the root *-tempt-* means "to despise" or "to look down on." ■ The store manager looked contemptuously at the shoplifter and picked up the phone to call the police.   **Page 472**

ORIGINAL SENTENCE: _____

_____

to facilitate (fə•sil′ə•tāt′) *v.* to make easier. ▶ The root of *facilitate* means "to do," and can be found in such other words as *facile* (easy), *facsimile* (a copy), and *factory.* ■ Having the proper supplies will facilitate your finishing the project on time. **Page 472**

ORIGINAL SENTENCE: _____

_____

ejaculated (i•jak′yə•lāt′id) *v.* past tense of *to ejaculate,* which means "to exclaim." ▶ The prefix *e-* is a variation of *ex-,* meaning "out"; the root *-jac-* means "to throw." Someone who ejaculates is "throwing out" words.   ■ "I can't wait for the concert!" Laura ejaculated.   **Page 472**

ORIGINAL SENTENCE: _____

_____

pretext (prē′tekst) *n.* an excuse; a false reason; a cover-up. ▶ This word derives from a Latin word meaning "pretend." ▶ Using the pretext that she had a headache, Yolanda said goodbye to her hostess and left the boring party.   **Page 473**

ORIGINAL SENTENCE: _____

_____

furtive (fur′tiv) *adj.* secretive; sneaky.
▶ *Furtive* is based on a Latin word meaning "thief." ■ I could tell from his <u>furtive</u> looks that the man was doing something he shouldn't. **Page 472**

ORIGINAL SENTENCE: _____

_____

intimation (in′tə•mā′shən) *n.* a hint; an indirect suggestion. ▶ This word is related to *intimate*, which means "private" or "personal." ■ Robert did not know how to respond to Barbara's <u>intimation</u> that she wanted to go out with him. **Page 474**

ORIGINAL SENTENCE: _____

_____

solicitude (sa•lis′ə•tōōd′) *n.* caring; concern. ▶ *Solicitude* is usually used to imply excessive caring and concern. ■ Stan resented his father's <u>solicitude</u>, because he knew he could take perfectly good care of himself. **Page 475**

ORIGINAL SENTENCE: _____

_____

supplications (sup′le•kā′shənz) *n. pl.* humble requests; appeals; pleas; prayers. ▶ The original meaning of this word was "to kneel," as in prayer. ■ Pete ignored the <u>supplications</u> of his dog and finished his steak dinner by himself. **Page 477**

ORIGINAL SENTENCE: _____

_____

PRACTICE TEST

Directions: In the blank at the right, write the vocabulary word that fits each definition at the left. *(10 points each)*

| malicious | ejaculated | solicitude | contemptuously | furtive |
| obliterating | pretext | supplications | to facilitate | intimation |

1. erasing, wiping out, or destroying

1. _____

2. prayers; pleas

2. _____

3. concern; caring

3. _____

4. spiteful; harmful

4. _____

5. scornfully

5. _____

6. a hint

6. _____

7. to make easier

7. _____

8. sneaky; hidden

8. _____

9. exclaimed

9. _____

10. an excuse

10. _____

THE MIRACLE WORKER, Act One   William Gibson
(Textbook page 494)

DEVELOPING VOCABULARY

Directions: Read carefully the explanation of each word. Then write a sentence of your own using that word. Include in your sentence clues to the meaning of the word.

oculist (äk′yə•list) *n.* old-fashioned term for eye doctor. ▶ Today an eye doctor is more likely to be called an *optometrist* or an *ophthalmologist.* ■ A fading wooden sign between the saloon and the livery stable pointed out the office of the <u>oculist</u>. **Page 497**

ORIGINAL SENTENCE: _____

_____

inarticulate (in′är•tik′yə•lit) *adj.* produced without the normal sounds of understandable speech. ▶ The prefix *in-* means "not." ■ At first the baby made only <u>inarticulate</u> sounds, but soon he was speaking in complete words and even sentences. **Page 499**

ORIGINAL SENTENCE: _____

_____

intimations (in′tə•mā′shəns) *n. pl.* hints; indirect suggestions. ▶ Do not confuse this word with *intimidation*, which is "the act of making someone afraid." ■ The teacher's <u>intimations</u> of a surprise test led Lucy to stay up until midnight memorizing names, dates, and facts. **Page 501**

ORIGINAL SENTENCE: _____

_____

pinafore (pin′ə•fōr) *n.* a sleeveless, apron-like garment, usually worn over a dress or blouse. ▶ This word is compounded of the English words *pin* ("attach") and *afore* ("in front"). ■ On her birthday, my little niece wore a new pink <u>pinafore</u> and black patent leather shoes. **Page 502**

ORIGINAL SENTENCE: _____

_____

caricature (kär′ə•kə•chər) *n.* an exaggerated picture of someone. ▶ A *caricature* is a drawing in which certain distinctive features are made larger as a way of criticizing or poking fun. ■ The artist drew a <u>caricature</u> of Eileen, with a grin so wide that her face was practically filled with teeth. **Page 508**

ORIGINAL SENTENCE: _____

_____

imperious (im•pir′e•əs) *adj.* overbearing; arrogant; proud. ▶ This word is based on a Latin root meaning "to command," the same root that *empire* is derived from. ■ Jorge's <u>imperious</u> attitude leads him to be very demanding with salespeople and waiters. **Page 508**

ORIGINAL SENTENCE: _____

_____

acute (ə•kyōot') *adj.* severe; intense. ▶ Another meaning of *acute* is "keen or shrewd." ■ The drought resulted in an <u>acute</u> shortage of corn and soybeans. **Page 495**

ORIGINAL SENTENCE: _____

_____

vivacious (vī•vā'shəs) *adj.* lively. ▶ The Latin root of this word means "to live." ■ Trixie, my <u>vivacious</u> cousin, is always chosen to be head cheerleader. **Page 496**

ORIGINAL SENTENCE: _____

_____

voluminous (və•lōo'mə•nəs) *adj.* large; bulky. ▶ As you might guess, *volume* is a related word. ■ The <u>voluminous</u> skirts worn by women at the turn of the century must have been terribly hot in the summer. **Page 508**

ORIGINAL SENTENCE: _____

_____

asperity (as•per'ə•tē) *n.* sharpness of temper; anger. ▶ Earlier forms of this word had the meaning "to push away." ■ Jack responded to everything his stepmother said with <u>asperity</u> and resentment. **Page 570**

ORIGINAL SENTENCE: _____

_____

PRACTICE TEST

Directions: Fill in the blank with the vocabulary word that best fits the meaning of the sentence. *(10 points each)*

acute   oculist   intimations   voluminous   caricature
vivacious   inarticulate   pinafore   imperious   asperity

1. _____ people seem to enjoy life so much.

2. The police could learn nothing from the injured man's _____ moans.

3. The stacks of computer printouts needed by some companies can be so

_____ that special warehouse space is needed.

4. Dale spoke sharply and with _____, which he regretted as soon as he saw the child begin to cry.

5. Peggy drew a funny _____ of the members of the football team.

6. Jo resented Florence's _____ tone.

7. A young girl of today is more likely to wear jeans than a _____.

8. There were _____ in the President's speech that a breakthrough in the nuclear test ban talks might soon occur.

9. A town _____ might have sold you wire-rimmed glasses, but certainly could not have offered you contact lenses!

10. The patient was brought to the emergency room in _____ pain.

THE MIRACLE WORKER, Act Two   William Gibson
(Textbook page 514)

DEVELOPING VOCABULARY

Directions: Read carefully the explanation of each word. Then write a sentence of your
own using that word. Include in your sentence clues to the meaning of the word.

nettled (net′′ld) *adj.* a form of *to nettle,*
which means "to irritate." ► This word
derives from the name of a cactus-like plant
with stinging hairs that irritate the skin.

■ Nettled by my little sister's childish
questions and restless behavior, I asked her to
play quietly while I finished my homework.
Page 529

ORIGINAL SENTENCE: _____

_____

temperance (tem′pər•əns) *n.* moderation;
self-restraint; not indulging too much.
► Frequently this word is used to refer
specifically to a commitment to avoid

drinking alcoholic beverages. ■ The
Surgeon General announced that temperance
in eating saturated fats could reduce the risk
of heart disease.   **Page 514**

ORIGINAL SENTENCE: _____

_____

nonplused (nän•plust′) *adj.* a form of *to
nonplus,* which means "to bewilder" or "to
confuse or embarrass." ► The prefix *non-*
means "not," and the root *-plus-* means

"further." ■ The assembly speaker was
nonplused by the students' snickering, and it
took him several minutes to regain his
composure.   **Page 517**

ORIGINAL SENTENCE: _____

_____

feigned (fānd) *adj.* pretended; simulated;
faked. ► This word comes from a Latin
root meaning "to shape," but now carries the
meaning "to shape reality into what you want

it to be." ■ This morning my little brother
stayed home from school with a feigned
illness.   **Page 517**

ORIGINAL SENTENCE: _____

_____

compunction (kəm•puŋk′shən) *n.* feeling
caused by a sense of guilt; remorse. ► The
base word of *compunction* is the same as in
puncture and implies "a pricking of the

conscience." ■ My father said he would
have no compunction about turning a drunk
driver in to the police.   **Page 520**

ORIGINAL SENTENCE: _____

_____

intractably (in•trak′tə•blē) *adv.* stubbornly.
► The prefix *in-* means "not," and the root
-tract- means "to pull," as in the word
tractor, which pulls plows and other

equipment. ■ Miguel clung intractably to
his position and refused to consider any
opposing arguments.   **Page 532**

ORIGINAL SENTENCE: _____

_____

glower (glou′ər) *n.* an angry stare. ► Most often *glower* is used in the verb form, meaning "to stare at in an angry way."

■ Professor Ellington was famous for her continual glower that kept students wondering what they had done wrong.   **Page 521**

ORIGINAL SENTENCE: _____

_____

to disinter (dis′in•tur′) *v.* to remove a body from its burial place. ► The prefix *dis-* here means "to do the opposite of." *Inter* is an English word that means "to bury."

■ When the police finally suspected that Mr. Kominsky had been murdered, they issued an order to disinter his body.   **Page 524**

ORIGINAL SENTENCE: _____

_____

impassively (im•pas′iv•lē) *adv.* without showing emotion; calmly; serenely. ► Do not confuse this word with *impasse*, which

means "a difficulty without solution."
■ The Buddhist monk sat impassively in the tranquil garden.   **Page 514**

ORIGINAL SENTENCE: _____

_____

paroxysm (par′ək•siz′m) *n.* a sudden outburst; a spasm. ► The prefix *para-,* meaning "beyond," can be found in other words such as *parapsychology.* ■ Suzanne

had not even finished telling the story before she convulsed in a paroxysm of laughter. **Page 530**

ORIGINAL SENTENCE: _____

_____

PRACTICE TEST

Directions: In front of each number, write **T** if the statement is true or **F** if the statement is false. *(10 points each)*

_____ **1.** A *paroxysm* of pain comes on suddenly and violently.

_____ **2.** An illness that continues *intractably* is hard to cure.

_____ **3.** If you want to *disinter* a body, you must first wrap it in clean cloth.

_____ **4.** A principal who feels *nettled* by the behavior of a group of students is likely to glare at them.

_____ **5.** A person with no *compunction* over cheating on a test will probably do it more than once.

_____ **6.** A *glower* is an expression of gratitude.

_____ **7.** When people are *nonplused*, they are often too confused to continue with what they are doing.

_____ **8.** *Feigned* affection is not sincere or genuine.

_____ **9.** Teachers are usually frustrated by students who sit *impassively*, because these students are not responsive.

_____**10.** A *temperance* movement encourages people to increase their consumption of alcoholic beverages.

THE MIRACLE WORKER, Act Three   William Gibson
(Textbook page 534)

DEVELOPING VOCABULARY

Directions: Read carefully the explanation of each word. Then write a sentence of your
own using that word. Include in your sentence clues to the meaning of the word.

audible (ô′də•b'l) *adj.* loud enough to be
heard. ▶ The word part -*aud*-, meaning "to
hear," appears in many familiar words
such as *audience, audio, audition, auditor,*
and *auditorium.* ■ The small girl's quiet
voice was barely audible.   **Page 534**

ORIGINAL SENTENCE: _____

_____

manipulates (mə•nip′yə•lāts′) *v.* handles;
manages skillfully. ▶ You will see the base
word -*man*- ("hand") in many other words,
including *manual* and *manuscript.* ■ Good
eye-to-hand coordination is needed to
manipulate the controls of a video game.
Page 537

ORIGINAL SENTENCE: _____

_____

simultaneously (sī′m'l•tā′nē•əs•lē) *adv.* at
the same time. ▶ This word and *same* are
derived from the same Greek word meaning
"together." ■ The arrival of my nephew
and the first landing of people on the moon
occurred simultaneously.   **Page 539**

ORIGINAL SENTENCE: _____

_____

trepidation (trep′ə•dā′shən) *n.* anxiety;
fearful uncertainty. ▶ The Latin root of this
word means "to tremble." ■ I entered the
classroom on the day of the test with great
trepidation.   **Page 542**

ORIGINAL SENTENCE: _____

_____

consummately (kən•sum′it•lē) *adv.* very
skillfully. ▶ *Consummately* is based on a
Latin root meaning "to finish." You can
remember the meaning of this word by
thinking that in order to do something
consummately, you must "finish" the
preparations. ■ After years of lessons and
practice, Joyce plays the cello consummately.
Page 542

ORIGINAL SENTENCE: _____

_____

transfixed (trans•fikst′) *adj.* a form of *to
transfix,* meaning "to make motionless."
▶ The original meaning of *transfix* was "to
pierce through with something pointed."
■ The circle of small children sat transfixed
by the beautiful story.   **Page 542**

ORIGINAL SENTENCE: _____

_____

groping (grōp′iŋ) **adj.** a form of *to grope,* which means "to feel about with the hands." ▶ *Grope* shares a common language ancestor with *grip* and *gripe*. ▪ When the thunderstorm caused the lights to go out, we immediately went into action, groping our way into the kitchen in search of candles. **Page 542**

ORIGINAL SENTENCE: _____

_____

resurrection (rez′ə•rek′shən) **n.** coming back to life; rising from the dead. ▶ The base word *-surg-,* on which both *resurrection* and *surge* are built, means "to rise or spring up." ▪ *Resurrection* and reincarnation are two different ways of imagining immortality. **Page 538**

ORIGINAL SENTENCE: _____

_____

PRACTICE TEST A

Directions: Circle the letter of the best meaning for each word. *(10 points each)*

1. consummately: **a.** very skillfully   **b.** without fear   **c.** loudly
   d. completely

2. simultaneously: **a.** forcefully   **b.** at the same place   **c.** at the same time
   d. for the same reasons

3. audible: **a.** able to be heard   **b.** able to be seen   **c.** able to be handled
   d. able to be done

4. transfixed: **a.** lessened   **b.** motionless   **c.** fearful
   d. rising from the dead

5. manipulates: **a.** attempts   **b.** handles   **c.** pleases   **d.** recognizes

PRACTICE TEST B

Directions: In the blank at the right, write the vocabulary word that is a synonym for the word at the left. *(10 points each)*

manipulates   transfixed   groping
trepidation   resurrection

1. anxiety   1. _____

2. handles   2. _____

3. motionless   3. _____

4. feeling   4. _____

5. rebirth   5. _____

VISITOR FROM FOREST HILLS   Neil Simon
(Textbook page 551)

DEVELOPING VOCABULARY

Directions: Read carefully the explanation of each word. Then write a sentence of your own using that word. Include in your sentence clues to the meaning of the word.

farce (färs) *n.* a humorous play based on a ridiculous situation. ▶ *Farce* has come to mean anything absurd or ridiculous, not just a play. ■ That new farce playing at the Oakville Repertory Theater is clever, but personally I prefer more realistic drama. **Page 549**

ORIGINAL SENTENCE: _____

_____

squabbling (skwäb′ə•liŋ) *n.* noisy quarreling over a small matter. ▶ This word is derived from a Swedish word meaning "a dispute." ■ The children's squabbling soon began to irritate their grandfather. **Page 550**

ORIGINAL SENTENCE: _____

_____

incredulously (in•krej′oo•ləs•lī) *adv.* in a manner showing doubt or disbelief. ▶ The prefix *in-* means "not," and the root *-cred-* means "to believe." ■ The cashier looked at Karen incredulously as she pulled out a one hundred dollar bill to pay for the record album. **Page 553**

ORIGINAL SENTENCE: _____

_____

brandishing (bran′dish•iŋ) *adj.* a form of *to brandish,* which means "to wave in a triumphant or threatening way." ▶ *To swing* and *to brandish* are similar in meaning; however, *swinging* implies a regular, uniform movement whereas *brandishing* suggests a threatening motion. ■ Brandishing a water pistol, the imaginative child pretended to be a cowboy. **Page 557**

ORIGINAL SENTENCE: _____

_____

interminable (in•tʉr′mi•nə•b′l) *adj.* without end; seemingly endless. ▶ The base word -term- means "end," as in *terminal* and *terminate.* ■ On the first day of camp the children squirmed as the counselor read an interminable list of rules. **Page 561**

ORIGINAL SENTENCE: _____

_____

vehemence (vē′ə•məns) *n.* intense feeling; fervor. ▶ This word can also be pronounced ve′hi•mənts. ■ Kathy's parents were surprised by the vehemence with which she declared that she planned to try out for the football team. **Page 560**

ORIGINAL SENTENCE: _____

_____

stereotype (ster′ē•ə•tīp′) *n.* a fixed idea about a person, thing, or event that does not allow for individual differences. ▶ A certain type of metal plate used for printing is also called a stereotype. ■ My older sister, who has platinum blond hair and a Ph.D. in physics, resents the <u>stereotype</u> of the dumb blond. **Page 550**

ORIGINAL SENTENCE: _____

_____

barricaded (bar′ə•kād′id) *adj.* a form of *to barricade,* which means "to shut in or keep out with a fence, wall, or other barrier." ▶ This word is probably related to *barrel,* because at one time barrels were used as barriers. ■ <u>Barricaded</u> in his room by a chest of drawers in front of the door, Tommy refused to come out for several hours. **Page 556**

ORIGINAL SENTENCE: _____

_____

gargoyle (gär′goil) *n.* a waterspout on a building, usually made to look like a grotesquely carved animal or fantastic creature. ▶ This word and *gargle* are both based on an Old French word for throat. ■ The Gothic chapel on the campus of Washington University is decorated with a number of interesting <u>gargoyles</u>. **Page 559**

ORIGINAL SENTENCE: _____

_____

despondently (di•spän′dənt•lē) *adv.* hopelessly; dejectedly. ▶ *Despondently* is the way someone acts who has given up trying because a situation looks hopeless. ■ Frank told us <u>despondently</u> that each of his college applications was rejected. **Page 560**

ORIGINAL SENTENCE: _____

_____

PRACTICE TEST

Directions: In front of each number, write the letter of the definition that best matches each vocabulary word. *(10 points each)*

_____ **1.** despondently

_____ **2.** gargoyle

_____ **3.** brandishing

_____ **4.** incredulously

_____ **5.** squabbling

_____ **6.** stereotype

_____ **7.** vehemence

_____ **8.** interminable

_____ **9.** farce

_____ **10.** barricaded

a. a play based on ridiculous situations

b. an unfair, inaccurate idea of people or things that does not allow for individual differences

c. an extended vacation

d. quarreling over something small

e. doubtingly; in a manner showing disbelief

f. shut in or kept out with a fence or wall

g. without the use of tools

h. waving in a threatening way

i. seeming to go on forever

j. to sort into groups

k. a waterspout

l. strong feeling; intensity

m. hopelessly; dejectedly

THE MOTHER   **Paddy Chayefsky**   (Textbook page 567)

DEVELOPING VOCABULARY

Directions: Read carefully the explanation of each word. Then write a sentence of your
own using that word. Include in your sentence clues to the meaning of the word.

fluidity (floo•id′ə•tē) *n.* the quality of
flowing smoothly like a liquid.   ▶ It is easy
to remember the meaning of *fluidity* if you
think of a fluid, such as water, flowing out of
a container.   ■ Tai Chi is a form of exercise
developed in China that is marked by great
fluidity.   **Page 566**

ORIGINAL SENTENCE: _____

_____

foyer (foi′ər) *n.* an entrance hall or lobby,
especially in a public building such as a
theater or hotel.   ▶ Since this word was
borrowed from French, many people use the
French pronunciation: foi′ā.   ■ I waited
twenty minutes for Lucy in the foyer of the
theater before I went in and took a seat.
Page 568

ORIGINAL SENTENCE: _____

_____

petulant (pech′oo•lənt) *adj.* impatient,
ill-humored, or irritable, especially over some
small annoyance.   ▶ The Latin root of this
word means "to attack."   ■ Grace
frequently becomes petulant when things do
not go her way.   **Page 570**

ORIGINAL SENTENCE: _____

_____

lenient (lē′ni•ənt) *adj.* not strict in
disciplining or punishing.   ▶ This word is
based on a Latin word meaning "soft."
■ Ms. Kowalski has a reputation for being
one of the most lenient teachers at Middleton
Junior High.   **Page 570**

ORIGINAL SENTENCE: _____

_____

montage (män•täzh′) *n.* set of things
(especially pictures) put together to create a
single effect.   ▶ Since both *montage* and
mount are based on the same root word, you
can remember the meaning of *montage* by
thinking of a group of pictures mounted
together.   ■ My art project was a montage
made from photographs I took on our trip to
Kenya.   **Page 573**

ORIGINAL SENTENCE: _____

_____

apprehensive (ap′rə•hen′siv) *adj.* worried or
fearful about the future.   ▶ The root of this
word means "to take hold of," and can also
be found in the verb *to apprehend,* which
means "to capture."   ■ As the time for her
performance at the music festival drew closer,
Beth became more and more apprehensive.
Page 574

ORIGINAL SENTENCE: _____

_____

covert (kuv′ərt) *adj.* secret; hidden. ▶ This word comes from a Middle English word that meant "to cover." It can also be pronounced kō′vərt. ■ A leading newspaper revealed that a <u>covert</u> plan to launch an unauthorized spacecraft had come close to being put into action. **Page 575**

ORIGINAL SENTENCE: _____

_____

staccato (stə•kät′ō) *adj.* made up of a rapid series of short, sharp sounds. ▶ *Staccato* was originally a music term borrowed from Italian. ■ The reporter heard the <u>staccato</u> sound of machine gun fire somewhere nearby. **Page 575**

ORIGINAL SENTENCE: _____

_____

meticulousness (mə•tik′yoo•ləs•nəs) *n.* excessive attention to detail. ▶ This word is based on a Latin word meaning "fear," and implies fearfulness that something is wrong or out of place. ■ Aunt Hazel's <u>meticulousness</u> was evident in the way she organized her closets. **Page 581**

ORIGINAL SENTENCE: _____

_____

valise (və•lēs′) *n.* an old-fashioned term for a small suitcase. ▶ This word was borrowed directly from the French language. ■ When the ticket agent asked if she had any luggage to check, Grandmother replied, "I only have this <u>valise</u>." **Page 582**

ORIGINAL SENTENCE: _____

_____

PRACTICE TEST

Directions: In the blank at the right, write the vocabulary word that fits each definition at the left. *(10 points each)*

| fluidity | petulant | montage | covert | meticulousness |
| foyer | lenient | apprehensive | staccato | valise |

1. great attention to detail　　　　　**1.** _____

2. a small suitcase　　　　　　　　　**2.** _____

3. smooth, liquid-like motion　　　　**3.** _____

4. an entrance hall　　　　　　　　　**4.** _____

5. made up of a rapid series of short sounds　　**5.** _____

6. hidden; secret　　　　　　　　　　**6.** _____

7. not strict; patient　　　　　　　　**7.** _____

8. impatient; ill-humored　　　　　　**8.** _____

9. worried; anxious　　　　　　　　　**9.** _____

10. images combined for one effect　　**10.** _____

THE TRAGEDY OF ROMEO AND JULIET, Act I
William Shakespeare   (Textbook page 602)

DEVELOPING VOCABULARY

Directions: Read carefully the explanation of each word. Then write a sentence of your own using that word. Include in your sentence clues to the meaning of the word.

humor (hyōō′mər) *n.* mood. ▶ Centuries ago people believed moods were caused by certain body fluids, called *humors*. This accounts for the word's present meaning of "moods." ■ Although yesterday he was happy, today Thomas is in a melancholy humor. **Page 608**

ORIGINAL SENTENCE: _____

_____

to mark (märk) *v.* to listen, observe, or take notice of. ▶ A more familiar meaning of this word is "to place a visible impression on a surface." ■ Speaking to the crowd that gathered after the fight, the swordsman exclaimed, "Mark well, countrymen!" **Page 617**

ORIGINAL SENTENCE: _____

_____

shrift (shrift) *n.* confession; the forgiveness given by a priest for sins confessed. ▶ This archaic word survives in common usage in the expression "to make short shrift of," which means "to finish a job quickly and impatiently." ■ The man's shrift brought him peace of mind, and he left the church feeling happy. **Page 609**

ORIGINAL SENTENCE: _____

_____

Soft! (sôft) *interj.* Quiet! Hush! Slow up! Stop! ▶ This meaning of *soft* is archaic, but it is close to the original meaning of the Old English word from which it is derived: *softe,* meaning "quiet" or "gentle." ■ Almost everyone remembers Romeo's line from the balcony scene: "But soft! What light through yonder window breaks?" **Page 611**

ORIGINAL SENTENCE: _____

_____

withal (with•ôl′) *prep.* with that; with. ▶ This meaning of *withal* is archaic, although the word is still used to mean "in addition" or "despite that." ■ The nurse, speaking of Juliet's mother, told Romeo, "I nursed her daughter that you talked withal." **Page 626**

ORIGINAL SENTENCE: _____

_____

Anon! (ə•nän′) *interj.* At once! Soon! Coming! ▶ This word is archaic, which means it is an old word that is no longer commonly used. ■ The peasant girl told her mother, "I'll be home <u>anon</u>, just as soon as I fill this bucket at the well." **Page 627**

ORIGINAL SENTENCE: _____

_____

Good-den (good•den) *interj.* an archaic word meaning "good evening." ▶ The first part of this word is a variation of *God,* which also appears in our current word *goodbye* (God be with you.) ■ Passing the priest on the cobblestone street, the merchant nodded and said, "<u>Good-den</u>." **Page 614**

ORIGINAL SENTENCE: _____

_____

PRACTICE TEST A

Directions: Circle the letter of the best meaning for each word. *(10 points each)*

1. shrift: **a.** beginning and end   **b.** today and tomorrow
   c. impurities left after mining   **d.** forgiveness for sins confessed

2. withal: **a.** money   **b.** with that   **c.** for   **d.** unto

3. humor: **a.** health   **b.** wisdom   **c.** mood   **d.** color

4. Anon!:   **a.** Terrific!   **b.** Coming!   **c.** Stop!   **d.** Quiet!

5. Good-den: **a.** good evening   **b.** good morning   **c.** God bless you
   d. God save the Queen

PRACTICE TEST B

Directions: In the blank at the right, write the vocabulary word that is a synonym for the word at the left. *(10 points each).*

humor   Anon!   to mark   Soft!   shrift

1. confession   1. _____

2. to listen   2. _____

3. mood   3. _____

4. Quiet!   4. _____

5. Soon!   5. _____

THE TRAGEDY OF ROMEO AND JULIET, Act II
William Shakespeare   (Textbook page 629)

DEVELOPING VOCABULARY

Directions: Read carefully the explanation of each word. Then write a sentence of your own using that word. Include in your sentence clues to the meaning of the word.

discourses (dis•kôrs′əs) *v.* utters or speaks. ▶ This meaning of *discourse* is now archaic, but the word is presently used as a noun to mean "communication of ideas and information, especially by talking" or "a lecture." ■ "Can you but discourse my name?" the lover begged.   **Page 631**

ORIGINAL SENTENCE: _____

_____

counsel (koun′s'l) *n.* private thoughts; secret plan. ▶ This meaning of *counsel* is rarely used today, except in the expression "to keep one's own counsel," meaning "to keep one's thoughts and plans to oneself." ■ "Never can you make me reveal my counsel," the man stated vehemently.   **Page 633**

ORIGINAL SENTENCE: _____

_____

proof (pro͞of) *adj.* armored or protected against; able to resist. ▶ This meaning of *proof,* while not frequently used, can be seen in the suffix *-proof.* When attached to a noun, *-proof* adds the meaning "protected against," as in *fireproof.* ■ "Say what you will, but I am proof against your words," declared the villager.   **Page 633**

ORIGINAL SENTENCE: _____

_____

discovered (dis•kuv′ərd) *v.* past participle of *to discover,* which means "to reveal." ▶ This meaning of *discover* is now rarely used. ■ The early morning light has discovered the losses of yesterday's battle.   **Page 634**

ORIGINAL SENTENCE: _____

_____

bounty (boun′tē) *n.* capacity for giving generously. ▶ *Bounty* can also mean "a generous gift," as well as "a reward given by the government for raising certain crops, capturing criminals, etc." ■ The mistress of the castle was much loved by the peasants for her bounty, especially at holiday time.   **Page 635**

ORIGINAL SENTENCE: _____

_____

baleful (bāl′fəl) *adj.* evil; threatening harm; poisonous. ▶ This word has no connection with the word *bale,* which means "a large bundle." Each entered Middle English from a different source. ■ Jonathan couldn't erase from his mind the stranger's baleful stare.   **Page 637**

ORIGINAL SENTENCE: _____

_____

grace (grās) *n.* favor; good will; approval. ▶ This word forms the basis of several common expressions such as "to fall from grace" (to do wrong) and "in the good graces of" (in favor with). ■ The knight hoped to win the grace of the princess by demonstrating his skill as a horseman. **Page 637**

ORIGINAL SENTENCE: _____

_____

bauble (bô′b′l) *n.* a showy but worthless thing; trinket; cheap jewel. ▶ The origin of this word is uncertain, but it may have come from a Latin word meaning "pretty." ■ "I think I'll go down to the mall and buy myself a bauble or two," Ms. Shatz told her husband. **Page 641**

ORIGINAL SENTENCE: _____

_____

Stay! (stā) *interj.* Wait! Pause! Delay! ▶ The original source of this word was a Latin word meaning "to stand." ■ "Stay!" the princess called, as she hurried to catch up. **Page 645**

ORIGINAL SENTENCE: _____

_____

confounds (kən•foundz′) *v.* destroys, defeats, or causes to fail. ▶ This meaning of *to confound* is archaic. Today, it means "to confuse" or "to mix up." ■ "The force of his army confounds us," the warrior cried. **Page 647**

ORIGINAL SENTENCE: _____

_____

PRACTICE TEST

Directions: In the blank at the right, write the vocabulary word that fits each definition at the left. *(10 points each)*

discourses	proof	bounty	grace	Stay!
counsel	discovered	baleful	bauble	confounds

1. private thoughts   1. _____

2. capacity for giving   2. _____

3. a trinket; cheap jewel   3. _____

4. destroys   4. _____

5. speaks   5. _____

6. protected against   6. _____

7. evil; threatening harm   7. _____

8. Wait!   8. _____

9. revealed   9. _____

10. favor; approval; good will   10. _____

THE TRAGEDY OF ROMEO AND JULIET, Act III
William Shakespeare   (Textbook page 650)

DEVELOPING VOCABULARY

Directions: Read carefully the explanation of each word. Then write a sentence of your own using that word. Include in your sentence clues to the meaning of the word.

doublet (dub′lit) **n.** a kind of jacket. ▶ A *doublet* is a garment that was worn by men from the 14th to the 16th centuries. It was closefitting and often sleeveless. ■ For the school play, the home economics classes made eight <u>doublets</u> and ten long dresses to be used as costumes.   **Page 650**

ORIGINAL SENTENCE: _____

_____

dissemblers (di•sem′blʉrz) **n. pl.** liars. ▶ The Latin verb *simulare*, which forms the root of this word and others such as *simulate*, means ''to pretend.'' ■ Philip is sometimes a <u>dissembler</u>, particularly when he thinks he has been caught doing something he shouldn't.   **Page 659**

ORIGINAL SENTENCE: _____

_____

strange (strānj) **adj.** unfamiliar. ▶ This use of *strange* is slightly different from its other meaning of ''peculiar; odd; extraordinary.'' ■ Ella and Martha were playing a game that was <u>strange</u> to me.   **Page 656**

ORIGINAL SENTENCE: _____

_____

civil (siv′′l) **adj.** well-behaved; courteous. ▶ You can remember the meaning of *civil* by associating it with *civilized*. ■ I don't expect her to be friendly to me after all the disagreements we've had, but she could at least be <u>civil</u>.   **Page 656**

ORIGINAL SENTENCE: _____

_____

fain (fān) **adv.** gladly; eagerly; willingly. ▶ Both the adverb and the adjective form (*fain*, meaning ''eager or glad'') are archaic. ■ As the man started to mount his horse, the maiden cried, ''I would <u>fain</u> follow you anywhere!''   **Page 659**

ORIGINAL SENTENCE: _____

_____

fond (fänd) **adj.** foolish. ▶ This use of *fond* appears rarely these days. More frequently it means ''tender, loving, or affectionate.'' ■ The <u>fond</u> young man believed that if he sold all his cows to buy the princess a golden bracelet, she would fall in love with him. **Page 661**

ORIGINAL SENTENCE: _____

_____

to sack (sak) *v.* to rob or plunder a captured city of everything of value. ▶ This word comes from a Latin word meaning ''bag.'' You can remember its meaning by thinking about invaders putting captured loot into bags to carry away. ■ The barbarians swept in from the north and began to sack the city. **Page 663**

ORIGINAL SENTENCE: _____

_____

entertained (en′tər•tānd′) *v.* past participle of *to entertain*, which means ''to consider; to allow oneself to think about; to have in mind.'' ▶ This meaning of *to entertain* is more closely related to its Latin root, which means ''to hold,'' than is the more familiar meaning: ''to amuse.'' ■ Mr. Gibson has entertained the possibility of dyeing his hair, but fears it will look silly. **Page 655**

ORIGINAL SENTENCE: _____

_____

spleen (splēn) *n.* anger; malice; spite. ▶ This meaning derives from the fact that the spleen, an organ next to the stomach, was once thought to be the location of certain emotions. ■ When Mildred gets angry, she directs her spleen toward the nearest person, whether or not he or she was the cause of the problem. **Page 655**

ORIGINAL SENTENCE: _____

_____

estate (ə•stāt′) *n.* situation; condition. ▶ This word is closely related to *state*, and both words are derived from the Latin word meaning ''to stand.'' ■ The peasant did not seem to mind his lowly estate. **Page 662**

ORIGINAL SENTENCE: _____

_____

PRACTICE TEST

Directions: In front of each number, write the letter of the definition that best matches each vocabulary word. *(10 points each)*

_____ **1.** dissemblers

_____ **2.** entertained

_____ **3.** fain

_____ **4.** civil

_____ **5.** to sack

_____ **6.** doublet

_____ **7.** estate

_____ **8.** spleen

_____ **9.** fond

_____**10.** strange

a. jacket

b. liars

c. exciting

d. unfamiliar

e. to plunder or rob

f. thought about, considered

g. sword

h. courteous; well-behaved

i. willingly

j. without enough energy

k. foolish

l. anger

m. situation

VOCABULARY ACTIVITY WORKSHEET

THE TRAGEDY OF ROMEO AND JULIET, Act IV
William Shakespeare   (Textbook page 676)

DEVELOPING VOCABULARY

Directions: Read carefully the explanation of each word. Then write a sentence of your own using that word. Include in your sentence clues to the meaning of the word.

God shield (gäd shēld) God forbid. ▶ This meaning of the verb *to shield* is rarely used. More often it means "to defend or protect." ■ The old man bowed low and said, "<u>God shield</u> that I would fail to recognize a person of royal blood."   **Page 677**

ORIGINAL SENTENCE: _____

_____

drift (drift) *n.* intentions.   ▶ A more familiar use of *drift* as a noun is to mean "a heap of snow or sand." ■ "I hope I have made clear my <u>drift</u>," the man said. **Page 679**

ORIGINAL SENTENCE: _____

_____

cunning (kun′iŋ) *adj.* skillful. ▶ Currently, this word is more frequently used to mean "sly" or "good at deceiving." ■ The prince bought all his shoes from one <u>cunning</u> cobbler named Zack.   **Page 679**

ORIGINAL SENTENCE: _____

_____

closet (kläz′it) *n.* private quarters. ▶ Today this word usually refers to a small storage room for clothes and supplies. ■ The young woman retired to her <u>closet</u> to pray. **Page 680**

ORIGINAL SENTENCE: _____

_____

orisons (ôr′i•z′nz) *n. pl.* prayers. ▶ This word derives from a Latin word meaning "a speech." ■ "God must have heard my <u>orisons</u>," exclaimed the young woman, "because today Father is well." **Page 681**

ORIGINAL SENTENCE: _____

_____

rosemary (rōz′mer′ē) *n.* a fragrant herb. ▶ Rosemary is used in cooking and perfumes. It is considered a symbol of remembrance. ■ Aunt Stella always has plenty of <u>rosemary</u> growing in her herb garden.   **Page 687**

ORIGINAL SENTENCE: _____

_____

lower (lou'ər) *n.* a frowning or threatening look. ▶ This work is somewhat similar to *glower*. A *lower* may appear ominous, whereas a *glower* is more angry and sullen. ■ The stranger's baleful <u>lower</u> made me want to run and hide. **Page 687**

ORIGINAL SENTENCE: _____

_____

fond nature (fänd nā'chər) foolish human nature. ▶ Both *fond* and *fun* come from the same Middle English word meaning "foolish." ■ "<u>Fond nature</u> leads us to do many unreasonable things," the priest said. **Page 687**

ORIGINAL SENTENCE: _____

_____

to carry (kar'ē) *v.* to endure. ▶ This meaning of *carry* is no longer used. ■ "No longer will I <u>carry</u> your insults," the knight said, striking his opponent with a single, deadly blow. **Page 688**

ORIGINAL SENTENCE: _____

_____

cry you mercy (krī yoo mur'sē) beg your pardon. ▶ The word *cry* here has the meaning "to plead for" rather than the more familiar meaning "to call out" or "to weep." ■ "I <u>cry you mercy</u>," said the knight. "I thought you were someone else." **Page 688**

ORIGINAL SENTENCE: _____

_____

PRACTICE TEST

Directions: Circle the letter of the best meaning for each word. *(10 points each)*

1. to carry: **a.** to handle   **b.** to endure   **c.** to try   **d.** to see

2. lower: **a.** frown   **b.** eyelid   **c.** legs   **d.** mood

3. God shield: **a.** God forgive us   **b.** God forbid   **c.** good evening   **d.** God take care of you

4. cunning: **a.** handsome   **b.** energetic   **c.** skillful   **d.** lazy

5. orisons: **a.** herbs   **b.** bones   **c.** enemies   **d.** prayers

6. cry you mercy: **a.** beg your pardon   **b.** offer you help   **c.** wish you well   **d.** ask God's blessing

7. fond nature: **a.** intelligent beings   **b.** foolish human nature   **c.** friendliness   **d.** skillfulness

8. rosemary: **a.** young girl   **b.** prayer   **c.** herb   **d.** meat

9. drift: **a.** intentions   **b.** grief   **c.** mental illness   **d.** boat

10. closet: **a.** chest of drawers   **b.** desk   **c.** kitchen   **d.** private quarters

THE TRAGEDY OF ROMEO AND JULIET, Act V
William Shakespeare   (Textbook page 690)

DEVELOPING VOCABULARY

Directions: Read carefully the explanation of each word. Then write a sentence of your
own using that word. Include in your sentence clues to the meaning of the word.

to presage (pri•sāj′) *v.* to predict, give
warning of, or foretell.   ▶ When used as a
noun, this word means "a sign or warning of
a future event," and is pronounced pres′ij.
■ Black clouds and heavy rain may presage a
tornado.   **Page 690**

ORIGINAL SENTENCE: _____

_____

to beseech (bi•sēch′) *v.* to beg.   ▶ This
word is closely related to the verb *to seek,*
which means "to look for" or "to ask for."
■ "I beseech you," cried the woman. "Spare
the life of my child."   **Page 690**

ORIGINAL SENTENCE: _____

_____

penury (pen′yə•rē) *n.* poverty.   ▶ Although
penury and *poverty* are synonyms, the first
word describes a more severe condition than
the second.   ■ The family's penury was a
serious threat to their health.   **Page 691**

ORIGINAL SENTENCE: _____

_____

loathsome (lōth′səm) *adj.* repulsive;
disgusting.   ▶ The verb *to loathe* means "to
hate." The suffix *-some* signals an adjective
form.   ■ Some people consider snakes to be
loathsome creatures, but others find them
fascinating and beautiful.   **Page 692**

ORIGINAL SENTENCE: _____

_____

obsequies (äb′sə•kwēz) *n. pl.* funeral rites or
ceremonies.   ▶ This word derives from the
same source as *obsequious,* which means
"overly submissive; servile," but the two
words are presently not related in meaning.
■ The obsequies of the Hindus often include
burning the body and sprinkling the ashes in
the holy Ganges River.   **Page 693**

ORIGINAL SENTENCE: _____

_____

ensign (en′sīn) *n.* a flag or banner.
▶ *Ensign* and *insignia,* which means
"symbols or badges of office or authority,"
have a common language ancestor.
■ England's ensign is often referred to as the
Union Jack, just as ours is sometimes called
the Stars and Stripes.   **Page 695**

ORIGINAL SENTENCE: _____

_____

maw (mô) *n.* the mouth. ► Originally *maw* meant "stomach," but it now refers to the throat and jaws as well, especially of an animal. ■ Unaware of the danger, the rabbit practically walked into the <u>maw</u> of the waiting lion. **Page 694**

ORIGINAL SENTENCE: _____

_____

morsel (môr's'l) *n.* a small piece. ► This word comes from a Latin word meaning "bite." You can remember it by thinking of an amount that is only big enough for one bite. ■ We feed the pigeons with <u>morsels</u> of bread left from our lunch. **Page 694**

ORIGINAL SENTENCE: _____

_____

ground (ground) *n.* a cause. ► When used in this way, the word is often plural: *grounds,* as in "You have grounds for concern." ■ "The <u>ground</u> of your dishonesty," stated the man to the shopkeeper, "is pure greed." **Page 699**

ORIGINAL SENTENCE: _____

_____

pallet (pal'it) *n.* a small bed or mattress placed directly on the floor. ► This word comes from an Old French word meaning "straw," because straw was often used as filling for mattresses. ■ When we visit my aunt and uncle, I sleep on a <u>pallet</u> because they do not have enough beds for everyone. **Page 696**

ORIGINAL SENTENCE: _____

_____

PRACTICE TEST

Directions: In front of each number, write **T** if the statement is true or **F** if the statement is false. *(10 points each)*

_____ **1.** A letter that *presages* the arrival of a mysterious stranger summarizes the stranger's ideas.

_____ **2.** If you are experiencing *penury,* a bank would probably be willing to issue you a credit card.

_____ **3.** If someone has generously given you something, there is no need to *beseech* him or her for it.

_____ **4.** The sweet smell of a spring day is generally considered *loathsome.*

_____ **5.** A state flag is an example of an *ensign.*

_____ **6.** *Obsequies* are particularly delicious when served with whipped cream.

_____ **7.** The opening of a cave could be compared to the *maw* of an animal.

_____ **8.** A *morsel* of food is enough to share with several friends.

_____ **9.** A wealthy person would probably sleep regularly on a *pallet.*

_____**10.** *Ground* is a word meaning "a cause."

THE ODYSSEY, Books 1–4   Homer   (Textbook page 721)

DEVELOPING VOCABULARY

Directions: Read carefully the explanation of each word. Then write a sentence of your own using that word. Include in your sentence clues to the meaning of the word.

lavished (lav′isht) **v.** past tense of *to lavish,* which means "to give generously." ▶ *Lavish* can also be used as an adjective, with the slightly different meaning of "very abundant, more than enough." ■ Mrs. Tulloch lavished expensive gifts on her favorite grandson.   **Page 724**

ORIGINAL SENTENCE: _____

_____

insolent (in′sə•lənt) **adj.** disrespectful; deliberately rude. ▶ Do not confuse *insolent* with the verb *insolate,* which means "to dry or bleach something by exposing it to the sun." ■ The insolent waiter refused to bring us water, so we reported him to the manager.   **Page 724**

ORIGINAL SENTENCE: _____

_____

lucid (loo′sid) **adj.** clear; easy to understand. ▶ This word comes from the same Latin root as *light.* ■ Ms. Rivera's history lectures are always interesting and lucid because she presents the information in a clear and lively way.   **Page 726**

ORIGINAL SENTENCE: _____

_____

to broach (brōch) **v.** to make a hole in; to tap; to introduce. ▶ Do not confuse this word with *brooch,* which refers to a type of jewelry that attaches with a pin. ■ The worker used a pointed tool and a hammer to broach the wooden barrel.   **Page 727**

ORIGINAL SENTENCE: _____

_____

prudently (prood′′nt•lē) **adv.** carefully; cautiously; with good judgment. ▶ A related word and synonym for *prudently* is *providently,* which means "in a way that provides for the future." ■ Receiving an allowance may help a child to learn to manage money prudently.   **Page 728**

ORIGINAL SENTENCE: _____

_____

to ponder (pän′dər) **v.** to think over; to weigh mentally; to consider carefully. ▶ *Ponder* suggests a careful consideration of a matter from all sides. ■ With his chin in his hands, David pondered whether a new bike was worth mowing lawns all summer.   **Page 724**

ORIGINAL SENTENCE: _____

_____

contending (kən•tend′iŋ) *n.* fighting; competing; struggling; arguing. ▶ *Contending* can also mean "holding to be a fact." ■ The two nations decided to put an end to their <u>contending</u> and sign a peace treaty. **Page 722**

ORIGINAL SENTENCE: _____

_____

din (din) *n.* a loud, continuous noise; clamor. ▶ *Din* has the connotation of noise that is a jumble of different sounds and is quite loud. ■ The <u>din</u> of the machinery was almost deafening. **Page 723**

ORIGINAL SENTENCE: _____

_____

to disperse (dis•pʉrs′) *v.* to scatter. ▶ The prefix *dis-* here means "out," and the Latin root *spargere* means "to scatter." ■ The sudden storm caused the crowd at the pep rally to <u>disperse</u> quickly. **Page 724**

ORIGINAL SENTENCE: _____

_____

host (hōst) *n.* a great number; a crowd; a multitude. ▶ A more familiar meaning of this word is "a person who entertains guests." ■ Our flight was delayed when a <u>host</u> of problems arose only moments before takeoff. **Page 730**

ORIGINAL SENTENCE: _____

_____

PRACTICE TEST

Directions: Fill in the blank with the vocabulary word that best fits the meaning of the sentence. *(10 points each)*

contending	to disperse	insolent	to broach	to ponder
din	lavished	lucid	prudently	host

1. The problem we had in math today was difficult; I had _____ it carefully before arriving at an answer.

2. In our school, any student who is _____ to a teacher or other student must write a note of apology.

3. The team knew that _____ with the Bears would be a challenge.

4. "For a _____ of reasons, including the possible hurricane, I cannot allow you to go on the camping trip," said Gary's mother.

5. Jarvis wrote a _____ essay in which he explained his ideas.

6. The boats created a _____ with their loud horns and whistles.

7. Linda _____ checked her pockets to make sure she had the keys.

8. The recipe said to stir the mixture in order _____ the dry ingredients through the liquid and shortening.

9. The farmer used a special tool _____ the cask of cider.

10. Monty's dog learned the tricks quickly because Monty _____ praise on her every time she performed correctly.

THE ODYSSEY, Book 5   Homer   (Textbook page 732)

DEVELOPING VOCABULARY

Directions: Read carefully the explanation of each word. Then write a sentence of your own using that word. Include in your sentence clues to the meaning of the word.

veered (vird) *v.* past tense of *to veer,* which means "to change direction." ▶ *To veer* can be used as a nautical term to mean "to change the direction of a ship by swinging its stern (rear) to the wind." ■ In order to avoid a collision, Buddy's father had to <u>veer</u> off the highway. **Page 732**

ORIGINAL SENTENCE: _____

_____

to douse (dous) *v.* to thrust into liquid; to throw liquid on. ▶ The everyday expression "to douse the lights" means "to put out the lights quickly." ■ To cool the glowing piece of iron, the blacksmith <u>doused</u> it in a pail of water. **Page 732**

ORIGINAL SENTENCE: _____

_____

mandate (man′dāt) *n.* an order or command. ▶ This word is a combination of two Latin roots: *manus,* meaning "hand," and *dare,* meaning "to give." ■ The new governor felt she had a <u>mandate</u> from the citizens to make improvements to the public schools. **Page 733**

ORIGINAL SENTENCE: _____

_____

forlorn (fər•lôrn′) *adj.* sad; lonely (usually because of abandonment). ▶ *Forlorn* comes from an Old English word meaning "to lose completely." You can remember the meaning of *forlorn* by imagining how a person would feel if he or she were deserted by friends and loved ones. ■ The <u>forlorn</u> little boy sat on the swing, waiting for a playmate to appear. **Page 734**

ORIGINAL SENTENCE: _____

_____

victuals (vit′′lz) *n. pl.* food supplies. ▶ *Victuals* derives from a Latin word meaning "food." It is now used mostly in informal speech. ■ In preparation for the long sea voyage, the captain made sure that adequate <u>victuals</u> had been stored on board. **Page 734**

ORIGINAL SENTENCE: _____

_____

versatile (vur′sə•t′l) *adj.* able to do many things; having many uses. ▶ British speakers usually pronounce this word vur′sə•tīl. ■ Rodney is a <u>versatile</u> musician: he can play the saxophone, the clarinet, and —in a pinch—the snare drums. **Page 734**

ORIGINAL SENTENCE: _____

_____

adversity (ad•vur′sə•tē) *n.* misfortune; suffering; affliction. ▶ The Latin root of this word means "turned opposite to." You can think of adversity as a set of circumstances that are the opposite of what a person would want them to be. ■ In times of adversity, you discover who your true friends are. **Page 734**

ORIGINAL SENTENCE: _____

_____

to pine (pīn) *v.* to long for; to yearn. ▶ When *pine* is used as a verb, it is usually followed by *for, after,* or an infinitive, such as *to have.* ■ The elderly man pined for the familiar sights of the farm he had once owned. **Page 734**

ORIGINAL SENTENCE: _____

_____

strategist (strat′ə•jist) *n.* a person skilled in careful, clever planning, or strategy. ▶ *Strategist* is often used to refer to someone who plans and directs large-scale military operations. ■ Although soldiers may do the actual fighting, a strategist must plan the overall approach an army will take. **Page 734**

ORIGINAL SENTENCE: _____

_____

shade (shād) *n.* a ghost. ▶ This unusual use of the familiar word *shade* is easy to understand if you think of a ghost as a shadow of a person who was once alive. ■ Halloween began as an observance of the time of year when shades were believed to wander over the earth visiting their living relatives. **Page 734**

ORIGINAL SENTENCE: _____

_____

PRACTICE TEST

Directions: In the blank at the right, write the vocabulary word that fits each definition at the left. *(10 points each)*

veered	victuals	strategist	mandate	adversity
to douse	versatile	shade	forlorn	to pine

1. an order or command   1. _____

2. sad and lonely   2. _____

3. food supplies; provisions   3. _____

4. to long for; to yearn   4. _____

5. skilled planner   5. _____

6. ghost   6. _____

7. changed direction   7. _____

8. misfortune; suffering   8. _____

9. to plunge into water   9. _____

10. able to do many things   10. _____

DEVELOPING VOCABULARY

Directions: Read carefully the explanation of each word. Then write a sentence of your own using that word. Include in your sentence clues to the meaning of the word.

oblivion (ə•bliv′ē•ən) *n.* the state of being forgotten or forgetting. ▶ A useful related word is *oblivious*, which means "not noticing," as in the sentence, "The girl was oblivious to the people around her." ■ Whenever I need to recall my grandparents' phone number, it seems to have disappeared into oblivion. **Page 736**

ORIGINAL SENTENCE: _____

_____

honeyed (hun′ēd) *adj.* sweet as honey; flattering. ▶ We use terms like "sweet talk" and "sugar coated" to refer to the practice of using pleasing words to influence people. Likewise, honeyed words are intended to flatter the listener. ■ The salesperson's honeyed words worked their magic on Ms. Carey, and she bought the car at once. **Page 738**

ORIGINAL SENTENCE: _____

_____

apparel (ə•per′əl) *n.* clothing. ▶ This word is closely related to *apparatus*, which refers to the materials or equipment needed for a specific use. ■ The doublet was a common item of men's apparel in Shakespeare's time. **Page 737**

ORIGINAL SENTENCE: _____

_____

prowls (proulz) *v.* moves about secretly and quietly; lurks. ▶ *Prowl* carries the connotation of looking for prey or loot, whereas *lurk* implies waiting with an evil purpose. ■ Late at night my cat prowls around in the yard looking for mice. **Page 738**

ORIGINAL SENTENCE: _____

_____

toil (toil) *n.* hard work; heavy labor. ▶ *Toil* implies long and exhausting work. ■ Before the invention of typesetting, years of toil were required to hand write a single copy of the Bible. **Page 739**

ORIGINAL SENTENCE: _____

_____

harmonious (här•mō′nē•əs) *adj.* fitting together without conflict; showing agreement of feelings, ideas, or actions. ▶ In music, harmony is a combination of two or more different tones that together produce a pleasing effect. ■ Open communication is necessary if two people are to achieve a harmonious relationship. **Page 739**

ORIGINAL SENTENCE: _____

_____

serenity (sə•ren′ə•tē) *n.* tranquillity; calmness. ▶ *Serenity* is derived from a Greek word meaning "dry." ■ I don't understand how the cafeteria supervisor can maintain such serenity in the middle of such chaos. **Page 739**

ORIGINAL SENTENCE: _____

_____

infused (in•fyo͞ozd′) *adj.* a form of *to infuse,* which means "to put one thing into another, so that it affects the entire thing." ▶ Originally, *infuse* referred to pouring a liquid into or onto something else, but now it is used primarily to refer to imparting ideas and feelings. ■ Infused with an enthusiasm for making the world a better place, the students began planning several community service projects. **Page 740**

ORIGINAL SENTENCE: _____

_____

averse (ə•vʉrs′) *adj.* opposed to; reluctant; unwilling. ▶ *Averse* is easily confused with *adverse,* which means "harmful," as in "the adverse effects of an experimental drug." ■ Mr. Kuchinsky strongly stated that he was averse to any plan that would require tearing down the beautiful old buildings in the neighborhood. **Page 741**

ORIGINAL SENTENCE: _____

_____

uncouth (un•ko͞oth′) *adj.* crude; uncultured. ▶ In Old English this word meant "not known." You can remember its meaning by thinking that good manners are "not known" by an uncouth person. ■ "Redneck," a slang term for an uncouth person, refers to someone who is sunburned from outdoor work. **Page 741**

ORIGINAL SENTENCE: _____

_____

PRACTICE TEST

Directions: In front of each number, write **T** if the statement is true or **F** if the statement is false. *(10 points each)*

_____ **1.** If you are *averse* to criticism, you are very willing to accept it.

_____ **2.** It is hard to remember something that has disappeared into *oblivion.*

_____ **3.** An *uncouth* person might pick his or her teeth with a fork during dinner.

_____ **4.** *Honeyed* words are useful when you want to pay someone a compliment.

_____ **5.** Days of *toil* on a farm are likely to leave you full of energy.

_____ **6.** A friend *infused* with love for the outdoors will probably want to go camping with you.

_____ **7.** A sweater is *apparel* that you might wear on a chilly day.

_____ **8.** A lion that *prowls* is less dangerous than one resting after dinner.

_____ **9.** A state park noted for its *serenity* is a good place to go if you want to relax.

_____**10.** *Harmonious* colors should be avoided when choosing paint for public areas such as bank lobbies and shopping malls.

THE ODYSSEY, Book 9   Homer   (Textbook page 745)

DEVELOPING VOCABULARY

Directions: Read carefully the explanation of each word. Then write a sentence of your own using that word. Include in your sentence clues to the meaning of the word.

formidable (fôr′mə•də•b'l) *adj.* causing fear, dread, or awe. ► When you pronounce this word, don't make the mistake of placing the stress on the second syllable. ■ Our team's most formidable opponents are the Lakeside Lions, who have been undefeated for the past three seasons. **Page 745**

ORIGINAL SENTENCE: _____

_____

guile (gīl) *n.* craftiness; using trickery when dealing with others. ► A related word, *to beguile,* means "to deceive or trick." ■ Through the use of guile and careful planning, the swindler was able to convince the couple to trust him with their life savings. **Page 745**

ORIGINAL SENTENCE: _____

_____

mustered (mus′tərd) *v.* past tense of *to muster,* which means "to gather together; to assemble." ► A common meaning of *to muster* is to call together troops for an inspection or roll call. ■ We could not muster enough players for a complete team. **Page 746**

ORIGINAL SENTENCE: _____

_____

to ravage (rav′ij) *v.* to ruin; to destroy; to devastate. ► *Ravage* is based on an Old French word meaning "to carry away." It implies destruction taking place over an extended period of time. ■ Wind and rain can ravage a wooden house that is not protected by paint. **Page 747**

ORIGINAL SENTENCE: _____

_____

gales (gālz) *n. pl.* strong winds. ► Technically, a gale blows from 32 to 63 miles per hour. ■ An unexpected gale blew the fishing boat off course. **Page 747**

ORIGINAL SENTENCE: _____

_____

dismembered (dis•mem′bərd) *v.* past tense of *to dismember,* which means "to divide into parts; to mutilate." ► One meaning of the word *member* is "body part." The prefix *dis-,* when added to a noun, turns it into a verb and here means "away." ■ The children will accidentally dismember the doll if they pull too hard on its arms and legs. **Page 748**

ORIGINAL SENTENCE: _____

_____

ninny (nin´ē) *n.* a foolish person. ▶ This word probably was created by running together the syllables of the words *an innocent.* ■ When it comes to buying clothes, Angela can be a real <u>ninny</u>; she always wants the newest fashion no matter how it looks on her. **Page 748**

ORIGINAL SENTENCE: _____

_____

sage (sāj) *adj.* displaying wisdom and good judgment. ▶ This word can also be a noun, meaning "a wise person." ■ My counselor gave me <u>sage</u> advice when he suggested that I take a course in auto mechanics. **Page 751**

ORIGINAL SENTENCE: _____

_____

bolted (bōlt´id) *v.* past tense of *to bolt,* which means "to run away; to dash out suddenly." ▶ Originally, this word meant "to shoot an arrow." You can remember its meaning by thinking of a person running away as quickly as an arrow moves through the air. ■ Every time I opened the door, the puppy <u>bolted</u> from the house and ran down the street. **Page 752**

ORIGINAL SENTENCE: _____

_____

meditations (med´ə•tā´shənz) *n. pl.* deep thoughts; contemplations; reflections. ▶ *Meditations* are usually thoughts on spiritual topics. ■ The nun spent part of her day in <u>meditation</u>. **Page 753**

ORIGINAL SENTENCE: _____

_____

PRACTICE TEST

Directions: In front of each number, write the letter of the definition that best matches each vocabulary word. *(10 points each)*

_____ **1.** ninny

_____ **2.** formidable

_____ **3.** meditations

_____ **4.** sage

_____ **5.** mustered

_____ **6.** guile

_____ **7.** dismembered

_____ **8.** to ravage

_____ **9.** gales

_____**10.** bolted

a. causing fear, dread, or awe

b. lonely

c. trickery; deception

d. assembled; gathered together

e. to prevent from happening

f. to destroy or devastate

g. strong winds

h. divided into parts

i. a strong leader

j. a foolish person

k. showing wisdom and good judgment

l. ran away quickly

m. deep thoughts; contemplations

THE ODYSSEY, Books 10–11   **Homer**   (Textbook page 757)

DEVELOPING VOCABULARY

Directions: Read carefully the explanation of each word. Then write a sentence of your own using that word. Include in your sentence clues to the meaning of the word.

snare (sner) *n.* a trap.. ► Originally this word referred to a means for catching small animals. Now it can mean anything that tricks, traps, or entangles a person in difficulties. ■ Work on the new recreation center was going smoothly, until last weekend when we hit a <u>snare</u>. **Page 758**

ORIGINAL SENTENCE: _____

_____

rancor (raŋ′kər) *n.* continuing and bitter hatred. ► A related word that is useful to know is *to rankle*, meaning "to cause long-lasting anger." ■ The work of the United Nations proves that even intense <u>rancor</u> can be overcome by serious efforts at peacemaking. **Page 760**

ORIGINAL SENTENCE: _____

_____

flitting (flit′tiŋ) *adj.* a form of *to flit*, which means "to fly lightly and quickly from one place to another." ► Do not confuse this word with *flirting*, which can mean "moving jerkily back and forth" or "playing at love." ■ <u>Flitting</u> from table to table, Michelle never stayed long enough to say more than a few words to anyone. **Page 759**

ORIGINAL SENTENCE: _____

_____

to atone (ə•tōn′) *v.* to make up for a wrongdoing; to make amends. ► This word is a combination of *at* and *one*, and refers to bringing back together two people who have become separated because of the actions of one of them. ■ Debra asked what she could do to <u>atone</u> for forgetting to invite me to her birthday party. **Page 761**

ORIGINAL SENTENCE: _____

_____

impalpable (im•pal′pə•b′l) *adj.* not capable of being felt or perceived. ► The prefix *im-* means "not," and the English word *palpate* means "to touch." ■ Although totally <u>impalpable</u>, nuclear radiation can be as deadly as the hard, cold steel of a bullet. **Page 762**

ORIGINAL SENTENCE: _____

_____

twinge (twinj) *n.* a sudden, brief pain. ► *Twinge* can also refer to a sudden, brief feeling of remorse or shame. ■ An occasional <u>twinge</u> in my lower leg reminds me of the skiing accident that put me in a cast last year. **Page 762**

ORIGINAL SENTENCE: _____

_____

fawned (fônd) *v.* past tense of *to fawn*, which means "to act in a servile way; to seek favor by flattery." ▶ Although this word is spelled the same way as *fawn*, meaning "a baby deer," the two words have very different meanings and developed from different origins. ■ Jed has a tendency to <u>fawn</u> on people whom he admires.   **Page 757**

ORIGINAL SENTENCE: _____

_____

beguiling (bi•gīl′iŋ) *adj.* a form of *to beguile*, which means "to trick, cheat, or deceive by the use of charm." ▶ This word contains the English word *guile*, which means "slyness or craftiness in dealing with others." ■ The handsome young politician had a <u>beguiling</u> manner that won him votes. **Page 757**

ORIGINAL SENTENCE: _____

_____

bereft (bi•reft′) *adj.* a form of *to bereave*, meaning "to rob; to be deprived of." ▶ A related word, *bereavement*, is the period of sadness that follows the death of a loved one. ■ The "F" on the final exam left Bob <u>bereft</u> of hope of passing world history.   **Page 761**

ORIGINAL SENTENCE: _____

_____

stealth (stelth) *n.* action or behavior that is secret, furtive, or sly. ▶ *Stealth* comes from the Middle English *stelen*, "to steal." ■ Through <u>stealth</u> and his knowledge of the company's computer system, Mr. Grandberry was able to obtain all the information needed to have the president arrested for fraud. **Page 758**

ORIGINAL SENTENCE: _____

_____

PRACTICE TEST

Directions: In the blank at the right, write the vocabulary word that fits each definition at the left. *(10 points each)*

fawned	flitting	snare	bereft	impalpable
beguiling	stealth	rancor	to atone	twinge

1. not capable of being felt   1. _____

2. to make up for a wrongdoing   2. _____

3. deceiving or charming   3. _____

4. flying quickly from place to place   4. _____

5. a sudden, brief pain   5. _____

6. sought to please by flattery   6. _____

7. deprived of; left alone   7. _____

8. lasting hatred   8. _____

9. a trap or trick   9. _____

10. secret, furtive action or behavior   10. _____

DEVELOPING VOCABULARY

Directions: Read carefully the explanation of each word. Then write a sentence of your own using that word. Include in your sentence clues to the meaning of the word.

haunting (hônt′iŋ) *adj.* a form of *to haunt*, meaning "to come back repeatedly." ▶ When thoughts, feelings, music, experiences, and so on, are difficult to forget, they are said to be "haunting." ■ The haunting memory of dancing with the beautiful girl kept the prince from falling in love again.   **Page 764**

ORIGINAL SENTENCE: _____

_____

kneaded (nēd′id) *adj.* a form of *to knead*, which means "to press or squeeze with the hands." ▶ *Knead*, *knob*, and *knot* can all be traced back to the same base word meaning "to form into a ball." ■ Kneaded properly, bread dough will rise into plump, smooth loaves.   **Page 763**

ORIGINAL SENTENCE: _____

_____

abominably (ə•bäm′ə•nə•blē) *adv.* hatefully; in a nasty, disagreeable, or loathsome way. ▶ This word derives from a Latin word meaning "inhuman." ■ Whenever we take my little brother to an expensive restaurant with us, he always acts so abominably that we vow never to do it again.   **Page 763**

ORIGINAL SENTENCE: _____

_____

promontory (präm′ən•tôr′ē) *n.* a peak of high land that juts out into a body of water. ▶ The Greek prefix *pro-* means "forward." ■ A lighthouse stood on a promontory at the entrance to the harbor.   **Page 763**

ORIGINAL SENTENCE: _____

_____

to muffle (muf′′l) *v.* to reduce the sound of. ▶ This word can also mean "to wrap up in a shawl or blanket so as to hide or keep warm." ■ Without special devices to muffle the sound of the machinery they operate, some factory workers would soon develop hearing problems.   **Page 764**

ORIGINAL SENTENCE: _____

_____

to baffle (baf′′l) *v.* to interfere with; to hinder. ▶ *Baffle* is more frequently used to mean "to confuse or puzzle." ■ The general massed his soldiers at the narrowest part of the valley, hoping to baffle the enemy's forward progress.   **Page 764**

ORIGINAL SENTENCE: _____

_____

ardor (är′dər) *n.* emotional warmth; passion; enthusiasm. ▶ The Latin root of this word meant "a flame." ■ The young woman expressed her ardor in long, impassioned love letters. **Page 766**

ORIGINAL SENTENCE: _____

_____

tumult (tōō′mult) *n.* uproar; noisy confusion. ▶ The Latin root of *tumult*, also found in *tumor*, means "to swell." ■ After the tumult of the political convention, a few days in the serenity of the lakeside resort was a welcomed relief. **Page 766**

ORIGINAL SENTENCE: _____

_____

to founder (foun′dər) *v.* to fill with water and sink; to break down, collapse, or fail. ▶ Do not confuse *founder* with *flounder*, which means "to stumble." ■ Despite the damage to its bow, the ship did not founder and was able to make it safely back to port. **Page 766**

ORIGINAL SENTENCE: _____

_____

maelstrom (māl′strəm) *n.* a large, violent whirlpool. ▶ This word has expanded in meaning to include any violently confused state of mind, emotion, or situation. ■ The tiny boat was caught in the maelstrom and promptly capsized. **Page 764**

ORIGINAL SENTENCE: _____

_____

PRACTICE TEST

Directions: Circle the letter of the best meaning for each word. *(10 points each)*

1. to founder: **a.** to arrive   **b.** to sink   **c.** to expand   **d.** to locate

2. promontory: **a.** high land jutting out into water   **b.** desert outpost
c. tree-covered mountain   **d.** narrow river or stream

3. haunting: **a.** easy to digest   **b.** difficult to forget   **c.** emotionally upsetting
d. soft to the touch

4. kneaded: **a.** required   **b.** hoped to find   **c.** pressed or squeezed
d. stitched with thread

5. tumult: **a.** uproar   **b.** vacation   **c.** large meeting   **d.** marketplace

6. abominably: **a.** invitingly   **b.** fiercely   **c.** intelligently   **d.** hatefully

7. maelstrom: **a.** type of soup   **b.** small, rocky island   **c.** violent whirlpool
d. debris found on a beach

8. to muffle: **a.** to reduce the price of   **b.** to reduce the noise of
c. to increase the amount of   **d.** to change the meaning of

9. to baffle: **a.** to prepare   **b.** to exhibit   **c.** to hinder   **d.** to restrict

10. ardor: **a.** grapevine   **b.** bird cage   **c.** confusion   **d.** emotional warmth

THE ODYSSEY, Books 16–17   **Homer**   (Textbook page 771)

DEVELOPING VOCABULARY

Directions: Read carefully the explanation of each word. Then write a sentence of your own using that word. Include in your sentence clues to the meaning of the word.

ruddy (rud'ē) *adj.* having a red or reddish color. ▶ *Rosy* and *ruddy* are synonyms, although *rosy* suggests the pinkness of a blush, whereas *ruddy* implies the reddish color of fair skin exposed to the outdoors. ■ My brother, a forest ranger, has brown hair, green eyes, and a <u>ruddy</u> complexion. **Page 772**

ORIGINAL SENTENCE: _____

_____

sweep (swēp) *n.* the range, scope, or area covered by something. ▶ This use of *sweep* is less frequent than its use as a verb meaning "clear away trash with a broom." ■ In front of the mansion was a long <u>sweep</u> of well-tended lawn. **Page 773**

ORIGINAL SENTENCE: _____

_____

uncomprehending (un•käm'prə•hend'iŋ) *adj.* a form of *to comprehend,* meaning "to understand," plus the prefix *un-,* meaning "not." ▶ The Latin root of this word means "to grasp." ■ The teacher knew when she saw their <u>uncomprehending</u> faces that she should never have attempted to explain such a difficult concept to the sixth graders. **Page 773**

ORIGINAL SENTENCE: _____

_____

meddling (med'liŋ) *adj.* a form of *to meddle,* which means "to interfere" or "to tamper." ▶ *Meddling* comes from a Latin word meaning "to mix." ■ <u>Meddling</u> friends are usually not appreciated; therefore, it is wise to stay out of other people's business. **Page 773**

ORIGINAL SENTENCE: _____

_____

ranging (rānj'iŋ) *adj.* a form of *to range,* meaning "to wander." ▶ *Range* has a wide variety of synonyms, including *roam, ramble, rove, stray,* and *meander.* ■ <u>Ranging</u> through the park looking for fallen timber to use for firewood, the scouts stumbled upon the entrance to a cave. **Page 773**

ORIGINAL SENTENCE: _____

_____

taloned (tal'ənd) *adj.* having claws. ▶ The Latin form of *talon* meant "ankle." It was borrowed by Old French and used to mean "heel." When it entered Middle English, it finally came to mean "claw." ■ Although they are beautiful, I find <u>taloned</u> birds like eagles and falcons somewhat frightening. **Page 773**

ORIGINAL SENTENCE: _____

_____

snuffling (snuf′′liŋ) *adj.* a form of *to snuffle*, which means "to breathe noisily." ▶ This word is a version of *to snuff*, which means "to sniff." ■ The snuffling dog picked up the scent of its master and began to wag its tail. **Page 771**

ORIGINAL SENTENCE: _____

_____

candor (kan′dər) *n.* honesty; directness; frankness. ▶ *Candor* comes from a Latin word meaning "whiteness" or "openness." ■ People who are accustomed to hiding their feelings may be surprised by your candor. **Page 772**

ORIGINAL SENTENCE: _____

_____

nestlings (nest′liŋz) *n. pl.* young birds. ▶ A different word spelled the same way as the singular of this word (*nestling*) is a form of the verb *to nestle* and means "settling down comfortably." ■ I enjoyed watching the mother bird bringing food back to her nestlings. **Page 773**

ORIGINAL SENTENCE: _____

_____

abroad (ə•brôd′) *adv.* outside one's own country. ▶ You can remember this word by thinking that travel to most foreign countries requires crossing a "broad" expanse of ocean. ■ Last summer my aunt and uncle took me with them on a trip abroad to China. **Page 771**

ORIGINAL SENTENCE: _____

_____

PRACTICE TEST

Directions: In front of each number, write the letter of the definition that best matches each vocabulary word. (*10 points each*)

_____ **1.** candor

_____ **2.** snuffling

_____ **3.** sweep

_____ **4.** ruddy

_____ **5.** meddling

_____ **6.** uncomprehending

_____ **7.** ranging

_____ **8.** taloned

_____ **9.** nestlings

_____ **10.** abroad

a. breathing noisily

b. honesty; frankness

c. red or reddish in color

d. outside one's own country

e. area covered by something

f. not understanding

g. lacking ambition

h. interfering; tampering

i. wandering

j. having lots of hair

k. having claws

l. baby birds

m. to separate into parts

THE ODYSSEY, Book 19   Homer   (Textbook page 776)

DEVELOPING VOCABULARY

Directions: Read carefully the explanation of each word. Then write a sentence of your own using that word. Include in your sentence clues to the meaning of the word.

laden (lād′′n) *adj.* a form of *to lade*, meaning "to load." ▶ *Laden* means "weighted down," and can be used to mean "psychologically burdened," as in "laden with worry." ■ <u>Laden</u> with equipment, the small pickup truck moved slowly up the hill.   **Page 777**

ORIGINAL SENTENCE: _____

_____

carriage (kar′ij) *n.* posture; bearing. ▶ A more familiar use of this word refers to something that carries people, such as a horse-drawn carriage or a baby carriage. ■ A self-confident person can often be recognized by his or her <u>carriage</u>.   **Page 777**

ORIGINAL SENTENCE: _____

_____

renowned (ri•nound′) *adj.* famous. ▶ The prefix *re-* means "again," and the Latin root *-nom-* means "name." ■ The <u>renowned</u> actor found it difficult to walk down the street without being recognized.   **Page 777**

ORIGINAL SENTENCE: _____

_____

suppliant (sup′lē•ənt) *n.* a person who makes a humble request. ▶ A related word with the same meaning is *supplicant*. Both words are based on a Latin root meaning "to kneel down" or "to pray." ■ The <u>suppliant</u> stood waiting for a response to his request.   **Page 778**

ORIGINAL SENTENCE: _____

_____

to endow (in•dou′) *v.* to provide; to furnish; to equip. ▶ This word shares its heritage with *donor*, someone who gives to others. ■ The wealthy family was able to <u>endow</u> the hospital with enough money to start a heart-transplant program.   **Page 778**

ORIGINAL SENTENCE: _____

_____

convulsed (kən•vulst′) *adj.* a form of *to convulse*, meaning "to shake violently; to cause spasms." ▶ This word comes from a Latin word meaning "to tear loose." ■ <u>Convulsed</u> from the earthquake, the ground heaved and tossed.   **Page 779**

ORIGINAL SENTENCE: _____

_____

realm (relm) *n.* kingdom. ▶ The origin of *realm* is the Latin word for royal. ■ On the day of the tournament, knights came from every corner of the <u>realm</u>.   **Page 778**

ORIGINAL SENTENCE: _____

_____

to suffice (sə•fīs′) *v.* to be enough. ► A more familiar form of this word is *sufficient*, which means "equal to what is needed." ■ Twenty or thirty dollars of spending money should <u>suffice</u> for the weekend trip. **Page 777**

ORIGINAL SENTENCE: _____

_____

maudlin (môd′lin) *adj.* tearfully sentimental. ► *Maudlin* is a shortened pronunciation of "Magdalene," a Biblical character often portrayed as weeping. ■ Lois becomes <u>maudlin</u> whenever she discusses her lost kitten. **Page 777**

ORIGINAL SENTENCE: _____

_____

heed (hēd) *n.* close attention. ► *Heed* evolved from a Greek word that means "hood," or something that furnishes protection. ■ I plan to give <u>heed</u> to the dentist's advice to brush regularly and avoid sweets. **Page 778**

ORIGINAL SENTENCE: _____

_____

PRACTICE TEST

Directions: Fill in the blank with the vocabulary word that best fits the meaning of the sentence. (*10 points each*)

laden	maudlin	renowned	suppliant	to endow
to suffice	carriage	heed	realm	convulsed

1. Some parents feel that their children do not pay _____ to their advice as often as they should.

2. John's _____ reaction to that sad love story surprised us.

3. Mr. Lopez returned from his orchard _____ with baskets of fresh peaches.

4. We saw a play in which a young _____ begs for a chance to sing in the chorus.

5. The assembly speaker was a(n) _____ authority on music.

6. Although only 14, Peter is tall and has the _____ of an adult.

7. The patient's body _____ with fits of coughing.

8. Taxpayers voted _____ the library with the money needed to open a new branch.

9. One quart of berries will have _____ for the blackberry pie.

10. The British monarch's _____ has been steadily shrinking since World War II because so many countries have achieved independence.

THE ODYSSEY, Book 21   **Homer**   (Textbook page 782)

DEVELOPING VOCABULARY

Directions: Read carefully the explanation of each word. Then write a sentence of your own using that word. Include in your sentence clues to the meaning of the word.

justification (jus′tə•fi•kā′shən) *n.* an acceptable reason, excuse, or defense. ▶ The Latin root on which *justification* is based means "to do what is just."

■ Linda's <u>justification</u> for her low grade was having missed eighteen days of school when she had the flu.   **Page 782**

ORIGINAL SENTENCE: _____

_____

courier (koor′ē•ər) *n.* a messenger. ▶ This word derives from the Latin word for run, because in ancient times messages were carried by runners. ■ My older brother has

a job as a <u>courier</u>, which sometimes requires him to ride his bike in heavy traffic. **Page 783**

ORIGINAL SENTENCE: _____

_____

adversities (ad•vur′sə•tēz) *n. pl.* misfortunes; hardships; calamities. ▶ This word is related to *adverse*, meaning "harmful." ■ The people of Ethiopia have

faced many forms of <u>adversity</u>—war, drought, starvation, and political upheaval. **Page 783**

ORIGINAL SENTENCE: _____

_____

longed (lôŋd) *v.* past tense of *to long*, which means "to want very much; to wish for; to yearn for." ▶ The root of *longed* is a

Greek word meaning "to reach." ■ After two months in Israel, my sister began to <u>long</u> for home.   **Page 783**

ORIGINAL SENTENCE: _____

_____

intervals (in′tər•v′lz) *n. pl.* periods of time between events. ▶ The Latin word from which *interval* evolved referred to the space between two walls. *Interval* can still be used

to denote distance as well as time. ■ At our school students are given five-minute <u>intervals</u> between classes.   **Page 784**

ORIGINAL SENTENCE: _____

_____

disdainful (dis•dān′fəl) *adj.* proud; scornful; filled with contempt. ▶ A disdainful person treats someone or something as though it

were beneath him or her. ■ One of the most irritating things about Brenda is the <u>disdainful</u> way she treats her classmates.   **Page 785**

ORIGINAL SENTENCE: _____

_____

heft (heft) *n.* weight; heaviness. ▶ *Heft* is related to the English verb *to heave*, which means "to lift." ■ Because of its great heft, the china cabinet could not be moved without the help of a furniture dolly. **Page 785**

ORIGINAL SENTENCE: _____

_____

vibrating (vī′brāt′iŋ) *adj.* a form of *to vibrate*, which means "to move rapidly back and forth." ▶ A useful related word is *vibrant*, which means "energetic; vivacious; vigorous." ■ The vibrating steering wheel caused me to suspect that one of the car's front tires was flat. **Page 785**

ORIGINAL SENTENCE: _____

_____

smote (smōt) *v.* past tense of *to smite*, which means "to strike or hit hard." ▶ The origin of this word is a Greek word meaning "to throw." ■ After the warrior smote the enemy soldier, he saw the copper band around the man's arm. **Page 785**

ORIGINAL SENTENCE: _____

_____

to adorn (ə•dôrn′) *v.* to decorate. ▶ The meaning of *adorn* differs slightly from the meaning of *decorate*. *To adorn* means to add something of beauty to something already beautiful. *To decorate* means to make something attractive that would otherwise be plain. ■ Throughout history women have used jewels, flowers, and ribbons to adorn their hair. **Page 785**

ORIGINAL SENTENCE: _____

_____

PRACTICE TEST

Directions: In front of each number, write the letter of the definition that best matches each vocabulary word. (*10 points each*)

_____ 1. to adorn	**a.** periods of time between events	**k.** scornful; filled with contempt
_____ 2. smote	**b.** wanted badly; yearned for	
_____ 3. adversities	**c.** an acceptable reason or excuse	**l.** foolish
_____ 4. vibrating	**d.** to make more beautiful	**m.** struck hard
_____ 5. intervals	**e.** moving rapidly back and forth	
_____ 6. heft	**f.** to supply with food	
_____ 7. disdainful	**g.** a messenger	
_____ 8. longed	**h.** hatred	
_____ 9. courier	**i.** hardships; misfortunes	
_____ 10. justification	**j.** weight; heaviness	

DEVELOPING VOCABULARY

Directions: Read carefully the explanation of each word. Then write a sentence of your own using that word. Include in your sentence clues to the meaning of the word.

wiliest (wī′lē•əst) *adj.* most sly; craftiest. ▶ This word is the adjective form of *wile*, which means "a sly trick" and derives from an Old English word meaning "magic."

■ In folk literature, the fox is often portrayed as the wiliest of the animals, full of tricks and slyness.   **Page 786**

ORIGINAL SENTENCE: _____

_____

revelry (rev′′l•rē) *n.* noisy merrymaking. ▶ The verb form of this word is *to revel*.

■ New Year's Eve is well known as a time for revelry.   **Page 786**

ORIGINAL SENTENCE: _____

_____

jostled (jäs′′ld) *v.* past tense of *to jostle*, which means "to push; to shove; to crowd against." ▶ *Jostle* can also be used as a noun to refer to a rough bump or shove.

■ Someone jostled Elizabeth in the cafeteria line, and she spilled her entire tray of food on the floor.   **Page 787**

ORIGINAL SENTENCE: _____

_____

craned (krānd) *v.* past tense of *to crane*, which means "to stretch one's neck." ▶ This word derives from the fact that birds known as cranes have long necks. It is usually used to suggest that someone is straining to see over something.   ■ With such a large crowd of people in front of me, I had to crane my neck first one way and then the other in order to see the parade. **Page 787**

ORIGINAL SENTENCE: _____

_____

restitution (res′tə•too′shən) *n.* repayment for loss or damage. ▶ This word is based on a Latin word meaning "to set up again" or "restore." ■ As restitution for the damage caused by their prank, the youths were required to pay 25 dollars each to the store owner.   **Page 788**

ORIGINAL SENTENCE: _____

_____

glowered (glou′ərd) *v.* past tense of *to glower*, which means "to scowl; to stare angrily." ▶ *Glower* can also be used as a noun, meaning "an angry stare." ■ When she is supervising study hall, Ms. Rella glowers at anyone who talks above a whisper. **Page 788**

ORIGINAL SENTENCE: _____

_____

ringleader (riŋ′lēd′ər) *n.* a person who leads others. ▶ This word is used chiefly to refer to situations in which the group is opposing authority, breaking laws, or engaging in mischief of some sort. ■ Nathan is the <u>ringleader</u> of the group who wrote their initials in paint on the side of the building. **Page 787**

ORIGINAL SENTENCE: _____

_____

aloft (ə•lôft′) *adv.* high up in the air. ▶ The word part *-loft* is derived from an Old Norse word meaning "air." ■ It is hard to keep a kite <u>aloft</u> when the wind is not strong. **Page 788**

ORIGINAL SENTENCE: _____

_____

shimmering (shim′ər•iŋ) *adj.* a form of *to shimmer,* which means "to shine with a soft, unsteady light." ▶ Do not confuse this word with *shimmying,* which means "shaking or wobbling." ■ We love to watch the <u>shimmering</u> moonlight through the trees across the lake. **Page 788**

ORIGINAL SENTENCE: _____

_____

veering (vir′iŋ) *adj.* a form of *to veer,* which means "to change direction; to shift; to swing around." ▶ This word is used by meteorologists to describe a clockwise shift in the wind. ■ <u>Veering</u> into the wrong lane, the truck almost hit an oncoming car. **Page 788**

ORIGINAL SENTENCE: _____

_____

PRACTICE TEST

Directions: In the blank at the right, write the vocabulary word that fits each definition at the left. *(10 points each)*

wiliest	jostled	restitution	ringleader	shimmering
revelry	craned	glowered	aloft	veering

1. repayment for loss or damage   1. _____

2. high up in the air   2. _____

3. craftiest; sliest   3. _____

4. stretched one's neck   4. _____

5. noisy merrymaking   5. _____

6. changing direction suddenly   6. _____

7. shining with an unsteady light   7. _____

8. the leader of a group   8. _____

9. stared angrily   9. _____

10. pushed or shoved   10. _____

THE ODYSSEY, Book 23   Homer   (Textbook page 789)

DEVELOPING VOCABULARY

Directions: Read carefully the explanation of each word. Then write a sentence of your
own using that word. Include in your sentence clues to the meaning of the word.

shuns (shunz) *v.* avoids; keeps away from.
▶ *Shun* and *avoid* are synonyms; however,
avoid stresses caution in keeping clear of
danger, whereas *shun* implies keeping away
as a matter of habit or policy.   ■ My friends
and I tend to <u>shun</u> the beach until after four
o'clock when the crowds thin out.
Page 789

ORIGINAL SENTENCE: _____

_____

tatters (tat′ərz) *n. pl.* torn pieces of cloth.
▶ This word is the plural form of *tatter*,
which can also be used as a verb (*to tatter*)
meaning "to make something ragged."
■ The poor man's clothes were nothing but
<u>tatters</u>.   **Page 789**

ORIGINAL SENTENCE: _____

_____

lavished (lav′isht) *v.* past tense of *to lavish*,
which means "to give generously."
▶ *Lavish* is derived from an Old French word
meaning "torrent of rain." You can
remember its meaning by thinking of presents
raining down on someone.   ■ The students
<u>lavished</u> gifts on Dr. Wang, the principal,
when she retired.   **Page 790**

ORIGINAL SENTENCE: _____

_____

lopped (läpt) *v.* past tense of *to lop*, which
means "to cut off."   ▶ This word primarily
refers to trimming trees by cutting off
branches. Generally it is followed by the
adverb *off*.   ■ To make the huge Christmas
tree fit into our living room, we <u>lopped</u> off
several branches.   **Page 791**

ORIGINAL SENTENCE: _____

_____

clotted (klät′tid) *adj.* a form of *to clot*,
meaning "to thicken and dry; to form into
lumps."   ▶ *Clot* refers especially to blood
or other liquids that undergo a process of
forming soft lumps or thickened areas within
the liquid.   ■ Because the wound was
covered with dirt and <u>clotted</u> blood, the
physician could not tell how extensive the
injury was.   **Page 791**

ORIGINAL SENTENCE: _____

_____

impostors (im•päs′tərz) *n. pl.* persons who
pretend to be someone or something they are
not.   ▶ The word comes from a Latin word
meaning "deception or fraud."   ■ One
month passed before the employees realized
that the stranger who claimed to be the
company's president was an <u>impostor</u>.
Page 791

ORIGINAL SENTENCE: _____

_____

tunic (tōō′nik) **n.** a loose garment, usually extending to the knees and sometimes tied or belted at the waist. ▶ Both men and women in ancient Greece and Rome wore tunics. ■ With Pablo's help I made a <u>tunic</u> to wear in the school play. **Page 790**

ORIGINAL SENTENCE: _____

_____

aloof (ə•lōōf′) **adj.** removed; distant; reserved; cool. ▶ Do not confuse *aloof* with *aloft,* which means "high up in the air." ■ Most people think Vicky is <u>aloof</u>, but I suspect she is just shy. **Page 790**

ORIGINAL SENTENCE: _____

_____

pliant (plī′ənt) **adj.** easily bent. ▶ Both *pliant* and its synonym *pliable* are based on a Latin word meaning "to fold." ■ The Cherokee Indians of eastern Tennessee make beautiful baskets from <u>pliant</u> strips of white oak. **Page 791**

ORIGINAL SENTENCE: _____

_____

tremulous (trem′yoo•ləs) **adj.** trembling; quivering; hence, fearful; timid. ▶ This word is closely related to *tremble,* which means "to shake." ■ In a <u>tremulous</u> voice Gloria began to recite the poem to the class. **Page 791**

ORIGINAL SENTENCE: _____

_____

PRACTICE TEST

Directions: In front of each number, write **T** if the statement is true or **F** if the statement is false. *(10 points each)*

_____ **1.** If *tatters* are what remain of some beautiful velvet draperies, the draperies will probably last for several more years.

_____ **2.** A wife who *lavished* gifts on her husband would expect him to be pleased.

_____ **3.** *Clotted* cream is very thin and watery.

_____ **4.** A *tremulous* sound is shaky.

_____ **5.** If someone you like *shuns* you, it makes you feel more self-confident.

_____ **6.** After you have *lopped* off the branches of a tree, it will look bigger and fuller than before.

_____ **7.** It is easier to shape and mold *pliant* metals than those that are not *pliant.*

_____ **8.** When an *aloof* person attends a party, he or she generally holds lively conversations with everyone there.

_____ **9.** A *tunic* is a weapon that was used by soldiers in ancient Greece.

_____ **10.** *Impostors* are people who are being perfectly honest about their identities.

THE ODYSSEY, Book 24   Homer   (Textbook page 792)

DEVELOPING VOCABULARY

Directions: Read carefully the explanation of each word. Then write a sentence of your own using that word. Include in your sentence clues to the meaning of the word.

sifted (sift′id) *v.* past tense of *to sift,* which means ''to separate the coarse parts from the fine parts.'' ▶ *Sift* is related to the noun *sieve,* which refers to a utensil with many small openings that is used to sift material. ■ Using a cast-off sieve, my little brother likes to <u>sift</u> the sand in his sandbox. **Page 792**

ORIGINAL SENTENCE: _____

_____

prickling (prik′liŋ) *adj.* a form of *to prickle,* meaning ''to cause to feel a tingling or stinging sensation.'' ▶ This word comes from an Old English word meaning ''a point.'' You can remember its meaning by thinking about how it feels to be touched with something that has a sharp point. ■ The doctor told my aunt that the <u>prickling</u> sensation in her legs was the result of a pinched nerve in her back. **Page 792**

ORIGINAL SENTENCE: _____

_____

wheedling (hwē′d′liŋ) *adj.* a form of *to wheedle,* which means ''to coax; to persuade by flattery.'' ▶ *Wheedle* was probably derived from a German word meaning ''to wave the fan, hence, to flatter.'' ■ <u>Wheedling</u> his parents with kind words, Roger talked them into buying him his own phone. **Page 792**

ORIGINAL SENTENCE: _____

_____

hue (hyōo) *n.* a shade of a color. ▶ This word originally meant ''general appearance,'' but over the years it has come to refer more specifically to color. ■ Carol asked the salesclerk if the store had sweaters in a <u>hue</u> that would match her skirt. **Page 792**

ORIGINAL SENTENCE: _____

_____

anointed (ə•noint′id) *v.* past tense of *to anoint,* which means ''to put oil or ointment on, usually in a religious ceremony.'' ▶ *Anoint* derives from a Latin word meaning ''to smear on.'' ■ As Mr. Ciccone lay dying, the priest <u>anointed</u> his body with holy oil and recited prayers. **Page 793**

ORIGINAL SENTENCE: _____

_____

girth (gʉrth) *n.* the distance around a person or thing; the circumference. ▶ This word comes from an Old Norse word meaning ''to encircle.'' ■ When the <u>girth</u> of a pine tree exceeds 31 inches, it can be sold for lumber. **Page 793**

ORIGINAL SENTENCE: _____

_____

stature (stach′ər) *n.* height. ▶ Noticing the similarity of this word to *statue* will help you remember its meaning. ■ People of short stature sometimes feel they must excel at everything they undertake in order to feel worthwhile. **Page 793**

ORIGINAL SENTENCE: _____

_____

skirmish (skʉr′mish) *n.* a brief fight. ▶ *Skirmish* differs from *battle* in that a skirmish is lighter, shorter, and involves fewer soldiers. ■ To divert the enemy's attention, one platoon started a skirmish near the river, while the rest of the troops crossed several miles downstream. **Page 793**

ORIGINAL SENTENCE: _____

_____

strewing (strōo′iŋ) *adj.* a form of *to strew,* which means "to scatter; to sprinkle." ▶ *Sprinkle* differs in meaning slightly from *scatter* and *strew. Sprinkle* implies causing something to fall in small drops, whereas *scatter* and *strew* suggests tossing something sideways in different directions. ■ Strewing flower petals in the aisle before the arrival of the bride, little Joanne looked especially sweet. **Page 793**

ORIGINAL SENTENCE: _____

_____

arbiter (är′bə•tər) *n.* a judge. ▶ An *arbiter* (or *arbitrator*) is a person chosen to settle a dispute. Usually, both sides have agreed to accept this person's decision. ■ Our student council president, Isabel Marquez, is often called upon to serve as arbiter in disagreements between students. **Page 794**

ORIGINAL SENTENCE: _____

_____

PRACTICE TEST

Directions: Circle the letter of the best meaning for each word. *(10 points each)*

1. hue: **a.** temperature   **b.** size   **c.** length   **d.** a shade of a color

2. wheedling: **a.** increasing in number   **b.** making less frightening
   c. persuading by flattery   **d.** limiting the number of

3. stature: **a.** temperature   **b.** shape   **c.** height   **d.** color

4. girth: **a.** distance across   **b.** distance around   **c.** distance to travel
   d. place to stay

5. anointed: **a.** applied oil   **b.** asked for mercy   **c.** settled an argument
   d. listened sympathetically

6. arbiter: **a.** shoemaker   **b.** person who pretends to be someone else
   c. person selected to settle a dispute   **d.** person who uses flattery

7. strewing: **a.** scattering   **b.** building   **c.** cooking slowly   **d.** destroying

8. skirmish: **a.** a brief letter   **b.** a brief answer   **c.** a long time
   d. a brief fight

9. prickling: **a.** soaking cucumbers in vinegar   **b.** causing a tingling feeling
   c. creating great enthusiasm   **d.** an open sore

10. sifted: **a.** separated fine from coarse parts   **b.** scattered widely
    c. fought in a large area   **d.** applied oil or ointment

ANIMAL FARM, Chapter I   George Orwell   (Textbook page 810)

DEVELOPING VOCABULARY

Directions: Read carefully the explanation of each word. Then write a sentence of your own using that word. Include in your sentence clues to the meaning of the word.

benevolent (bə•nev′ə•lənt) *adj.* kindly; inclined to do good. ▶ The Latin root -*bene*- means "good." ■ It is curious that grandparents are usually portrayed as benevolent and stepparents are often portrayed as evil. **Page 810**

ORIGINAL SENTENCE: _____

_____

ensconced (in•skänst′) *adj.* a form of *to ensconce*, which means "to settle comfortably, snugly, or securely." ▶ This word is based on a Dutch word meaning "fortress or shelter." ■ Ensconced in a corner of the sofa, I read a science fiction novel. **Page 810**

ORIGINAL SENTENCE: _____

_____

cynical (sin′i•k′l) *adj.* believing that people are motivated primarily by selfishness. ▶ A cynical person doubts the sincerity of others and questions the value of living. ■ Ever since my father was cheated out of a great deal of money by his business partner, he has been rather cynical. **Page 810**

ORIGINAL SENTENCE: _____

_____

abolished (ə•bäl′isht) *adj.* a form of *to abolish*, which means "to do away with." ▶ *Abolish* derives from a Latin word that means "destroy." ■ Abolished in some states, the death penalty still exists in others. **Page 811**

ORIGINAL SENTENCE: _____

_____

to tyrannize (tir′ə•nīz′) *v.* to govern harshly with absolute power. ▶ The base word *tyranny* implies two qualities: unlimited power or authority and cruelty and severity. ■ Hitler tyrannized the people of many countries in Europe before he was finally defeated in 1945. **Page 812**

ORIGINAL SENTENCE: _____

_____

scullery (skul′ər•ē) *n.* a small room near the kitchen, where pots and pans are cleaned and stored. ▶ *Scullery* comes from a Latin word meaning "tray." The word is seldom used today. ■ Working in the scullery was the least attractive job in the household. **Page 810**.

ORIGINAL SENTENCE: _____

_____

preliminary (pri•lim′ə•ner′ē) *adj.* introductory; leading up to the main action. ▶ The prefix *pre-* means "before." ■ Chet was eliminated in the <u>preliminary</u> round of judging in the talent contest, but Pauline made it to the finals. **Page 813**

ORIGINAL SENTENCE: _____

_____

resolution (rez′ə•lōō′shən) *n.* firmness of will. ▶ A related adjective, *resolute*, means "determined or resolved." ■ The <u>resolution</u> of the British people helped them survive the dark days of World War II. **Page 812**

ORIGINAL SENTENCE: _____

_____

plaited (plāt′id) *adj.* braided. ▶ This word is based on a Latin word that means "to fold." ■ Until she was almost grown, Maya wore her hair <u>plaited</u>. **Page 811**

ORIGINAL SENTENCE: _____

_____

paddock (pad′ək) *n.* a small, enclosed area for animals. ▶ Specifically, a paddock is an enclosure near a stable or race track where horses are exercised. ■ She caught a glimpse of Golden Boy as he was being led to the <u>paddock</u> by his trainer. **Page 810**

ORIGINAL SENTENCE: _____

_____

PRACTICE TEST

Directions: In front of each number, write the letter of the definition that best matches each vocabulary word. *(10 points each)*

_____ 1. scullery

_____ 2. resolution

_____ 3. tyrannize

_____ 4. abolished

_____ 5. cynical

_____ 6. benevolent

_____ 7. preliminary

_____ 8. paddock

_____ 9. plaited

_____10. ensconced

a. kindly

b. having a sense of humor

c. settled comfortably

d. doubting the sincerity of people's motives

e. done away with completely

f. rule cruelly with unlimited power

g. make an exchange

h. introductory; coming before

i. firmness of will

j. a burial place

k. braided

l. a room where pots are scrubbed

m. an enclosure for animals

ANIMAL FARM, Chapter II   George Orwell   (Textbook page 813)

DEVELOPING VOCABULARY

Directions: Read carefully the explanation of each word. Then write a sentence of your own using that word. Include in your sentence clues to the meaning of the word.

vivacious (vi•vā′shəs) *adj.* lively; full of life; energetic. ► This word is based on a Latin word that means "to live." ■ In choosing cheerleaders for this year's squad, we looked for people who were especially <u>vivacious</u>. **Page 813**

ORIGINAL SENTENCE: _____

_____

expounded (ik•spound′id) *v.* past tense of *to expound*, which means "to state or explain in detail." ► *Expound* is derived from the prefix *ex-*, meaning "out," and the Latin root *ponere*, meaning "to put." ■ The class listened while Mr. Morrelli <u>expounded</u> his theory of why dinosaurs became extinct. **Page 814**

ORIGINAL SENTENCE: _____

_____

pre-eminent (prē•em′ə•nənt) *adj.* surpassing others. ► The English word *eminent* means "lofty." The prefix *pre-* adds the meaning "forward" or "ahead." ■ Today we watched a videotaped interview with the <u>pre-eminent</u> authority on British constitutional government. **Page 813**

ORIGINAL SENTENCE: _____

_____

apathy (ap′ə•thē) *n.* lack of interest; indifference. ► *Apathy* comes from a Greek word meaning "without emotion." ■ Because they encountered so much <u>apathy</u> among the other students, the committee decided not to proceed with their plans. **Page 814**

ORIGINAL SENTENCE: _____

_____

disheartened (dis•här′t′nd) *adj.* a form of *to dishearten*, which means "to discourage; to take away the enthusiasm of." ► The prefix *dis-* here means "to cause to be the opposite of," and *hearten* means "to cheer up or encourage." ■ The rest of the team felt <u>disheartened</u> by the news that the quarterback would not be able to play. **Page 814**

ORIGINAL SENTENCE: _____

_____

gamboled (gam′b'ld) *v.* past tense of *to gambol*, which means "to jump and skip about in play." ► Do not confuse *gambol* with its homonym *gamble*, which means "to play games of chance for money." ■ In the early summer the lambs would <u>gambol</u> in the lush green meadow. **Page 815**

ORIGINAL SENTENCE: _____

_____

situated (sich′o͞o•wāt′id) *adj.* located. ▶ This word is based on a Latin word meaning "to place." ■ Columbia, Missouri, is <u>situated</u> roughly halfway between St. Louis and Kansas City. **Page 814**

ORIGINAL SENTENCE: _____

_____

frothing (frôth′iŋ) *adj.* a form of *to froth*, which means "to produce foam." ▶ A related word, *frothy*, means "foamy" or "light, trifling, or worthless." ■ Some detergents contain special chemicals to produce <u>frothing</u> suds. **Page 816**

ORIGINAL SENTENCE: _____

_____

nimble (nim′b'l) *adj.* quick and light in movement; agile. ▶ This word comes from an Old English word meaning "to take or seize." ■ To be successful at gymnastics, a person must be very <u>nimble</u>. **Page 814**

ORIGINAL SENTENCE: _____

_____

tormentors (tôr•men′tərz) *n. pl.* torturers; those who cause others pain, anxiety, or suffering. ▶ The Latin root of this word meant "an instrument of torture." ■ The new recruits considered the drill sergeant to be a <u>tormentor.</u> **Page 814**

ORIGINAL SENTENCE: _____

_____

PRACTICE TEST

Directions: Fill in the blank with the vocabulary word that best fits the meaning of the sentence. *(10 points each)*

vivacious	pre-eminent	disheartened	gamboled	nimble
expounded	apathy	situated	frothing	tormentors

1. The children _____ like colts frolicking on a spring morning.

2. The amusement park is _____ six miles from downtown.

3. The girls were _____ that no one would help them.

4. The _____ cello player was greeted with thunderous applause.

5. Pedro _____ on why the voting age should be reduced to 16.

6. My _____ cousin was chosen for her high energy level.

7. Dad finally succeeded in killing his _____, the mosquitoes.

8. Sheila doubted whether she was _____ enough to climb down.

9. Detergent poured into the fountain produced a _____ mess.

10. Although many people were starving as a result of the drought, the reaction in other parts of the world was generally one of _____.

ANIMAL FARM, Chapter III   George Orwell
(Textbook page 818)

DEVELOPING VOCABULARY

Directions: Read carefully the explanation of each word. Then write a sentence of your own using that word. Include in your sentence clues to the meaning of the word.

parasitical (par′ə•sit′i•kəl) *adj.* living at the expense of others. ▶ *Parasitical* and *parasitic* are both adjective forms of the noun *parasite.* ■ A leech is a type of parasitical worm that lives off the blood of other animals. **Page 818**

ORIGINAL SENTENCE: _____

_____

shirked (shʉrkt) *v.* past tense of *to shirk,* which means "to neglect a duty; to evade work." ▶ The origin of this word was probably a German word meaning "rascal." ■ Once elected class president, you will have certain responsibilities that you cannot shirk. **Page 818**

ORIGINAL SENTENCE: _____

_____

cryptic (krip′tik) *adj.* having a hidden meaning; mysterious. ▶ This word is derived from the same Greek word (meaning hidden) as *crypt,* an underground chamber serving as a burial place. ■ The only clue the detectives had was a cryptic note that said, "The pink penguin walks at midnight." **Page 818**

ORIGINAL SENTENCE: _____

_____

resolved (ri•zälv′d) *v.* past tense of *to resolve,* which means "to decide; to reach an agreement." ▶ This word is based on the prefix *re-* (again) plus the Latin root *-solv-,* meaning "to release." ■ The group finally resolved to pay for the pizza by each of us contributing two dollars. **Page 819**

ORIGINAL SENTENCE: _____

_____

propulsion (prə•pul′shən) *n.* a driving force; a forward motion. ▶ *Propulsion* is based on the prefix *pro-* (forward) and a Latin root meaning "to drive." ■ Large ocean liners depend on steam turbines for propulsion. **Page 820**

ORIGINAL SENTENCE: _____

_____

manipulation (mə•nip′yə•lā′shən) *n.* skillful handling or operation. ▶ The Latin word *manus* means "hand." ■ Operating a construction crane requires good coordination and careful manipulation. **Page 820**

ORIGINAL SENTENCE: _____

_____

maxim (mak′sim) **n.** a concise statement of truth or rule of conduct. ▶ The Latin root of *maxim* means "greatest," and can be found in other English words such as *maximum* and *magnify*. ■ "Honesty is the best policy" is one of the <u>maxims</u> by which I try to live. **Page 819**

ORIGINAL SENTENCE: _____

_____

grudging (gruj′iŋ) **adj.** a form of *to grudge,* which means "to give with reluctance." ▶ This word is related in origin to the word *grouch.* ■ My parents gave only <u>grudging</u> approval to my enrolling in karate class. **Page 818**

ORIGINAL SENTENCE: _____

_____

seclusion (si•kloo′zhən) **n.** being kept apart from others; isolation. ▶ This word is based on two Latin word parts that combine to mean "to close off." ■ The witness was kept in <u>seclusion</u> until after the trial. **Page 820**

ORIGINAL SENTENCE: _____

_____

acute (ə•kyoot′) **adj.** sharp; severe; intense. ▶ *Acute* is derived from a Latin verb meaning "to sharpen." ■ My father's ulcer causes him <u>acute</u> pain if he eats spicy foods or drinks coffee. **Page 818**

ORIGINAL SENTENCE: _____

_____

PRACTICE TEST

Directions: Circle the letter of the best meaning for each word. *(10 points each)*

1. grudging: **a.** hateful   **b.** excellent   **c.** skillful   **d.** reluctant

2. cryptic: **a.** silent   **b.** ancient   **c.** hidden   **d.** early

3. shirked: **a.** removed a piece of clothing   **b.** neglected or evaded
   c. found a solution for   **d.** separated into its parts

4. acute: **a.** attractive   **b.** lasting   **c.** puzzling   **d.** sharp

5. parasitical: **a.** living at the expense of others   **b.** existing in another place
   c. inclined to be bossy   **d.** practical

6. manipulation: **a.** thorough understanding   **b.** skillful handling
   c. warm affection   **d.** spiritual development

7. maxim: **a.** highest point   **b.** most important reason
   c. concise statement of truth   **d.** change in direction

8. resolved: **a.** encouraged   **b.** refused   **c.** brought into the open
   d. reached an agreement

9. propulsion: **a.** forward motion   **b.** complex problem
   c. lengthy explanation   **d.** intense pain

10. seclusion: **a.** being kept apart from others   **b.** being forced to do something
    wrong   **c.** being kept waiting   **d.** trying to one's best

ANIMAL FARM, Chapter IV   George Orwell   (Textbook page 820)

DEVELOPING VOCABULARY

Directions: Read carefully the explanation of each word. Then write a sentence of your own using that word. Include in your sentence clues to the meaning of the word.

tractable (trak′tə•b'l) *adj.* easily managed; obedient. ▶ The Latin root of *tractable* is a verb meaning "to drag or haul." ■ A dog will be more <u>tractable</u> if you approach it with kindness.   **Page 821**

ORIGINAL SENTENCE: _____

_____

irrepressible (ir′i•pres′ə•b'l) *adj.* uncontrollable. ▶ *Ir-*, like *il-* and *im-*, is a variation of the prefix *in-*, meaning "not." ■ Lorrie has an <u>irrepressible</u> sense of humor; she is forever making jokes.   **Page 821**

ORIGINAL SENTENCE: _____

_____

maneuver (mə•noo′vər) *n.* a movement intended as a skillful step toward some goal. ▶ This word is derived from Latin words meaning "to work by hand." ■ Sharon made a <u>maneuver</u> with the truck that allowed us to attach a tow rope to the disabled car. **Page 821**

ORIGINAL SENTENCE: _____

_____

vengeance (ven′jəns) *n.* action taken in return for an injury or offense. ▶ A synonym for *vengeance*, based on the same Latin root, is *revenge*. ■ When he discovered that his skateboard had been broken, he declared that he wanted <u>vengeance</u>.   **Page 822**

ORIGINAL SENTENCE: _____

_____

ignominious (ig′nə•min′ē•əs) *adj.* shameful; dishonorable. ▶ This word comes from a Latin word meaning "loss of one's name." You can remember this word by thinking of the way a person is viewed when his or her "good name," or reputation, has been lost. ■ Although the mayor had been highly respected before his arrest, the citizens scorned him when they learned of his <u>ignominious</u> action.   **Page 822**

ORIGINAL SENTENCE: _____

_____

impromptu (im•prämp′too) *adj.* without preparation. ▶ English speakers borrowed this word from French, although originally it came from a Latin word meaning "in readiness." ■ At the party after the game, the coach made an <u>impromptu</u> speech on the value of failures as well as successes. **Page 822**

ORIGINAL SENTENCE: _____

_____

adjoined (ə•joind′) *v.* past tense of *to adjoin*, which means "to be next to." ▶ Note that the first *d* in this word is silent. ■ When I was growing up, our house adjoined my father's dental office. **Page 821**

ORIGINAL SENTENCE: _____

_____

to scorn (skôrn) *v.* to make fun of; to look down on. ▶ *To scorn* has a number of synonyms, including *to despise, to disdain,* and *to hate*. ■ Mr. Ortiz scorned the offer of help by demanding, "Where were you when I really needed you!" **Page 821**

ORIGINAL SENTENCE: _____

_____

monstrous (män′strəs) *adj.* huge. ▶ The Latin word on which *monstrous* is based means "to warn." ■ The stuffed animal, with its small head and monstrous tail, looked comical. **Page 820**

ORIGINAL SENTENCE: _____

_____

posthumously (päs′choo•məs•lē) *adv.* after death. ▶ The prefix *post-* means "after," as in *postpone, postscript* (P.S.), *postmeridian* (P.M.), and *postindustrial*. ■ The writer's last novel was published posthumously. **Page 823**

ORIGINAL SENTENCE: _____

_____

PRACTICE TEST

Directions: In the blank at the right, write the vocabulary word that fits each definition at the left. *(10 points each)*

| adjoined | tractable | maneuver | ignominious | monstrous |
| scorn | irrepressible | vengeance | impromptu | posthumously |

1. skillful move toward a goal   1. _____

2. uncontrollable   2. _____

3. without preparation   3. _____

4. easily managed; obedient   4. _____

5. shameful; dishonorable   5. _____

6. was situated next to   6. _____

7. despise; look down upon   7. _____

8. huge   8. _____

9. after death   9. _____

10. revenge; punishment in return for an offense   10. _____

ANIMAL FARM, Chapter V   **George Orwell**   (Textbook page 825)

DEVELOPING VOCABULARY

Directions: Read carefully the explanation of each word. Then write a sentence of your own using that word. Include in your sentence clues to the meaning of the word.

pretext (prē′tekst) *n.* a false reason; an excuse. ▶ This word is based on a Latin word meaning "to pretend." ■ Angelo's pretext for calling Sarah was to get the next day's history assignment, but he really just wanted to get better acquainted. **Page 825**

ORIGINAL SENTENCE: _____

_____

blithely (blīth′lē) *adv.* in a carefree or unconcerned manner. ▶ *Blithe* has remained a part of the English language virtually unchanged for approximately 800 years. ■ Even though we had warned her of the danger, Marilyn blithely walked to the edge of the cliff and peered over. **Page 825**

ORIGINAL SENTENCE: _____

_____

ratified (rat′ə•fīd′) *v.* past participle of *to ratify*, which means "to approve; to confirm formally." ▶ The Latin origin of this word is a word meaning "to make a rate." ■ Although the president signed the treaty, it never officially took effect because it was not ratified by the Senate. **Page 825**

ORIGINAL SENTENCE: _____

_____

innovations (in′ə•vā′shənz) *n. pl.* introductions of new ways of doing things. ▶ The Latin root *nov-* means "new." It is also found in such words as *novelty* and *novice.* ■ Teachers at Roosevelt Junior High are introducing a number of educational innovations such as small group instruction, independent study, and self-paced learning. **Page 825**

ORIGINAL SENTENCE: _____

_____

aloof (ə•lo̅o̅f′) *adv.* at a distance; apart. ▶ Do not confuse *aloof* with *aloft,* which means "high up in the air." ■ Some people believe that to be a good teacher one should not try to be a pal to the students, but instead stay aloof. **Page 826**

ORIGINAL SENTENCE: _____

_____

faction (fak′shən) *n.* a group of people working for a common goal within a larger group. ▶ This word is based on a Latin verb meaning "to do." ■ The student government is made up of three competing factions, a situation that makes cooperation almost impossible. **Page 826**

ORIGINAL SENTENCE: _____

_____

restive (res′tiv) *adj.* nervous; restless; uneasy. ▶ *Restive* has somewhat the same meaning as *restless,* but also conveys the idea of being impatient and therefore hard to control or keep in order. ■ The crowd became increasingly <u>restive</u> as they waited for the doors of the arena to be opened. **Page 826**

ORIGINAL SENTENCE: _____

_____

sordid (sôr′did) *adj.* filthy; dirty; mean. ▶ The Latin word on which *sordid* is based means "filth." ■ The sailor told his life story, a <u>sordid</u> tale of poverty, crime, and sorrow. **Page 827**

ORIGINAL SENTENCE: _____

_____

articulate (är•tik′yə•lit) *adj.* able to express oneself easily and clearly. ▶ This word is based on a Latin root meaning "to speak distinctly." ■ The students chose Carmen as their spokesperson, since she is the most <u>articulate</u> member of the group. **Page 827**

ORIGINAL SENTENCE: _____

_____

disinterred (dis′in•turd′) *v.* past participle of *to disinter,* which means "to unearth." ▶ The basic meaning of this word is "to dig up (a body) from a grave," but it can also mean "to bring into the open (anything that has been hidden)." ■ After months of research, the reporter had <u>disinterred</u> the facts about an attempt to bribe a government official. **Page 828**

ORIGINAL SENTENCE: _____

_____

PRACTICE TEST

Directions: In front of each number, write **T** if the statement is true or **F** if the statement is false. *(10 points each)*

_____ **1.** An *articulate* person needs to take speech lessons, since he or she does not speak well.

_____ **2.** A *faction* is a group of people with a common purpose within a larger group.

_____ **3.** If you use a *pretext* for something you do, it's probably because you don't want the real reason to be known.

_____ **4.** When a plan has to be *ratified,* it has to be discarded.

_____ **5.** If you want a task to turn out well, you will do it *blithely.*

_____ **6.** After a fossil is *disinterred,* it remains in the ground.

_____ **7.** *Innovations* are new ways of doing things.

_____ **8.** People who treat everyone they meet as though they are lifelong friends hold themselves *aloof.*

_____ **9.** A *restive* class of third-graders is easy to deal with.

_____ **10.** A person with a *sordid* past is likely to want to hide it.

ANIMAL FARM, Chapter VI   George Orwell   (Textbook page 830)

DEVELOPING VOCABULARY

Directions: Read carefully the explanation of each word. Then write a sentence of your own using that word. Include in your sentence clues to the meaning of the word.

matted (mat′id) *adj.* a form of *to mat*, which means "to closely tangle together into a thick mass." ▶ This word is related to the English noun *mat*, which can refer to any densely woven material. ■ The team of geologists had to hack their way through <u>matted</u> vines and thick undergrowth in order to get back to the trail.   **Page 830**

ORIGINAL SENTENCE: _____

_____

procured (prō•kyoord′) *v.* past participle of *to procure*, which means "to obtain." ▶ This word comes from a Latin word meaning "to take care of or to attend to." ■ These beautiful oranges were <u>procured</u> by my aunt when she visited a grove in Florida. **Page 831**

ORIGINAL SENTENCE: _____

_____

commissions (kə•mish′ənz) *n. pl.* payments, usually a percentage of the sale of something, made to the person making the sale. ▶ The Latin word from which *commission* evolved meant "to bring together in a contest." ■ The real estate agent who sold our house earned a <u>commission</u> of six percent. **Page 831**

ORIGINAL SENTENCE: _____

_____

compensated (käm′pən•sāt′id) *v.* past tense of *to compensate*, which means "to make up for." ▶ This word is often used to mean "paying someone back for a loss." ■ The insurance company paid my mother $5,000 to <u>compensate</u> her for the salary she did not earn while she was injured.   **Page 832**

ORIGINAL SENTENCE: _____

_____

perpendicularity (pur′pən•dik′yə•lar′ət•ē) *n.* being vertical or at a 90 degree angle to something else. ▶ The Latin word on which this word is based means "to weigh carefully." ■ The <u>perpendicularity</u> of the mountain made it impossible to climb. **Page 832**

ORIGINAL SENTENCE: _____

_____

arable (ar′ə•b′l) *adj.* suitable for plowing and producing crops. ▶ The Latin root of this word means "to plow." You can remember the meaning of *arable* by visualizing a tractor plowing a field. ■ Some countries have difficulty feeding their people because the amount of <u>arable</u> land they have is limited.   **Page 830**

ORIGINAL SENTENCE: _____

_____

broker (brō′kər) *n.* a person who buys and sells for other people. ► *Broker* comes from an Old French word that originally meant "wine dealer." ■ It is very difficult to purchase stocks and bonds without going through a broker. **Page 831**

ORIGINAL SENTENCE: _____

bankrupt (baŋk′rupt′) *adj.* unable to pay one's debts. ► The Latin root *-rupt-* means "broken." ■ Although he worked hard to make the new business successful, Mr. Pauley eventually became bankrupt. **Page 831**

ORIGINAL SENTENCE: _____

simultaneously (sī′m′l•tā′nē•əs•lē) *adv.* happening at the same time. ► The basis of this word, a Latin root *-simul-*, means "same." ■ The doorbell and the telephone rang simultaneously. **Page 831**

ORIGINAL SENTENCE: _____

repose (ri•pōz′) *n.* rest; sleep. ► The prefix *re-* means "again," and the Latin root *-pose-* means "to stop or rest." ■ Mrs. Swancott lay in repose on the sofa, eating a sandwich and watching TV. **Page 832**

ORIGINAL SENTENCE: _____

PRACTICE TEST

Directions: In front of each number, write the letter of the definition that best matches each vocabulary word. *(10 points each)*

_____ **1.** arable

_____ **2.** perpendicularity

_____ **3.** repose

_____ **4.** matted

_____ **5.** compensated

_____ **6.** commissions

_____ **7.** simultaneously

_____ **8.** bankrupt

_____ **9.** broker

_____ **10.** procured

a. being vertical

b. high level of energy

c. made up for

d. rest or sleep

e. a person who buys and sells for others

f. unable to pay one's debts

g. tangled in a thick mass

h. to pay attention to

i. obtained

j. suitable for growing crops

k. occurring at the same time

l. disloyal

m. percentages of money earned on a sale

ANIMAL FARM, Chapter VII   George Orwell   (Textbook page 833)

DEVELOPING VOCABULARY

Directions: Read carefully the explanation of each word. Then write a sentence of your own using that word. Include in your sentence clues to the meaning of the word.

emboldened (im•bōl′d′nd) *adj.* a form of *to embolden*, which means "to give courage to." ▶ The prefix *em-* adds emphasis to the meaning of the base word (*bold*). The suffix -*en* is used to change the adjective to a verb. ■ Emboldened by his anger, Rafael was able to confront the boys who had been teasing his sister.   **Page 834**

ORIGINAL SENTENCE: _____

_____

infanticide (in•fan′tə•sīd′) *n.* the murder of a baby. ▶ The suffix -*cide* adds the meaning "to kill" (as in *homicide*). ■ Years ago in some societies, infanticide was used to control the number of female children.   **Page 834**

ORIGINAL SENTENCE: _____

_____

capitulated (kə•pich′ə•lāt′id) *v.* past tense of *to capitulate*, which means "to give up." ▶ A synonym for *capitulated* is *yielded*. ■ When it became obvious that the cause was lost, the leader capitulated.   **Page 834**

ORIGINAL SENTENCE: _____

_____

stupefied (stōō′pə•fīd′) *adj.* a form of *to stupefy*, meaning "to stun or to amaze." ▶ Both *stupefy* and *stupid* are based on a Latin word meaning "to be stunned." ■ Stupefied, the audience watched the dangerous tricks that the daredevil attempted.   **Page 835**

ORIGINAL SENTENCE: _____

_____

to formulate (fôr′myə•lāt′) *v.* to put into words; to express in a systematic way. ▶ You can remember the meaning of *to formulate* by thinking of it as a synonym for the familiar term *to form*. ■ The committee met to formulate a plan for persuading the cafeteria manager to serve hamburgers every day.   **Page 835**

ORIGINAL SENTENCE: _____

_____

graphically (graf′i•k′l•lē) *adv.* vividly; producing a picture with words. ▶ This word comes from a Greek root meaning "drawing." ■ Jerome described the auto accident so graphically that we all felt as though we had seen it ourselves.   **Page 836**

ORIGINAL SENTENCE: _____

_____

cowered (kou′ərd) *v.* past tense of *to cower*, which means "to crouch in fear or shame." ▶ This word is easy to remember because it so closely resembles the familiar word *coward*. ■ When the fight broke out, we <u>cowered</u> behind the car. **Page 836**

ORIGINAL SENTENCE: _____

_____

secreted (si•krēt′id) *v.* past participle of *to secrete*, which means "to hide or conceal." ▶ The verb *to secrete* can also refer to the action of glands that release fluids. ■ The bank robbers had <u>secreted</u> their stolen money in an abandoned building. **Page 836**

ORIGINAL SENTENCE: _____

_____

pervading (pər•vād′iŋ) *adj.* a form of *to pervade*, meaning "to spread throughout all parts of." ▶ The prefix *per-* means "through." ■ With concerns about the crime rate <u>pervading</u> the community, the mayor decided to take action. **Page 835**

ORIGINAL SENTENCE: _____

_____

retribution (ret′rə•byoo′shən) *n.* deserved punishment. ▶ The prefix *re-* means "back," and the Latin root *-tribu-* means "to pay." ■ Some people believe that epidemics are <u>retribution</u> for wrongdoings by society. **Page 837**

ORIGINAL SENTENCE: _____

_____

PRACTICE TEST

Directions: Fill in the blank with the vocabulary word that best fits the meaning of the sentence. (*10 points each*)

emboldened	capitulated	to formulate	cowered	pervading
infanticide	stupefied	graphically	secreted	retribution

1. Nancy guessed that losing her purse was _____ for going to the mall without telling her mother.

2. _____ the chemistry lab was the odor of rotten eggs.

3. The gambler _____ an ace of spades in his sleeve.

4. The boy _____ behind his mother when he saw the doctor.

5. The story _____ depicts the final hours of the *Titanic*.

6. The scientists tried _____ ideas that would lead to a better understanding of certain diseases.

7. The urging of the other students _____ Shirley, and she stood up to express her opinion.

8. _____ is illegal in the United States.

9. When he was clearly losing, the candidate formally _____

10. The investigators were _____ when they learned how much money was missing from the bank.

ANIMAL FARM, Chapter VIII   **George Orwell**   **(Textbook page 840)**

DEVELOPING VOCABULARY

Directions: Read carefully the explanation of each word. Then write a sentence of your own using that word. Include in your sentence clues to the meaning of the word.

decree (di•krē′) **n.** an official order. ▶ The prefix *de-* here means "from" and the Latin word *cernere* means "to judge"; thus, this word originally referred to a decision issued by a judge. ■ The king issued a <u>decree</u> that all young men in the realm would have to spend two years as soldiers. **Page 844**

ORIGINAL SENTENCE: _____

_____

skulking (skulk′iŋ) **v.** present participle of *to skulk*, which means "to hide or sneak around with some evil purpose; to lurk." ▶ *Skulk* derives from a German word meaning "to stay out of school." ■ The pickpocket was <u>skulking</u> in the doorway, waiting for the right moment to strike. **Page 841**

ORIGINAL SENTENCE: _____

_____

impending (im•pen′diŋ) **adj.** a form of *to impend*, meaning "to be about to happen." ▶ The Latin root *-pend-* means "to hang." ■ The rumble of thunder and the flash of lightning signaled an <u>impending</u> storm. **Page 841**

ORIGINAL SENTENCE: _____

_____

pensioner (pen′shən•ər) **n.** a person who receives payment for previous services. ▶ A *pension* is often compensation given to former soldiers or retired persons. ■ Because Mrs. Azzarito is a <u>pensioner</u>, she has little extra money to spend on luxuries. **Page 842**

ORIGINAL SENTENCE: _____

_____

hullabaloo (hul′ə•bə•lōō′) **n.** loud noise and confusion; hubbub. ▶ This word was created as an imitation of the sound it describes. ■ The crowd raised a <u>hullabaloo</u> about the delay in starting the concert. **Page 842**

ORIGINAL SENTENCE: _____

_____

wistful (wist′fəl) **adj.** showing vague yearning or longing. ▶ Do not confuse this word with *wishful*, which has a somewhat related meaning. ■ The <u>wistful</u> look on the child's face let me know at once that she longed to be invited to play with the others. **Page 842**

ORIGINAL SENTENCE: _____

_____

conciliatory (kən•sil′ə•tôr′ē) **adj.** gaining good will by friendly actions. ► The basis of this word is a Latin word meaning "to bring together." ■ I interpreted Ed's phone call as a conciliatory gesture and decided to forget our disagreement. **Page 842**

ORIGINAL SENTENCE: _____

_____

unscathed (un•skāthd′) **adj.** not hurt; unharmed. ► The root of this word is based on an Old Norse word meaning "harm." The prefix *un-* means "not." ■ It is a miracle that the family all walked away from the accident unscathed. **Page 843**

ORIGINAL SENTENCE: _____

_____

unaccountably (un′ə•koun′tə•blē) **adj.** in a manner that cannot be explained; mysteriously. ► *To account* means "to give satisfactory reasons for." ■ Mr. Sumner, who is usually grouchy on Mondays, was unaccountably cheerful today. **Page 843**

ORIGINAL SENTENCE: _____

_____

lamentation (lam′ən•tā′shən) **n.** weeping; wailing. ► A book of the Bible named Lamentations is found in the Old Testament and is attributed to Jeremiah. ■ The death of the president produced widespread lamentation through the nation. **Page 844**

ORIGINAL SENTENCE: _____

_____

PRACTICE TEST

Directions: Fill in the blank with the vocabulary word that best fits the meaning of the sentence. (*10 points each*)

decree	impending	hullabaloo	wistful	unaccountably
skulking	pensioner	conciliatory	unscathed	lamentation

1. The weather has been _____ dry this summer; no one knows why.

2. Although he spent months in combat, my uncle returned _____.

3. When Trina gets that _____ expression on her face, I know she is daydreaming about becoming a ballerina.

4. The band worked hard because of the _____ contest.

5. Police discovered that the strange man who was _____ near the entrance to the park was selling drugs.

6. The mayor signed a _____ that no water could be used to wash cars or water lawns until the water shortage ended.

7. The _____ had enjoyed his work but was now glad to retire.

8. Hearing a great _____, Mr. Kahler stepped out to investigate.

9. The _____ of the child whose cat had died was heartbreaking.

10. As a(n) _____ move, Ms. Stevens invited her neighbor to sit down and discuss the conflict with her.

124 Vocabulary Activity Worksheet: *Elements of Literature, Third Course*

HRW MATERIAL COPYRIGHTED UNDER NOTICE APPEARING EARLIER IN THIS WORK.

ANIMAL FARM, Chapter IX   **George Orwell**   **(Textbook page 845)**

DEVELOPING VOCABULARY

Directions: Read carefully the explanation of each word. Then write a sentence of your own using that word. Include in your sentence clues to the meaning of the word.

formulated (fôr′myə•lāt′id) *v.* past tense of *to formulate,* which means "to put into words; to express in a systematic way." ▶ The suffix *-ate* means "cause to become." ■ The young child tried to <u>formulate</u> a theory to explain the setting of the sun. **Page 845**

ORIGINAL SENTENCE: _____

_____

devotees (dev′ə•tēz′) *n. pl.* persons who are strongly dedicated to something. ▶ The suffix *-ee* adds the meaning "a person who is," as in the word *interviewee*. ■ Both Professor Breckel and his wife are <u>devotees</u> of early 19th century drama. **Page 846**

ORIGINAL SENTENCE: _____

_____

complicity (kəm•plis′ə•tē) *n.* partnership in wrongdoing. ▶ You can remember this word by associating it with *accomplice,* which means "a partner in crime." ■ Anthony was given an "F" on the test because of his <u>complicity</u> in the scheme to take a copy from the teacher's desk. **Page 846**

ORIGINAL SENTENCE: _____

_____

stratagem (strat′ə•jəm) *n.* a trick or scheme for achieving a purpose. ▶ The Greek word from which *stratagem* derives originally referred to a plan used by the general of an army. ■ The embezzler had discovered an almost perfect <u>stratagem</u> for covering up the large amounts of money he was taking from the bank. **Page 846**

ORIGINAL SENTENCE: _____

_____

professed (prə•fest′) *v.* past tense of *to profess,* which means "to declare openly." ▶ *Profess* sometimes carries the connotation of insincerity, as though the person is declaring something that is not really the truth. ■ The man <u>professed</u> to be a scholar, but he never opened a book. **Page 848**

ORIGINAL SENTENCE: _____

_____

knacker (nak′ər) *n.* a person who buys worn-out horses and sells them for dog food and other uses. ▶ This word is chiefly used by British speakers. It can also refer to someone who buys and wrecks old homes and sells their materials. ■ Sir James turned away the <u>knacker</u>, who offered him 18 pounds for Old Dobin. **Page 848**

ORIGINAL SENTENCE: _____

_____

demeanor (di•mēn′ər) *n.* conduct; outward behavior; bearing. ► The Middle English origins of this word meant "to rule or govern oneself." ■ Although she is only 12, Brigitte has the demeanor of an adult. **Page 849**

ORIGINAL SENTENCE: _____

_____

knoll (nōl) *n.* a mound; a small hill. ► *Knoll* comes from the same sources as *knot.* ■ The grave was dug on a tree-covered knoll near the back of the cemetery. **Page 847**

ORIGINAL SENTENCE: _____

_____

tempered (tem′pərd) *v.* past participle of *to temper,* which means "to reduce in intensity; to soften." ► *Temper* comes from a Latin word meaning "to regulate." ■ Lynn has tempered the remarks she plans to make to the committee, so that they will take her seriously. **Page 849**

ORIGINAL SENTENCE: _____

_____

lamented (lə•men′tid) *adj.* a form of *to lament,* which means "to mourn." ► The Latin word on which this word is based meant "wailing." ■ Our team's loss to Fairfield was more highly lamented than its loss to Milltown, because we have always beaten Fairfield in the past. **Page 849**

ORIGINAL SENTENCE: _____

_____

PRACTICE TEST

Directions: Circle the letter of the best meaning for each word. *(10 points each)*

1. tempered: **a.** exploded **b.** softened **c.** demanded **d.** angered

2. knacker: **a.** person who buys stocks and bonds **b.** person who buys worn-out horses **c.** waterproof boot **d.** person who understands computers

3. formulated: **a.** expressed in a systematic way **b.** explained in general terms **c.** solved after careful study **d.** written down

4. complicity: **a.** reward for bravery **b.** refusal to do what is expected **c.** participation in wrongdoing **d.** hiding one's true feelings

5. demeanor: **a.** deep feelings **b.** expectations **c.** outward behavior **d.** cruel treatment of others

6. lamented: **a.** praised **b.** remembered **c.** mourned **d.** understood

7. knoll: **a.** horse-trader **b.** sound a bell makes **c.** pasture land **d.** small hill

8. professed: **a.** declared openly **b.** refused to speak **c.** asked for one's hand in marriage **d.** moved ahead

9. stratagem: **a.** weapon **b.** jewel **c.** wish **d.** trick

10. devotees: **a.** newcomers **b.** strong supporters **c.** critics **d.** teachers

ANIMAL FARM, Chapter X   George Orwell   (Textbook page 851)

DEVELOPING VOCABULARY

Directions: Read carefully the explanation of each word. Then write a sentence of your own using that word. Include in your sentence clues to the meaning of the word.

upstanding (up•stan′diŋ) *adj.* honorable. ▶ This word is a compound of two familiar English words. The meaning is derived from the notion that a person who stands up straight is of good character. ■ It is important to elect an <u>upstanding</u> person to the city council. **Page 851**

ORIGINAL SENTENCE: _____

_____

frugally (froo′gə•lē) *adv.* sparingly; in a manner that avoids unnecessary expense. ▶ This word comes from the Latin word for fruit. ■ Most pensioners discover that they must live very <u>frugally</u>. **Page 851**

ORIGINAL SENTENCE: _____

_____

imperishable (im•per′ish•ə•b'l) *adj.* not likely to die or decay; indestructible. ▶ The prefix *im-* means "not." The English word *perishable* refers to something, such as food, that can spoil. ■ Only <u>imperishable</u> food should be sent through the mail. **Page 852**

ORIGINAL SENTENCE: _____

_____

deputation (dep′yoo•tā′shən) *n.* a group of persons sent to represent others. ▶ This word is closely related to *deputy*, meaning "a person appointed to act in place of another." ■ The senator met with a <u>deputation</u> of health care workers who expressed concerns about the effects of acid rain. **Page 853**

ORIGINAL SENTENCE: _____

_____

misgiving (mis•giv′iŋ) *n.* a feeling of fear, doubt, or suspicion. ▶ This word is generally used in the plural form: *misgivings*. ■ When I heard her plans, I had a number of <u>misgivings</u> about participating. **Page 853**

ORIGINAL SENTENCE: _____

_____

dispelled (dis•peld′) *adj.* a form of *to dispell*, which means "to scatter; to drive away." ▶ The prefix *dis-* means "apart" and the Latin root *-pel-* means "to drive." ■ My mother's doubts were <u>dispelled</u> when I suggested she call Donna's mother to confirm our plans. **Page 853**

ORIGINAL SENTENCE: _____

_____

witticism (wit′ə•siz′m) *n.* a joke; a humorous remark. ► The suffix *-cism* (often spelled *-ism*) means "an example of" or "an instance of." ■ I don't think Charlotte appreciated Mark's witticism about her haircut. **Page 854**

ORIGINAL SENTENCE: _____

_____

gratified (grat′ə•fīd′) *adj.* a form of *to gratify,* meaning "to give pleasure or satisfaction to." ► The Latin root of this word means "pleasing." ■ The director said she was very gratified by the orchestra's performance, especially since it was their first concert. **Page 854**

ORIGINAL SENTENCE: _____

_____

intimated (in′tə•māt′id) *v.* past tense of *to intimate,* which means "to suggest; to make known indirectly; to hint." ► Do not confuse this verb with the adjective *intimate,* meaning "private and personal." ■ Mary Beth was furious that anyone would intimate that she had not written the essay herself. **Page 854**

ORIGINAL SENTENCE: _____

_____

subversive (səb•vʉr′siv) *adj.* seeking to undermine, overthrow, or destroy. ► The prefix *sub-* means "below." You can remember this word by thinking about a force "from below" overthrowing a government. ■ The secret police arrested the man suspected of making subversive comments about his government. **Page 854**

ORIGINAL SENTENCE: _____

_____

PRACTICE TEST

Directions: In the blank at the right, write the vocabulary word that fits each definition at the left. *(10 points each)*

upstanding	imperishable	misgiving	witticism	intimated
frugally	deputation	dispelled	gratified	subversive

1. pleased; satisfied

1. _____

2. scattered and driven away

2. _____

3. not able to be destroyed

3. _____

4. overthrowing or undermining

4. _____

5. hinted

5. _____

6. a humorous remark

6. _____

7. a feeling of fear or doubt

7. _____

8. a group sent to represent others

8. _____

9. without unnecessary expense

9. _____

10. honorable; of good character

10. _____

Workbook

ELEMENTS OF LITERATURE

THIRD COURSE

ACKNOWLEDGMENTS

For permission to reprint copyrighted material, grateful acknowledgment is made to the following sources:

Atheneum Publishers, Inc.: From *The Miracle Worker* by William Gibson. Copyright © 1956, 1957, by William Gibson; copyright © 1959, 1960 by Tamarack Productions, Ltd., and George S. Klein and Leo Garel, as Trustees under three separate Deeds of Trust.

Virginia Barber Literary Agency and McGraw-Hill Ryerson Limited: From ''Red Dress' from *Dance of the Happy Shades* by Alice Munro. Copyright © 1968 by Alice Munro. Published by Penguin Books in the United States and Canada.

Susan Chayefsky: From *The Mother*, slightly adapted from *Television Plays* by Paddy Chayefsky. Copyright © 1955 by Paddy Chayefsky.

Delacorte Press/Seymour Lawrence: From ''The Making of Annie Sullivan'' (Retitled: '' 'Annie' '') in *Helen and Teacher: The Story of Helen Keller and Annie Sullivan Macy* by Joseph P. Lash. Copyright © 1980 by Joseph P. Lash.

Doubleday, a division of Bantam, Doubleday, Dell Publishing Group, Inc. From *The Odyssey* by Homer, translated by Robert Fitzgerald. Copyright © 1960 by Robert Fitzgerald. From ''The Lesson of the Moth'' from *Archy and Mehitabel* by Don Marquis. Copyright 1927 by *Doubleday, a division of Bantam, Doubleday, Dell Publishing Group, Inc.* From ''The Bat'' from *The Collected Poems of Theodore Roethke* by Theodore Roethke. Copyright 1938 by Theodore Roethke. From ''Highway: Michigan'' from *The Collected Poems of Theodore Roethke*. Copyright 1940 by Theodore Roethke. From ''March 1st'' from *Flying Inland* by Kathleen Spivack. Copyright © 1965, 1966, 1967, 1968, 1970, 1971 by Kathleen Spivack. Originally published in *The New Yorker*.

Doubleday, a division of Bantam, Doubleday, Dell Publishing Group, Inc. and Curtis Brown Ltd., on behalf of Daphne du Maurier: From ''The Birds'' from *Kiss Me Again, Stranger* by Daphne du Maurier, Copyright 1952 by Daphne du Maurier.

E.P. Dutton, a division of New American Library and Jonathan Cape Ltd.: From Chapter XV, ''The Avalanche'' (Retitled: ''Annapurna'') in *Annapurna* by Maurice Herzog, translated by Nea Morin and Janet Adam Smith. Copyright 1952 by E. P. Dutton; renewed 1980 by E. P. Dutton.

Farrar, Straus & Giroux, Inc.: Adapted and abridged from *Coming into the Country* by John McPhee. Copyright © 1976, 1977 by John McPhee. Originally published in *The New Yorker*. From ''The Washwoman'' from *A Day of Pleasure* by Isaac Bashevis Singer. Copyright © 1963, 1965, 1966, 1969 by Isaac Bashevis Singer.

Michael Gibson, on behalf of the Estate of Wilfrid Wilson Gibson: From ''Flannan Isle'' by Wilfrid Wilson Gibson.

Donald Hall: From ''The Old Pilot's Death'' from *The Alligator Bride* by Donald Hall. Published by Harper & Row, Publisher, Inc.

Harcourt Brace Jovanovich, Inc.: From ''Fog'' from *Chicago Poems* by Carl Sandburg. Copyright © 1916 by Holt, Rinehart and Winston, Inc.; renewed 1944 by Carl Sandburg. From ''Women'' from *Revolutionary Petunias & Other Poems* by Alice Walker. Copyright © 1970 by Alice Walker. From ''Thirteen: Summer II'' (''The Hat'') from *Cress Delahanty* by Jessamyn West. Copyright 1948, 1976 by Jessamyn West. From ''Boy at the Window'' from *Things of This World* by Richard Wilbur. Copyright 1952 by the New Yorker Magazine, Inc.; renewed 1980 by Richard Wilbur.

Harper & Row, Publishers, Inc.: From pp. 5-9 in *Pilgrim at Tinker Creek* (Retitled: ''The Giant Water Bug'') by Annie Dillard. Copyright © 1974 by Annie Dillard. From ''Old Christmas'' from *Lonesome Water* by Roy Helton. Copyright 1930 by Harper & Row, Publishers, Inc.; renewed 1958 by Roy Helton. From ''Fifteen'' from *Stories That Could Be True* by William Stafford. Copyright © 1964 by William E. Stafford. From *Life on the Mississippi* by Mark Twain.

continued on page 198

USING THE WORKBOOK

This comprehensive *Workbook* accompanies *Elements of Literature*, Third Course.

For each selection in the student anthology—whether short story, poetry, nonfiction, drama, epic, or novel—a two-page *Workbook* lesson is provided. Each *Workbook* lesson is keyed to a specific central literary element in that selection, and gives in-depth practice on identifying and applying the element. You will find these literary skills identified in the Table of Contents, as well as in the main heading of each worksheet.

The *Workbook* begins with a special series of lessons on Previewing the Anthology. These lessons—on everything from Using the Indexes to Identifying Genres—will be invaluable aids for users of the anthology, helping them to get the most out of the text, and to understand how to use the different parts of the book, including the various features within selections, such as the headnotes and study questions.

Each of the *Workbook* lessons on individual selections begins with some instruction or other identification of the literary element(s) being studied, then provides two different practice activities: Understanding and Applying. The first section, Understanding, does precisely that—helps the user to understand and identify the important literary concept(s) being focused on. The second section, Applying, provides hands-on practice in using the literary element, a sure means of "anchoring" the term in memory. Many lessons also include an optional feature, Reader's Response, which, in keeping with the overall response-centered approach of the literature anthology allows for a personal, immediate reaction to some aspect of the literary work being studied. The various parts of each *Workbook* lesson combine to further students' comprehension of the important literary elements that are essential to understanding how literature "works," what it means, and how it can best be appreciated.

CONTENTS

UNIT FOUR: THE ELEMENTS OF DRAMA

UNIT FIVE: WILLIAM SHAKESPEARE

UNIT SIX: THE ELEMENTS OF THE EPIC

UNIT SEVEN: THE ELEMENTS OF A NOVEL

PREVIEWING THE ANTHOLOGY

Using the Table of Contents (page xi)

The **Table of Contents** of your anthology lists the units you will study, as well as the titles and authors of the selections in each unit, and the page on which each begins. A section in the back of the book called **Writing About Literature** provides information related to that topic. **A Handbook of Literary Terms** gives definitions, discussions, and examples of key literary terms, while the **Glossary** defines, in alphabetical order, words from the selections that may be difficult or unfamiliar.

Understanding the Anthology's Organization

Use the spaces provided to answer the following questions.

1. How many units are included in your anthology? _____

2. How do units five, six, and seven differ from earlier units?

   _____

3. Which unit contains two poems by Robert Frost? _____

4. Who wrote the personal essay "The Night the Bed Fell"? _____

5. Which unit might contain a short story by Saki (H.H. Munro)? _____
   Does the unit include a selection from this author? _____

6. How are the selections organized within the first two units?

   _____

7. What type of literature is contained in Unit Three? _____

8. On which page in the text are similes and metaphors introduced? _____

9. In what part of the book would you find the definition of the word *preclude*?

   _____

10. In what section of the book would you find a discussion of the literary device of personification? _____

Workbook: Elements of Literature, Third Course

HRW material copyrighted under notice appearing earlier in this work.

1

Applying Skills

Use the Table of Contents to find the page number you would first turn to in each of the following situations. Use the space provided to write your answers.

1. Your teacher has told you to read the introduction to The Elements of Nonfiction for homework. _____

2. In writing an essay, you are unsure how to credit a quotation you want to include. _____

3. In reading a selection you come across the word *abate*, and you don't know what it means.

   _____

4. You have forgotten the name of a character in the short story "The Hat." _____

5. You want to reread the poem "The Shell." _____

PREVIEWING THE ANTHOLOGY

Using the Indexes (page 887)

The four **indexes** in your anthology are alphabetical listings of material with page numbers showing where the material begins. The **Index of Skills** lists five major types of skills materials. The **Index of Features** lists special background materials on various authors and selections. The **Index of Fine Art** lists paintings and other works of fine art found within the text. The **Index of Authors and Titles** lists both individual selections in the anthology and their authors.

Understanding the Indexes

Use the indexes in your anthology to answer the following questions.

1. On what page does the Index of Features begin? _____

2. Which of the five major types of skills taught in this anthology is itself divided into five subsections? _____

3. On what page can you find a comment about the writer Dorothy Johnson? _____

4. How are the works of the twenty unknown artists listed? _____

5. On what pages can you find paintings by Charles Burchfield? _____

6. On what page will you find information about poet Lynne Alvarez? _____

7. On what page does the selection from *The Odyssey* begin? _____

8. How many selections by Maya Angelou are included in the anthology? _____

Applying Skills

Name the index that you might use in response to each of the following directions from your teacher. Write your answers in the space provided.

1. This morning we are going to read *Visitor from Forest Hills*. _____

2. In preparation for reading *Animal Farm*, let's look at some propaganda techniques.

   _____

3. Compare the Claude Monet paintings. _____

4. Before you begin the selection, be certain that you read the author biography.

   _____

5. For tomorrow, be certain that you know what a "Jack-in-the-box" character is.

   _____

Workbook: Elements of Literature, Third Course

HRW material copyrighted under notice appearing earlier in this work.

3

Genres

The **genres**, or forms of literature, that you will study in this anthology are the **short story**, **poetry**, **nonfiction**, **drama**, the **epic**, and the **novel**. An entire unit in your anthology is devoted to each of these genres. Read the following brief descriptions of each of the six genres you will study.

Short Story   A short prose narrative built on a plot that includes the basic situation, complications, climax, and resolution.

Poetry   A kind of writing that uses rhythmic, compressed language, including figures of speech and imagery designed to appeal to emotion and imagination.

Nonfiction   Prose writing that deals with real people, events, and places.

Drama   A story written in dialogue with stage directions, intended to be acted out in front of an audience.

Epic   A long story told in poetry which relates the great deeds of a larger-than-life hero who embodies the values of a particular society.

Novel   A long fictional story (usually more than 100 pages in length) that uses all the elements of storytelling: plot, character, setting, theme, and point of view.

Further information on each genre and its elements can be found in the introductions to the units and in the Handbook of Literary Terms in the back of the anthology (p. 866).

Understanding Genres

Below are listed five of the six genres already discussed. Identify the genre to which each of the following passages belongs by placing the correct letter of the genre in the blank before each passage.

a. Epic   **d.** Drama
b. Short Story   **e.** Poetry
c. Nonfiction

_____ **1.** "Sing in me, Muse, and through me tell the story / of that man skilled in all ways of contending, the wanderer, harried for years on end, / after he plundered the stronghold / on the proud height of Troy."

_____ **2.** "In 1880, when Annie Sullivan, aged fourteen, was permitted to enroll in the Perkins Institution for the Blind in South Boston and began her schooling, she discovered that history for her schoolmates was the Civil War."

_____ **3.** " 'Good morning, madam,' said Holmes, cheerily. 'My name is Sherlock Holmes. This is my intimate friend and associate, Dr. Watson, before whom you can speak as freely as before myself.' "

_____ 4. "I had read about the giant water bug, but never seen one. 'Giant water bug' is really the name of the creature, which is an enormous, heavy-bodied beetle. It eats insects, tadpoles, fish and frogs."

_____ 5. "A violet by the mossy stone
　　　Half hidden from the eye!
　　Fair as a star, when only one
　　　Is shining in the sky."

_____ 6. **Benvolio.**　By my head, here come the Capulets.
　　 Mercutio.　By my heel, I care not.

Applying Skills

On the space provided, write **short story**, **poetry**, **nonfiction**, **drama**, **epic**, or **novel** to identify the genre.

1. To write a modern American _____, you must decide on the values that are important to Americans, and create a hero who embodies those values.

2. To write _____, you must check facts and dates carefully.

3. If you have to take time to figure out proper stage directions, you are writing

   _____.

4. You would most likely interview people about their experiences if you were

   writing _____.

5. If you have to decide how to get a character out of a tight spot within 9 pages, you are

   probably writing (a, an) _____.

6. If you are on page 436 of a long story about the relationships among three generations of an

   American family, you are probably reading (a, an) _____.

7. Rhythm and the use of figurative language are key features of _____.

8. A work about the readjustment of Vietnam veterans to American society, based on the

   results of ten years of research, is an example of _____.

9. A long tale about an extraordinary Greek hero who wanders for years before regaining his

   rightful home and kingdom is an example of (a, an) _____.

10. If you wanted to write a science fiction story about an intergalactic war that involves ten

    generations of Earth people, you would probably write (a, an) _____

    rather than (a, an) _____.

Workbook: Elements of Literature, Third Course

HRW material copyrighted under notice appearing earlier in this work.

5

PREVIEWING THE ANTHOLOGY

Previewing the Unit

Use your textbook to answer the following questions.

1. What does the opening page of each unit contain?

   _____

   _____

2. The first left-hand page of each unit contains a Unit Outline. Look at the outline for Unit One on page 2. Does it include the titles of the literary selections in the unit? _____
   What does it contain?

   _____

   _____

3. Look through The Art of Storytelling section of Unit One (pp. 3-5). How are important literary terms highlighted?

   _____

   _____

4. What five methods of creating characters will be discussed in Section Three of Unit One? (See page 2.)

   _____

   _____

5. What four major headings appear in each section labeled Responding to the Story? (See pages 29-30, for example.)

   _____

   _____

6. What special feature appears on page 31?

   _____

7. How are specialized or difficult words in the selections explained? (See page 6.)

   _____

   _____

Applying Skills

Use pages 2 and 3 of your textbook to answer the following questions about Unit One.

1. On what page will you find a discussion of situational irony? _____
   Under what literary element is it discussed?

   _____

2. At the end of which section will you find Exercises in Critical Thinking and Writing dealing with point of view? _____

3. What writer is quoted at the beginning of the introduction to Unit One? _____

4. On what page does the introduction to the element of theme begin? _____

5. How would you expect the word *exposition* to be printed on page 5?

   _____

Workbook: Elements of Literature, Third Course

HRW material copyrighted under notice appearing earlier in this work.

7

Previewing a Selection

Previewing a story before you read it can whet your appetite and heighten your anticipation for reading.

1. Scan the story "Poison," beginning on page 6. List words or phrases that catch your eye. DO NOT STOP TO READ A PASSAGE.

_____

_____

_____

_____

_____

_____

_____

_____

_____

_____

2. What hint about the story do you get in the footnote on page 6?

_____

_____

3. What do you think has happened to the man pictured in the illustration on pages 6-7? Does this illustration make you want to read the story?

_____

_____

_____

4. So far, what do you think the story will be about?

_____

_____

Applying Skills

In each box below, explain what that feature contributes to your feelings and ideas about the story. Combine your ideas and thoughts from each box to write in the center box your own purpose for reading the story.

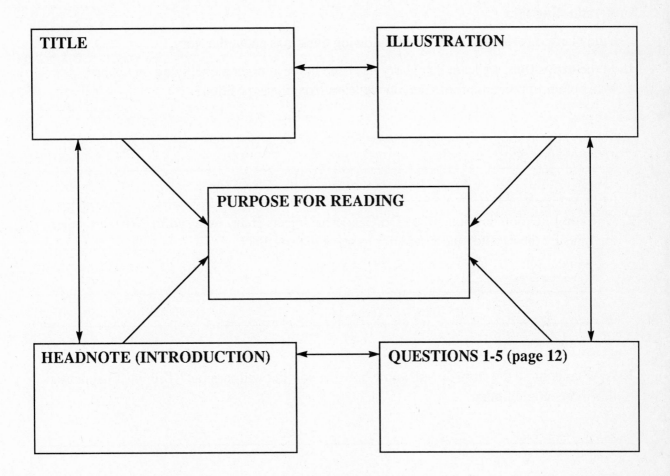

Workbook: Elements of Literature, Third Course

HRW material copyrighted under notice appearing earlier in this work.

9

The Four Parts of Plot

The four parts of **plot** are exposition, complication, climax, and resolution. In the **exposition**, we learn the basic situation and are introduced to the characters and their conflict(s). In the **complication**, the characters take some action to resolve the conflict and meet with problems. The **climax** is the key scene of the story. The **resolution**, which occurs at the end of the story, is the point when we know what is going to happen to the characters.

Understanding Plot

Use the blanks provided to answer the following questions about the story.

1. In the **exposition**, we learn that Harry has been home at night alone, lying on his bed. What other important information do we learn from the exposition?

   _____

   _____

   _____

2. One **complication** develops when Dr. Ganderbai injects Harry with serum. What are other attempts by the narrator and the doctor to solve the conflict?

   _____

   _____

   _____

3. At what point in the story do you know how the conflict will turn out? Tell what happens at this moment of **climax**.

   _____

   _____

   _____

4. Conflicts in a story are not always resolved. There are really two conflicts in "Poison." One conflict is obvious, but the other is just as important to the plot, if not more so. What are the two conflicts in "Poison"? Which of these two conflicts has a **resolution**? Which conflict does not have a resolution?

   _____

   _____

Applying Skills

Below is the exposition of a short story plot. Read the basic situation. Then, in the chart that follows, jot down ideas for possible complications and for a possible climax and resolution.

Exposition: Late at night in a small, almost deserted bus depot, a teenager, with a guitar and a small suitcase, tries to board a bus. With no ticket or money, the teenager asks the driver for a ride to the nearest city, seventy miles away, where a friend waits with money. The driver refuses.

Complications

Climax

Resolution

Workbook: Elements of Literature, Third Course

HRW material copyrighted under notice appearing earlier in this work.

11

THE ADVENTURE OF
THE SPECKLED BAND Arthur Conan Doyle (page 14)

Suspense

Suspense is the anxiety about what is going to happen that readers feel as they read a story or watch a drama. Suspense builds as various **complications** arise in the plot. The reader's anxious uncertainty is not relieved until the **climax** of the story.

Understanding Suspense

Use the blanks provided to answer the following questions about the story.

1. What physical details indicate that the fear that haunts Helen has been with her for a long time?

   _____

   _____

   _____

2. Which aspects of Dr. Roylott's character contribute to our sense of anxiety about Helen Stoner's safety in his house?

   _____

   _____

   _____

3. What specific event so frightens Helen that she goes to see Holmes?

   _____

   _____

   _____

4. When Holmes strikes a light and begins lashing at the bell pull, Watson does not see anything on the cord, but he makes an observation about Holmes that heightens suspense. What does he notice about Holmes's face?

   _____

   _____

   _____

   _____

Applying Skills

Read the situation sketched below. Then suggest an event of plot development that would heighten suspense.

A four-year-old child is playing with a paper airplane in an apartment on the fourteenth floor of an old building. It is summer, and windows are open. While the child's mother answers the telephone in the next room, the child puts the paper airplane in flight. What happens next?

_____

_____

_____

_____

_____

Reader's Response

Assign a number from **1** to **10** to indicate how suspenseful you found each of the following events in the story. (A **10** would be the most suspenseful.)

_____ As Holmes and Watson approach the Roylott house, something leaps from a clump of bushes in front of them.

_____ Dr. Roylott twists a poker out of shape in the apartment shared by Holmes and Watson.

_____ Holmes shouts, "You see it, Watson? . . . You see it?"

_____ Holmes discovers that the bell rope in Julia Stoner's room is a dummy.

Workbook: Elements of Literature, Third Course

HRW material copyrighted under notice appearing earlier in this work.

13

Inferring Details of Plot

Writers sometimes **foreshadow**, or hint at, events that will occur later in a story in order to whet the reader's interest or create suspense. Being alert for clues to important plot details will enhance your enjoyment and understanding of a story or drama.

Understanding Plot Details

1. What is the first unusual thing that Nat notices about the birds flocking around Mr. Trigg's tractor?

_____

_____

_____

2. What two ominous events occur on the first night when Nat opens the bedroom window to investigate the tapping sound?

_____

_____

_____

3. When Nat goes down to the beach to bury the dead birds, he sees a strange and frightening sight off shore. What is it?

_____

_____

_____

4. What future discovery do these sentences foreshadow? "[Nat] noticed grimly that every windowpane was shattered. Only the boards had kept the birds from breaking in." (p. 47)

_____

_____

_____

_____

Applying Skills

Imagine you are writing a story about four high school students who get caught in a blizzard while driving home from a basketball game. At this point in the story, the game has just ended, and the four students walk outside toward the parking lot. Supply one or two details that will enable your readers to infer what is going to happen.

_____

_____

_____

_____

_____

Reader's Response

Indicate with a check mark the sentence below that you feel gives the strongest hint of frightening events to come.

_____ **1.** ". . . there was not one bird upon the sill but half a dozen; they flew straight into his face, attacking him." (p. 34)

_____ **2.** "The sky was hard and leaden, and the brown hills that had gleamed in the sun the day before looked dark and bare." (p. 35)

_____ **3.** " 'No,' [Nat] said, 'it's not going to snow. This is a black winter, not a white one.' " (p. 36)

Workbook: Elements of Literature, Third Course

HRW material copyrighted under notice appearing earlier in this work.

15

Methods of Characterization

The process of letting the reader know what the people in a story are really like is called **characterization**. A writer may tell the reader what a character is like in so many words, but more often the writer will show this by telling what the character looks like, says, and does.

Understanding Characterization

Read each passage below. Then circle the lettered word or phrase that best completes the statement about the character's appearance or personality that the passage describes.

1. "She is wearing tennis shoes and a shapeless gray sweater over a summery calico dress." (p. 62)
   The narrator's friend is _____ about her appearance.

   a. particular   **b.** vain   **c.** indifferent

2. "She is small and sprightly, like a bantam hen; but, due to a long, youthful illness, her shoulders are pitifully hunched." (p. 62)
   She is somewhat _____.

   a. stooped   **b.** athletic   **c.** overweight

3. "In addition to never having seen a movie, she has never: eaten in a restaurant, traveled more than five miles from home, received or sent a telegram, read anything except funny papers and the Bible, worn cosmetics, cursed, wished someone harm . . . ." (p. 63)
   The passage indicates that she is _____.

   a. sophisticated   **b.** unworldly   **c.** cynical

4. " 'We can't mess around with thirteen. The cakes will fall. Or put somebody in the cemetery. Why, I wouldn't dream of getting out of bed on the thirteenth.' " (p. 64)
   The narrator's friend is _____.

   a. confident   **b.** lazy   **c.** superstitious

5. " 'Buddy, are you awake?' It is my friend, calling from her room, which is next to mine; and an instant later she is sitting on my bed holding a candle. 'Well, I can't sleep a hoot,' she declares. 'My mind's jumping like a jack rabbit. Buddy, do you think Mrs. Roosevelt will serve our cake at dinner?' " (p. 68)
   The narrator's friend is _____.

   a. political   **b.** childlike   **c.** cautious

Applying Skills

Think of a friend or relative of whom you are fond. Then jot down in the space provided several details describing that person's appearance, personal traits, and characteristic actions or behaviors.

Appearance	Personal Traits	Actions

Reader's Response

Some readers think that the final paragraph of "A Christmas Memory" is excessively sentimental and that the piece would be better if it ended with the preceding paragraph. Tell whether you agree or disagree and give your reason in one or two sentences.

_____

_____

_____

_____

_____

_____

Workbook: Elements of Literature, Third Course

HRW material copyrighted under notice appearing earlier in this work.

17

Methods of Characterization

A writer may sometimes tell us exactly what a character is like: funny, courageous, evil, kind, and so on. Doing so is called **direct characterization**. More often, the writer will let us listen to what characters say and watch what they do. These observations allow us to draw our own conclusions about the kind of people the characters are. This method is known as **indirect characterization**. A writer can indirectly reveal a character's personality in five ways:

1. By letting us hear the character speak.

2. By describing how the character looks and dresses.

3. By letting us listen to the character's inner thoughts and feelings.

4. By revealing what other people in the story think or say about the character.

5. By showing us what the character does—how he or she acts.

Understanding Indirect Characterization

In the space before each passage from "María Tepache," write the number given above that corresponds to the method of indirect characterization used in each passage. For example, if the writer lets us hear the character speak, write a **1** on the blank.

_____ 1. " 'I can read and eat with a spoon, but I'm not one of those women meant to live in homes that would be like cathedrals if they had bells.' " (p. 72)

_____ 2. "She wiped sweat from her forehead with a fold of her apron, and began to fan herself. Then she motioned me to a plate filled with refried beans, rice, and blanquillos." (p. 75)

_____ 3. "The gray-haired woman wore a blue dress that was cut straight and came to her knees, and she had on huaraches." (p. 72)

_____ 4. " '. . . what spider has stung you—you look sad and burdened like the woodcutter's burro,' [María] said." (p. 72)

_____ 5. " 'I wasn't one of those model Mexican wives who leave their wills in the church . . . .' " (p. 74)

_____ 6. "She asked me where I was from, her face intent with strong interest." (p. 72)

_____ 7. "There was lightning, vivid flashes that scarred the sky, and I could see San Antonio's lights golden as oil lamps beyond the New Braunfels Bridge." (p. 74)

_____ 8. " 'May the Indian Virgin . . . protect you and cover you with her mantle,' [María] said. . . ." (p. 75)

Applying Skills

Write a sentence of *direct* characterization that is more or less equivalent to each indirect characterization below.

1. The old man frequently grew red in the face. He would then clench his fists and scream abuses at the top of his voice.

_____

_____

2. "I like to come here alone and sit on this rock when I have problems," Alicia confided. "It's a good place for me to think things out."

_____

_____

3. "I don't blame you for dozing off," the lecturer said. "I sometimes drop off during this lecture myself."

_____

_____

Workbook: Elements of Literature, Third Course

HRW material copyrighted under notice appearing earlier in this work.

19

Static and Dynamic Characters

Some characters seem the same on the last page of a story as they did on the first. These are known as **static characters**. Other characters change because of what happens to them in the story. Characters who change as a result of the story's events are known as **dynamic characters**.

Understanding Static and Dynamic Characters

Use the space provided to answer each of the following questions.

1. Which character in "Thank You, M'am" is a static character—one who remains much the same throughout the story?

2. Which character is a dynamic character—one who changes because of what happens in the story? How does that character change?

3. List three details from the story that indicate that Roger's "contact" with Mrs. Jones is having a positive effect on him.

4. When Roger offers to go to the store for Mrs. Jones, is he thinking about running off with at least a little bit of money? Give reasons to support your answer.

Applying Skills

Most of the characters in comic strips and television sitcoms are static characters who do not change much. Pick one of these characters that you are quite familiar with. Then imagine a situation or series of situations in which that character behaves like a dynamic character, changing as a result of what has happened to him or her. Outline your scenario in a few sentences in the space provided.

_____

_____

_____

_____

_____

_____

Reader's Response

Do you think Roger will follow Mrs. Jones's advice not to snatch any more purses? Explain your answer in a few sentences, using evidence from the story.

_____

_____

_____

_____

_____

_____

_____

_____

_____

_____

Workbook: Elements of Literature, Third Course

Analyzing Character

When you analyze **character**, you determine aspects of the character based on what the author says about the character, on what the character says and does, and on what other characters say and do in relationship to that character.

Understanding Character

Each of the following boxes represents an aspect of the character of Granny in "Blues Ain't No Mockin Bird." Analyze the set of details listed below to determine the appropriate aspect of her character and write that aspect in the box that follows the details. The first one has been done for you.

(Granny:) " 'Go tell that man we ain't a bunch of trees. ' " (p. 81)

(Photographer:) " 'Mind if we shoot a bit around her? '
'I do indeed,' said Granny with no smile." (p. 83)

" 'Now, aunty,' Camera said . . . .
(Granny:) 'Your mama and I are not related.' " (p. 83)

1. | Granny is a proud and dignified woman.

" 'I don't know about the thing, the it, and the stuff,' said Granny . . . . 'Just the people here is what I tend to consider.' " (p. 81)

(Granny:) " 'Taking pictures of the man in his misery about to jump, cause life is so bad and people been messin with him so bad.' " (p. 83)

2. |

(Granny:) " 'Let's get on away from here before I kill me somebody.' " (p. 83)

(Narrator:) "Granny going crazy, and Granddaddy Cain pullin her off the people, saying, 'Now, now, Cora.' " (p. 83)

(Narrator:) "And we figure any minute, . . . Granny gonna bust through that screen with somethin in her hand and murder on her mind." (p. 84)

3. |

Applying Skills

The photographers obviously upset and irritated Granny greatly. Describe how another, more sensitive photographer might have approached Granny without alienating her. Consider Granny's character in your response: What methods might work with a person of her character and temperament?

_____

_____

_____

_____

_____

_____

_____

Reader's Response

How would you feel about your private life being filmed for a documentary? Would you enjoy the experience or resent the invasion of your privacy?

_____

_____

_____

_____

_____

The Function of Setting

The time and place of a story make up its **setting**. In some stories, the setting merely provides a believable background for the action. In other stories, setting plays a more important role by creating a mood or helping to reveal character. In "Top Man," the setting—the slopes of an unconquered mountain peak—serves as one source of conflict the characters struggle to overcome.

Understanding Setting

For dramatic effect, author Ullman gives the mountain K3 certain characteristics of a living being. Underline the words in the following descriptions that help to create the impression that the mountain is a living creature.

1. ". . . every man of us was for the first time aware of it, not as a picture in his mind but as a thing, an antagonist. " (p. 97)

2. "It was a flawlessly clear Himalayan night and K3 tiered up in the blackness like a monstrous sentinel lighted from within." (p. 98)

3. "Osborn attacked the mountain, head on. Nace studied it, sparred with it, wore it down." (p. 103)

4. "The mountain . . . was no longer a mere giant of rock and ice; it had become a living thing, an enemy, watching us, waiting for us, hostile, relentless." (p. 104)

5. "With fiendishly malignant timing . . . the mountain hurled at us its last line of defense." (p. 104)

Applying Skills

Many stories pit human beings in an external conflict with a force of nature. In the spaces below, indicate a *situation* in which one or more characters struggle against nature, the *aspect of nature* that is the antagonist, and the character's *goal*. One has been done for you as an example.

Character/Situation	Aspect of Nature	Goal of Character(s)
1. stranded motorist	blizzard	survival
2.		
3.		

Reader's Response

Whom do you think would be credited as the first to climb K3—Nace, whose ax was found at the summit, or Osborn, who put it there? State your reasons for thinking as you do.

_____

_____

_____

_____

_____

_____

_____

_____

_____

Setting and Character

The way in which characters in a story react to their **setting** (time and place) can provide revealing insights into what they are like. The differing approaches of Nace and Osborn in conquering K3 in "Top Man" highlighted basic differences in their characters. In a less dramatic way, the characters in "Antaeus" reveal themselves in relation to the setting of the story.

Understanding Setting and Character

Read each passage below. Then circle the letter of the word or phrase that best completes each statement.

1. " 'You mean you ain't got no fields to raise nothing in?—no watermelons or nothing?' "
   (p. 113)
   T. J. finds the idea of not growing things ____.
   a. silly   **b.** hard to imagine   **c.** uninteresting

2. " 'Who'd want to have their own acre of cotton and corn? That's just work. What can you do with an acre of cotton and corn?' " (p. 113)
   Blackie's response to T.J. reveals that he ____.
   a. wants to pick a fight   **b.** loves city life   **c.** has no idea of what farming means to T.J.

3. "Only rich people had roof gardens, we knew, and the idea of our own private domain excited them." (p. 113)
   Unlike T.J., the other boys see a roof garden as ____.
   a. a place to grow things   **b.** an exciting private possession   **c.** a way of pretending to be rich

4. "'We could play on it and take sunbaths on it. Like having our own lawn. Lots of people got lawns.' " (p. 115)
   Blackie defends growing grass on the roof of the building because he ____.
   a. thinks it would be easier   **b.** wants a lawn to use for   **c.** knows that grass seeds
   than growing crops   recreation as others do   will be easy to obtain

5. " 'I did have it in mind to raise some corn and vegetables. But we'll plant grass.' " (p. 115)
   T.J. agrees to grow grass because he ____.
   a. wants to grow *something*   **b.** is afraid of losing his friends   **c.** knows the roof garden is doomed anyway

6. " We couldn't keep from looking at it, unable to believe that we had created this delicate growth. " (p. 115)
   The boys were fascinated by the growing grass because they ____.
   a. had not seen much   **b.** knew it wouldn't last   **c.** were amazed that they
   grass before   long   were responsible for
                                   making it happen

Applying Skills

Suppose you are one of the group with the roof garden. Suppose also that you and your friends decide to try to save your garden. How would you go about it? Whose help would you seek? Remember this is wartime, and food is precious. In the space below, list a few ideas for saving the roof garden. What character traits would be revealed by such an undertaking?

_____

_____

_____

_____

_____

_____

_____

_____

_____

_____

_____

_____

Inferring Details of Setting and Culture

It doesn't require much imagination to visualize the **setting** of a story that takes place in modern times and in a familiar place. But when the story has an unfamiliar setting, you need to reason as well as imagine in order to visualize the physical or cultural environment of the story. The writer will usually supply key details to create a sense of place, but it is up to the reader to fill in the picture the writer has sketched by inferring other details of setting. When a setting is strikingly different from the reader's experience, such details may include descriptions of customs or lifestyle. Being able to make use of the clues provided by the writer to visualize a strange or exotic setting and culture is an important and satisfying reading skill.

Understanding Details of Setting and Culture

Below are details of setting and culture taken directly from the story. Use these details to make a logical inference about setting or culture to complete the statement in the box that follows the details. The first one has been done for you.

"The hag gave him stinking, rancid grease. . . . He applied it gingerly to his bruised and sun-seared body. Now he thought, I smell like the rest of them." (p. 121)

1.	Most of the Indians in camp smelled of rancid grease.

"Before riding into camp they stopped and dressed in their regalia. . .they painted their faces black." (p. 121)

"The white man had watched warriors in their triumph. He knew what to do. [He] smeared his face with grease and charcoal." (p. 124)

2.	To celebrate a triumph,

"The Crows were wealthy in horses, prosperous, and contented." (p. 122)

"He set about courting her, realizing how desperately poor he was both in property and honor. He owned no horse. . . ." (p. 124)

"The white man could not wait for some far-off time when he might have either horses or meat to give away." (p. 124)

3.	In Crow society,

Workbook: Elements of Literature, Third Course

28

HRW material copyrighted under notice appearing earlier in this work.

"This is the way the captive white man acquired wealth and honor. . .[He] dashed forward to strike the still-groaning man with his bow, to count first coup." (p. 124)

"The white man was called to settle an argument . . . as to which of [the boys] had struck second coup. . . ." (p. 124)

"[Yellow Robe's] honors were many. He captured horses in an enemy camp, led two successful raids, counted first coup and snatched a gun from the hand of an enemy tribesman." (p. 127)

4.	To count coup

Applying Skills

Write a few sentences describing a place well-known to you but probably unfamiliar to your classmates. Give key descriptive details and include a few clues from which your readers will be able to infer other details of setting.

_____

_____

_____

_____

_____

_____

_____

_____

_____

_____

_____

_____

_____

Workbook: Elements of Literature, Third Course

HRW material copyrighted under notice appearing earlier in this work.

29

First-Person Point of View

In a story told from the **first-person point of view**, one of the characters does the talking using the first-person pronoun *I*. In a first-person narrative, the speaker's voice is part of the story. We can know only what that person knows and observe only what he or she observes. "Correspondence" is a special kind of first-person narrative, called an **epistolary form**, which is made up entirely of letters. The letters tell us a lot about Henky—partly from what she confides to her correspondent and partly from the way she phrases things.

Understanding Characterization Through Point of View

Use the spaces provided to answer the following questions about "Correspondence."

1. Near the end of her first letter to Manoel, Henky states, "I feel I already know you so well," even though she really knows nothing about him. What does this tell you about her?

   _____

   _____

2. In her first letter, Henky's apology that her Spanish is weak reveals that she doesn't know as much about Brazil as she thinks. Why?

   _____

   _____

3. What does the wording of the following excerpt from Henky's letter of December 29 tell you about her? "I realize how communications can sometimes go astray . . . . But perchance there is some reason I do not know about."

   _____

   _____

4. In her second letter, Henky writes that she finds it peculiar that the seasons are opposite in Brazil and the United States. She adds "Of course you are used to it." What is amusing about this phrase?

   _____

   _____

   _____

Applying Skills

Put yourself in Henky's place—ten years after the writing of these letters. Write the first paragraph of your first-person account describing your long-ago correspondence with Manoel. Remember, this time you are writing a *personal recollection*, not a letter.

_____

_____

_____

_____

_____

_____

_____

_____

_____

Reader's Response

How would you feel if you had written several letters to a pen pal and received no reply? Would you have written a letter like Henky's final one or simply stopped writing after the second or third one?

_____

_____

_____

_____

_____

_____

_____

_____

Workbook: Elements of Literature, Third Course

HRW material copyrighted under notice appearing earlier in this work.

31

Third-Person Point of View

One kind of third-person narrator is the **omniscient** (all-knowing) narrator, who lets the reader see into the minds and hearts of all the important characters in a story or novel. The omniscient narrator is not a character in the story and never uses the first-person pronoun *I*.

Understanding Omniscient Point of View

Read the following passages from each section of the story. Then complete the chart that follows by identifying the character (Cress, Mr. Delahanty, or Mrs. Delahanty) who is speaking or thinking in each passage and what the passage reveals about that character's attitude or feelings at that point in the story. The first one has been done for you.

Beginning

1. " 'I mean that the hat was never intended for a thirteen-year-old girl. It's for an older—woman.' " (p. 144)

2. "The hat was summertime . . . . The person wearing it would be languorous, gentle, and delicate." (p. 144)

Middle

3. " 'I can only hope, Cress, the shoe won't be too decidedly on the other foot.' " (p. 146)

4. " 'You're all right, Crescent . . . . That hat's a little unusual, but I don't know that I'd want a daughter of mine trigged out like everyone else. Have a good time. And I hope you see Edwin.' " (p. 146)

End

5. " 'It wouldn't have been so bad though if that Edwin hadn't had to turn up in time to see it all.' " (p. 150)

6. " 'And whenever I wear this hat, he'll remember.' " (p. 150)

Workbook: Elements of Literature, Third Course

32

HRW material copyrighted under notice appearing earlier in this work.

CHARACTER	ATTITUDE
B E G I N N I N G 1. _____ Mrs. Delahanty 2. _____	She thinks the hat is unsuitable for Cress. _____ _____ _____
M I D D L E 3. _____ 4. _____	_____ _____ _____ _____ _____
5. _____ E N D 6. _____	_____ _____ _____ _____ _____

Applying Skills

Describe why an omniscient narrator is able to give the reader a more detailed description of the part of the story after the hat descends into the aquarium than if the story were narrated in the first person by Cress.

_____

_____

_____

_____

_____

_____

Workbook: Elements of Literature, Third Course

HRW material copyrighted under notice appearing earlier in this work.

33

THE OLD DEMON   Pearl S. Buck   (page 153)

Evaluating Point of View

A story told from the **third-person limited** point of view focuses on the thoughts and feelings of a single character. In this respect, it resembles a first-person narrative, which limits the reader to the thoughts and observations of the narrator only. Third-person limited point of view differs, however, by giving us the viewpoint of a narrator who knows the thoughts and feelings of the main character while remaining outside the story to comment and explain. This way of telling a story permits the writer to express shades of meaning that even a wise old woman like Mrs. Wang in "The Old Demon" could hardly be expected to express in her own words.

Understanding Third-Person Limited Point of View

Read the following excerpts from "The Old Demon." Evaluate how the use of third-person limited point of view rather than first-person narrative affects the telling of the story. In some cases, point of view may not affect the telling of the story. The first one has been done for you.

1. "Everyone listened to her since she was the oldest woman in the village and whatever she said settled something." (p. 153)

   It might seem conceited of Mrs. Wang to claim that whatever she said settled something;

   the observation comes naturally from an outside observer.

   _____

2. "The first time she was seventeen and a bride, and her husband had shouted to her to come . . . up the dike, and she had come, blushing and twisting her hands together. . . ." (p. 154)

   _____

   _____

   _____

3. " 'I can't run,' she remarked. 'I haven't run in seventy years, since before my feet were bound.' " (p. 156)

   _____

   _____

   _____

4. " 'Are you dead?' she inquired politely." (p. 157)

_____

_____

_____

5. "Then she felt it seize her and lift her up to the sky. It was beneath her and around her. It rolled her joyfully hither and thither, and then, holding her close and enfolded, it went rushing against the enemy." (p. 160)

_____

_____

_____

Applying Skills

Use details from the following background information and first-person narrative to rewrite a paragraph from the third-person limited point of view.

Background: Broudy, a forty-year-old writer who lives mainly in New York City, takes a winter hike through woodland in Vermont.

First-person narrative:
It was just after daybreak and snowing lightly when I started hiking through the Vermont woods. The path I followed was all that remained of an old logging road. It was quite distinct for the first few hundred yards, but it gradually faded away under leaves and underbrush. Eventually, I realized that the snow was falling thicker and faster and that I was lost.

Third-person limited narrative:

_____

_____

_____

_____

_____

_____

_____

_____

_____

_____

Workbook: Elements of Literature, Third Course

HRW material copyrighted under notice appearing earlier in this work.

35

Finding the Theme

The **theme** of a story is the central idea it expresses. It is not the same as the subject, or topic, of a story, which can usually be stated in a word or phrase. Childhood, the relationship between brothers, and war are all subjects. The theme of a story makes some statement about the story's meaning; it usually must be expressed in a sentence.

The writer does not usually state the theme of a story in so many words. Instead, he or she uses the words and action of the story to convey the theme. Identifying the theme of a story is important in understanding the meaning of the work.

Understanding A Story's Theme

Use the space provided to answer the following questions.

1. Why does the narrator persist in trying to make Doodle like other boys?

_____

_____

_____

2. Why does the narrator abandon Doodle in the thunderstorm?

_____

_____

_____

3. In what ways is Doodle like the scarlet ibis?

_____

_____

_____

_____

4. The narrator makes the following statement: " . . . pride is a wonderful, terrible thing, a seed that bears two vines, life and death." What insight does this statement give you to the story's theme? (p. 172)

_____

_____

_____

_____

Applying Skills

A theme may be correctly stated in more than one way, but it usually requires at least one sentence. Below, write one or more sentences that state the theme of "The Scarlet Ibis."

_____

_____

_____

_____

_____

Reader's Response

Do you think the narrator of "The Scarlet Ibis" pushed Doodle too hard to become more like other children, or did his actions help Doodle grow? Do you blame the narrator for Doodle's death? Explain your answers.

_____

_____

_____

_____

_____

_____

_____

_____

Workbook: Elements of Literature, Third Course

Theme and Plot

The connected series of events that make up a story form its **plot**. The underlying meaning or central idea that this series of events conveys to the reader is the story's **theme**. The theme of a story is the writer's comment on experience—his or her reason for telling the story. Instead of stating the theme in so many words, the writer lets us discover it for ourselves as we share the experience of the characters.

Understanding Theme and Plot

Classify each of the following elements of "The Bridge" according to its function of either advancing the plot or developing the theme. Write a **P** on the space provided next to each item that advances the plot of the story. Write a **T** on the space provided next to each item that develops the theme of the story.

_____ **1.** Gramma says Kostya is "scared of everything."

_____ **2.** Kostya had begun to avoid people.

_____ **3.** Kostya goes for a last bike ride.

_____ **4.** The girl begins to pedal faster.

_____ **5.** The girl starts to ride across the unfinished bridge.

_____ **6.** Kostya gets off his bike and dives into the river.

_____ **7.** Kostya learns that he can accomplish tasks.

_____ **8.** The girl shows confidence in him as he rescues her.

_____ **9.** Kostya walks back onto the bridge without fear.

_____ **10.** The girl is impressed by Kostya's future plans.

_____ **11.** Kostya no longer dreads going to his uncle.

_____ **12.** Kostya discovers an unknown tenderness within himself.

Applying Skills

Suppose you wished to write a story with the following underlying theme: "As one grows older, the fear of death decreases." What kind of plot would you invent to develop this theme? Mention a few specific events that might be part of the plot.

_____

_____

_____

_____

_____

_____

_____

_____

_____

_____

Reader's Response

"The Bridge" is a **rite-of-passage** story. It concerns a single event in the life of a young man named Kostya. As a result of this event, his life changes and he becomes an adult. Do you think a single event can dramatically shape the course of one's life? Have you ever had such an experience? If so, describe the experience.

_____

_____

_____

_____

_____

_____

Workbook: Elements of Literature, Third Course

Making Inferences About Theme

The **theme,** or central idea, of most stories is not stated outright. The reader must discover it by reflecting on the meaning of the events that occur within the story or the changes that the main characters undergo. Since the writer wants readers to grasp the underlying meaning of the story, he or she provides many clues in the course of telling the story. An experienced reader searches for such clues and uses them to infer the theme of the story.

Understanding a Story's Theme

Use the space provided to answer the following questions about the story.

1. What did the narrator and her friend Lonnie hope to learn from completing magazine questionnaires?

_____

_____

_____

2. Why is the narrator so uncomfortable in high school?

_____

_____

_____

3. What does the narrator mind most about being deserted by Mason Williams on the dance floor?

_____

_____

_____

4. Explain in your own words what the narrator means when she states "Then he turned back to town, never knowing he had been my rescuer, that he had brought me from Mary Fortune's territory into the ordinary world." (p. 193)

_____

_____

_____

Applying Skills

Describe in a short paragraph what the narrator's life in high school might have been like if she had remained in "Mary Fortune's territory."

_____

_____

_____

_____

_____

_____

_____

_____

Reader's Response

In a few sentences, describe what you think the narrator told her mother about the night's events. Do you think she would have told her friend Lonnie everything?

_____

_____

_____

_____

_____

_____

_____

_____

Workbook: Elements of Literature, Third Course

HRW material copyrighted under notice appearing earlier in this work.

41

Irony

The difference between what we expect and what actually happens is the essence of **irony**. Irony is a fundamental element in literature, as it is in life. Things seldom turn out the way we had planned. Writers use irony as a comment on the unpredictability of life itself.

Understanding Irony

Answer the following questions about the use of irony in the two stories by James Thurber.

1. What is unusual or ironic about the very first paragraph of "The Little Girl and the Wolf"?

_____

_____

_____

_____

2. In "The Princess and the Tin Box," how does the king's requirement of a gift from the suitors differ from other similar fairy tales?

_____

_____

_____

_____

3. Find the irony in the following description of the fifth prince and explain what it adds to the story.
"[He] was the son of a poor king whose realm had been overrun by mice and locusts and wizards and mining engineers so that there was nothing much of value left in it."

_____

_____

_____

_____

4. Do you think the Princess's initial reaction of interest and delight in the tin box and its contents was genuine? What is ironic about her reaction and subsequent decision?

_____

_____

_____

5. What is the usual last line of a fairy tale following the wedding of the prince and princess?

_____

_____

_____

6. How is the last line of "The Princess and the Tin Box" both ironic and consistent with the rest of the story?

_____

_____

_____

Applying Skills

Write a new moral for "The Princess and the Tin Box." Be sure your moral is consistent with the story. Try to make your moral ironic.

_____

_____

_____

_____

Reader's Response

Did you think the Princess was going to select the tin box and marry the prince who brought it? Why or why not?

_____

_____

_____

_____

Workbook: Elements of Literature, Third Course

HRW material copyrighted under notice appearing earlier in this work.

43

THE SNIPER   Liam O'Flaherty   (page 206)

Situational Irony

Situational irony occurs when a situation that is expected to happen is the opposite of what actually does happen. A civil war might be considered to be an example of situational irony because the combatants are fellow citizens, who might be expected to be comrades rather than enemies.

Understanding Situational irony

Complete the following chart, supplying whichever is missing—the expected outcome of the situation described or the actual ironic outcome in the story. The first one has been done for you.

Situation	Expected Outcome	Ironic Outcome
1. The Irish want to be free of British rule.	The Irish fight the British.	The Irish engage in civil war.
2. An old woman tells a soldier in an armored car the sniper's location.	The sniper will be killed.	
3. The sniper's bullets are unable to pierce the steel of an armored car.		The man opens the turret, exposing himself to sniper's fire.
4. The sniper must expose himself to fire at the soldier in the car.	Having succeeded, the sniper will quickly take cover.	
5. The sniper is curious as to the identity of the man he has just killed on the opposite roof.	The dead man may be someone the sniper knew in the army.	

Applying Skills

Stories about a wish being granted often involve situational irony. Think of an example of a wish fulfillment from fairy tales, myths, or other stories you have read and point out the irony in the story's outcome.

_____

_____

_____

Workbook: Elements of Literature, Third Course

44   HRW material copyrighted under notice appearing earlier in this work.

Reader's Response

"The Sniper" illustrates how civil wars can divide families. In fact, the sniper actually kills a man who turns out to be his own brother. What do you think the sniper's reaction was after discovering he had killed his brother? Do you think he would have continued fighting? Why or why not?

_____

_____

_____

_____

_____

_____

_____

_____

_____

_____

_____

_____

_____

Dramatic and Verbal Irony

Verbal irony occurs when a writer or speaker says one thing but really means something completely different. **Dramatic irony** occurs when the audience or speaker knows something important that a character in a story or play is unaware of.

Understanding Dramatic and Verbal Irony

Identify each quotation from the story as an example of either verbal or dramatic irony, and explain why it is ironic. The first one has been done for you.

1. Montresor "implores" Fortunato to turn back from the vaults because of his health—

" 'Enough,' [Fortunato] said; 'the cough is a mere nothing; it will not kill me. I shall not die of a cough.' " (p. 211)

dramatic irony

Fortunato is unaware of the truth he has spoken—truly a cough will not be the cause of his

death.

2. Montresor gives Fortunato a draft of wine, and Fortunato makes a toast—

" 'I drink,' [Fortunato] said, 'to the buried that repose around us.' " (p. 211)

_____

_____

_____

3. Fortunato asks Montresor about his family coat of arms—

" 'And the motto?'
'Nemo ne impune lacessit.'
'Good!' [Fortunato] said." (p. 212)

_____

_____

_____

4. Montresor emphasizes the dampness of the vault and once again "implores" Fortunato to turn back—

" 'The drops of moisture trickle among the bones. Come, we will go back ere it is too late. Your cough—' " (p. 213)

_____

_____

_____

5. Montresor has just secured Fortunato to a granite rock—

" 'But I must first render you all the little attentions in my power.' " (p. 214)

_____

_____

_____

Applying Skills

One of the ironies of the story is that Fortunato contributes to his own end. In what ways does he do so?

_____

_____

_____

_____

Reader's Response

At what point in the story did you realize that this was the night Montresor had chosen for his revenge? Explain how you knew.

_____

_____

_____

_____

_____

_____

Workbook: Elements of Literature, Third Course

HRW material copyrighted under notice appearing earlier in this work.

47

THE NECKLACE   Guy de Maupassant   (page 218)

Situational Irony

Situational irony produces surprise. We are led to expect one thing, yet something quite different happens. When irony is used simply to give a story a surprise twist at the end, we may be amused but might not take the story seriously. On the other hand, when irony is essential for developing the theme of a story or when it dramatizes the unpredictability of life, it becomes a powerful tool for the writer.

Understanding Situational Irony

Use the spaces provided to answer the following questions about "The Necklace."

1. How would you describe Mathilde's character at the beginning of "The Necklace"?

_____

_____

2. How does Mathilde deal with the enormous debt she and her husband have to repay?

_____

_____

3. Describe Mathilde's character at the end of the story.

_____

_____

4. Explain what is ironic about the change in Mathilde's circumstances during the course of the story.

_____

_____

5. The last line of the story is especially ironic. Explain why.

_____

_____

_____

_____

Applying Skills

Situational irony occurs when what we expect to happen is in fact the opposite of what takes place. For each of the situations at the left below, write an ironic outcome. The first one has been done for you.

SITUATION	IRONIC OUTCOME
The venom of a poisonous snake causes many deaths.	The venom is used to develop an antidote to the snake's bite.
An antiwar activist is drafted to serve in the army.	
A lonely man accepts an offer of marriage.	
An expensive city manager is hired to help bail a community out of financial difficulty.	

Reader's Response

In "The Necklace" the actions of the main character are motivated by human vanity. Explain how Mme. Loisel's obsession with appearances leads to her own downfall. Also note how judging by appearances adds to the irony of this story.

_____

_____

_____

_____

_____

_____

_____

_____

The Five Senses

A strong and vivid **image** will usually appeal to one of the five senses, enabling the reader mentally to see, hear, smell, taste, or feel the experience the image describes.

Understanding Images

Write each of the following images from the poem in the column of the sense to which it appeals. (In some cases, an image may appeal to more than one sense.)

"hooded against the frost"   "the river mutters"

"shadowy spruce"   "icy bed"

"the long moon drifts"   "when morning climbs/the limbs"

SIGHT	HEARING	TOUCH

Applying Skills

Create images of your own for experiences that might occur in the setting of the poem "If the Owl Calls Again." Write images that will appeal to at least three of the five senses.

Sight _____

_____

Hearing _____

_____

Touch _____

_____

Smell _____

_____

Taste _____

_____

Reader's Response

The setting of "If the Owl Calls Again" is obviously a cold environment. Reread the poem and substitute a spring or summer image for each wintery image in the poem. Does changing the setting affect the tone or overall feeling created by the poem? Explain your answers.

_____

_____

_____

_____

_____

_____

_____

_____

_____

_____

_____

_____

_____

Imagery and Theme

The combination of **images** — or sensory descriptions — in a poem builds a single, unified effect. This cumulative effect supports the central idea — or **theme** — of the poem.

Understanding Imagery and Theme

Write the sense (sight, sound, touch, taste, or smell) to which each of the following images appeals. Then explain what feelings or associations each image calls up.

1. "the attic of an aging house" _____

_____

_____

2. "His fingers made a hat about his head" _____

_____

_____

3. "He loops in crazy figures" _____

_____

_____

4. "he brushes up against a screen" _____

_____

_____

5. "mice with wings can wear a human face" _____

_____

_____

Workbook: Elements of Literature, Third Course

52   HRW material copyrighted under notice appearing earlier in this work.

Applying Skills

In your own words, state the theme of the poem. Explain how the images support that theme.

_____

_____

_____

_____

_____

_____

Reader's Response

How did the poem make *you* feel about bats? What specific details contributed to that feeling?

_____

_____

_____

_____

_____

_____

_____

_____

_____

Workbook: Elements of Literature, Third Course

HRW material copyrighted under notice appearing earlier in this work.

53

Imagery and Feelings

Writers often use **imagery** to create an overall tone, impression, or mood. Images within a poem may be selected to create or suggest certain specific feelings.

Understanding Imagery and Feelings

Answer the following questions about the poem.

1. In "Poem to be Read at 3 A.M.," the speaker gives three examples of isolated lights. Explain how each one contributes to the feeling of loneliness in the poem.

    a. "the diner/On the outskirts [of town]"

    _____

    _____

    _____

    b. "dark but/For my headlights"

    _____

    _____

    _____

    c. "up in/One second-story room/A single light"

    _____

    _____

    _____

2. How do the words "sick or/Perhaps reading" add to the feeling of loneliness?

    _____

    _____

    _____

3. What other kinds of lights might a driver expect to see in a small town at 3 A.M.?

_____

_____

How might the presence of these other lights change the narrator's feeling?

_____

_____

_____

4. How does the speaker try to bridge the loneliness?

_____

_____

_____

Applying Skills

Choose any three of the light sources listed below. Write an image that gives a feeling about the kind of light that would come from each one.

a camp fire   a neon sign

a movie marquee   a crystal chandelier

a night-light   oriental lanterns

a bare bulb in a ceiling fixture   Christmas-tree lights

1. _____

_____

_____

2. _____

_____

_____

3. _____

_____

_____

Workbook: Elements of Literature, Third Course

HRW material copyrighted under notice appearing earlier in this work.

55

Imagery and Setting

Imagery is often used to create vivid mental pictures of a scene or a place in time. Through the use of such striking images, the **setting** of a story or poem is clearly and effectively revealed.

Understanding Imagery and Setting

Answer the following questions about the poem.

1. In what setting is the speaker?

_____

_____

2. What feature of that setting forms the central image of the poem?

_____

_____

3. The central image of the poem functions on two levels: the literal, physical level and an internal, personal level. Explain how the image works on each level.

literal _____

_____

internal _____

_____

4. How does the setting of the poem make it easy for the speaker to fail to help the blind man?

_____

_____

_____

_____

Applying Skills

In her short, passing observation of the man, the speaker notices a number of significant details: the dog, the man's grip on the leash, his gray gloves, his cane, and the mound of snow. She recognizes the man's blindness and, from the tension in his body, imagines his silent plea for help.

Think of someone you observed briefly while passing by on a bus or in a car. Record the images of the scene and what you imagined of that person's situation and thoughts.

_____

_____

_____

_____

_____

_____

_____

_____

_____

_____

_____

_____

_____

_____

_____

Analyzing Imagery

Images are vivid descriptions that appeal to the senses. They often allow the reader to view everyday objects in a new light. Through the use of imagery, the writer may provide insight into the world around us.

Understanding Images

Answer the following questions about "Southbound on the Freeway."

1. What reality does each of the following images describe?

IMAGE	REALITY
a. the round rolling feet	
b. The front eyes	
c. the red eyes in back	
d. the creature with the revolving red eye	
e. the dark diagrams with white lines	
f. the measuring tapes	
g. the hiss of the creatures	
h. the creatures themselves	
i. the soft shapes inside the creatures	

2. Why is the nighttime setting essential to the imagery of the poem?

_____

_____

_____

3. How would you explain to the Orbitville tourist the reality of the scene?

_____

_____

_____

_____

_____

Applying Skills

The tourist describes only two types of creatures, using only the revolving fifth eye to distinguish between them. Think of two other different types of "creatures" the tourist from Orbitville might observe on the freeway. Using the basic imagery found in the poem, invent a distinguishing feature for each one.

_____

_____

_____

_____

_____

_____

_____

_____

_____

Similes

A **simile** compares two unlike things. A simile may point out one way in which the things compared are similar and startle us into thinking about the subject in a new way. A simile makes its comparison explicitly, usually with a word such as *like, as, resembles,* or *than.* In "Harlem," Langston Hughes uses a series of similes to describe the fate of a "dream deferred" — that is, a hope or ambition that must be put off, perhaps indefinitely.

Understanding Similes

Answer each question in the space provided.

1. What do the images "a raisin in the sun," "fester like a sore," "rotten meat," and a piece of stale candy have in common?

_____

_____

_____

2. What does the simile comparing a dream deferred to a "heavy load" suggest?

_____

_____

_____

3. The last line of the poem makes an implied comparison. What object explodes after being left alone for a time?

_____

_____

_____

4. How do the first five similes of the poem differ from the comparison made in the last line?

_____

_____

_____

5. Why is the poem called "Harlem"?

_____

_____

_____

Applying Skills

Write a sentence with an appropriate simile that describes each of the following:

A hoped-for result _____

_____

A welcome sight _____

_____

Workbook: Elements of Literature, Third Course

HRW material copyrighted under notice appearing earlier in this work.

61

A NARROW FELLOW IN THE GRASS   Emily Dickinson   (page 254)

Metaphors

A **metaphor** is a special kind of comparison between two unlike things. Instead of saying A is like B, as a simile does, a metaphor boldly states or implies that A *is* B. The unexpected linking of two seemingly unrelated things causes us to view the subject under consideration in a new way. In "A Narrow Fellow in the Grass," Emily Dickinson uses a series of metaphors to create the impression of a sudden encounter with a snake.

Understanding Metaphors

Circle the letter of the word or phrase that best completes each statement.

1. By likening the snake to "a spotted shaft," the poet emphasizes the snake's
   a. round, sleek shape   **b.** ability to fly through the air like an arrow   **c.** deadly rattles

2. "A floor too cool for corn" means
   a. a damp granary floor   **b.** land that receives little sunshine   **c.** snow-covered earth

3. "A whip-lash/Unbraiding in the sun" describes the _____ of the snake.
   a. uncoiling   **b.** stroking   **c.** rapid movement

4. "And zero at the bone" refers to
   a. bone-chilling fear   **b.** lack of a backbone   **c.** wind chill

Applying Skills

Write a sentence using an appropriate metaphor to describe one of the following:

1. The mind of an old person with many memories

_____

_____

2. A room filled with feverishly active people

_____

_____

3. A single line of people

_____

_____

_____

Reader's Response

Do you think "tighter breathing" and "zero at the bone" are apt descriptions of how you would feel if you suddenly noticed a snake just ahead of you? Create your own metaphor that reveals how you would feel in this situation.

_____

_____

_____

_____

_____

_____

_____

_____

_____

Workbook: Elements of Literature, Third Course

HRW material copyrighted under notice appearing earlier in this work.

63

Implied Metaphors

An **implied metaphor** suggests a comparison without actually saying A *is* B. In "Women," the struggle of black women to improve the lot of their children is likened to the efforts of army commanders to gain victory in warfare.

Understanding Implied Metaphors

Answer the following questions about the poem.

1. What does the poet mean by saying the women had "fists as well as/Hands"?

_____

_____

2. Explain the poem's metaphors of battering down doors and ironing "starched white/shirts."

_____

_____

_____

_____

3. Who might the "generals" be that the women are said to have "headdragged"?

_____

_____

_____

4. What is meant by "A place for us"?

_____

_____

5. Explain the meaning of "How they knew what we/*Must* know/Without knowing a page/ Of it /Themselves."

_____

_____

_____

Applying Skills

Indicate an aspect of human life for which each of the following activities could serve as an implied metaphor. The first one has been done for you.

1. Making a journey

   life as a whole
   _____

2. A potter molding objects out of clay

   _____

   _____

   _____

3. A guide showing visitors works of art in a museum

   _____

   _____

   _____

THE OLD PILOT'S DEATH   Donald Hall   (page 258)

Extended Metaphors

An **extended metaphor** is a metaphor that is continued and developed over several lines of writing or throughout an entire poem. In "The Old Pilot's Death," a final flight is an extended metaphor for the pilot's death.

Understanding Extended Metaphors

Answer the following questions about the poem.

1. If you did not know the title of this poem, what kind of experience would you think was being described? List at least three details that contribute to this impression.

   _____

   _____

   _____

   _____

2. What is suggested by the simile "He . . . sits like an egg in a nest of canvas"?

   _____

   _____

3. Which details suggest that flying is something the pilot did long ago?

   _____

   _____

4. Reread these lines and then answer the questions that follow.

   > "He feels the old fear, and rising over the fields
   > the old gratitude. In the distance, circling
   > in a beam of late sun like birds migrating,
   > there are the wings of a thousand biplanes."

   a. What, besides a safe take-off, does the pilot have to be grateful for?

   _____

   b. Why is the simile of the migrating birds particularly appropriate?

   _____

   _____

c. What does the detail of a "beam of late sun" suggest?

_____

_____

Applying Skills

Develop an extended metaphor of your own. Remember, a metaphor compares two unlike things. An extended metaphor is developed over several lines of writing. Write two or three sentences or lines of poetry to extend your chosen metaphor.

_____

_____

_____

_____

_____

_____

_____

Reader's Response

How do you feel about the attitude toward death expressed in "The Old Pilot's Death"?

_____

_____

_____

_____

_____

_____

Metaphors and Theme

Metaphors begin as comparisons, but effective metaphors do much more than describe. A good metaphor provides an insight into the nature of the main subject of the poem or story. In "She Dwelt Among the Untrodden Ways," a metaphor simply but powerfully expresses the **theme**, or central insight, of the poem.

Understanding Theme Through Metaphors

1. The central metaphor of the poem compares Lucy to a single violet. Some attributes of the violet are listed at the left below. In the space provided, indicate how each attribute applies to the young girl. The first one has been done for you as an example.

   a. delicately beautiful

   a. We are told that Lucy is "fair." _____

   _____

   b. short-lived

   b. _____

   _____

   c. almost hidden by the "mossy stone"

   c. _____

   _____

   d. solitary

   d. _____

   _____

2. What effect does the simile in lines 7 and 8 have on the metaphor comparing Lucy to a violet?

   _____

   _____

   _____

3. What is the central theme of the metaphor in stanza 2?

   _____

   _____

   _____

   _____

Applying Skills

List attributes of a large oak tree that might make it an appropriate metaphor for an elderly person who has long been the head of a family.

_____

_____

_____

_____

_____

_____

_____

Reader's Response

Do you think that Lucy was a real person or an imaginary creation of the poet? If you believe she was a real person, do you think the poet was in love with her or did he simply admire her beautiful, simple life?

_____

_____

_____

_____

_____

_____

_____

Implied Metaphors

An **implied metaphor** does not make a direct comparison. Instead, it uses words and images that suggest what the nature of the comparison is. In "Fog" and "The yellow fog . . .," two very different poets use the same implied metaphor to describe fog in the city.

Understanding Implied Metaphors

Answer the following questions about the two poems in the space provided.

1. Which poet is more specific in making his comparison? Explain.

_____

_____

2. What does Sandburg suggest by saying that the fog comes "on little cat feet"?

_____

_____

3. List the catlike actions or parts of a cat's anatomy that each poet attributes to fog.

Sandburg _____

Eliot _____

_____

Applying Skills

Write a sentence or two containing an implied metaphor of a bird or animal to describe one of the following:

1. Clouds moving rapidly across the sky

2. An airliner taking off

3. A jittery, constantly moving person

4. A faithful, uncomplaining companion

_____

_____

_____

_____

Reader's Response

The poems "Fog" and "The yellow fog . . ." both create a certain emotional response. In your own words, explain the feeling created by comparing the movement of fog to the behavior of a cat in these poems.

_____

_____

_____

_____

_____

_____

_____

_____

_____

Evaluating Metaphors

When you evaluate a **metaphor**, you judge the aptness of the comparison and the extent to which the use of the metaphor provides an insight into the nature of the subject. If the metaphor is extended, you must judge whether the development is logical and consistent.

Understanding Metaphors

Circle the letter of the word or phrase that best completes each statement.

1. The central metaphor in "The Seven Ages of Man" is _____.
   a. direct   b. indirect   c. implied

2. The metaphor is extended _____.
   a. throughout the poem   b. through the first eight lines   c. through the first 15 lines

3. The metaphor in line 14 which compares reputation to a bubble suggests that one's reputation is _____.
   a. permanent   b. fragile   c. worthless

4. The "cannon's mouth" in line 15 is a special kind of metaphor called *metonymy*, which substitutes an associated thing for the thing itself. A reporter uses metonymy when he or she uses "White House" to mean "the President and his administration." In this instance, *cannon's mouth* stands for _____.
   a. a braggard   b. an oracle   c. the dangers of war

5. "Sighing like furnace" is an example of _____.
   a. metonymy   b. an implied metaphor   c. a simile

Applying Skills

Identify the two metaphors in the following lines from a poem by Ben Jonson. Explain what is being compared and evaluate the effectiveness of the metaphors.

from "On My First Son"

Farewell, thou child of my right hand, and joy;
My sin was too much hope of thee, loved boy:
Seven years thou wert lent to me, and I thee pay,
Exacted by thy fate, on the just day.

Rest in soft peace, and asked, say, "Here doth lie
Ben Jonson his best piece of poetry."

_____

_____

_____

Reader's Response

In the poem "The Seven Ages of Man," the speaker mocks each stage of life and the overall tone of the poem is pessimistic. Select two of the ages described in the poem and rewrite them to reflect a more optimistic and joyful view of life.

_____

_____

_____

_____

_____

_____

_____

_____

_____

_____

_____

_____

_____

_____

_____

_____

_____

_____

Personification

Personification is a kind of metaphor in which an object, quality, or idea is talked about as if it were human. The effect is to engage our sympathy or add interest or meaning to aspects of the nonhuman world.

Understanding Personification

Answer the following questions about "The Legend of the Paper Plates" in the spaces provided.

1. Identify what is being personified by each of the following:

   a. "all the family"   (line 3) _____

   b. "the patriarchs"   (line 7) _____

   c. "the young people"   (line 9) _____

   d. "ten million offspring"   (line 16) _____

   e. "them"   (line 17) _____

2. Explain the meaning of the fourth stanza of the poem (lines 11-16).

   _____

   _____

   _____

   _____

3. Contrast the description of the paper plates in lines 20-23 with qualities of the "ancestors" stated or implied in lines 3 and 4.

Ancestors	Paper Plates
proud, bushy, strong	
	identical
long-lived	

Workbook: Elements of Literature, Third Course

74

HRW material copyrighted under notice appearing earlier in this work.

4. In what way is the title of this poem ironic?

_____

_____

_____

5. What is the overall effect of personification in this poem?

_____

_____

_____

Applying Skills

In a few lines, personify one of the following, attributing human characteristics to the object or idea.

1. An old house, vacant after many years of occupancy

2. A much-used school or office computer

3. A violin that once belonged to a brilliant musician

4. A nonhuman thing or quality of your choice

_____

_____

_____

_____

Reader's Response

It is likely you will continue using paper plates. But will you think of this poem and experience a pang of guilt the next time you see or use a paper plate?

_____

_____

_____

_____

_____

_____

Workbook: Elements of Literature, Third Course

Personifying Nature

Throughout history some cultures have believed that trees, rivers, mountains, and other features of nature possessed spirits. Perhaps a fragment of the same impulse sometimes leads writers to personify trees and other natural objects. **Personifications** differ in the extent to which we are asked to think of the natural object as having human form. In "A Pastoral," a few human characteristics are assigned to an apple tree, but the tree remains a tree.

Understanding Personification

Complete each of the following statements about the poem "A Pastoral."

1. The speaker of the poem calls the old tree wise because _____

_____

2. The successive orchard men who mark the tree for cutting want it removed because _____

_____

3. One reason the speaker refers to the tree as a "showy veteran" is that _____

_____

_____

4. The speaker says he will *defer* the tree's removal, rather than *prevent* it because _____

_____

5. Three expressions in the last stanza that personify the tree are _____

_____

6. As the apple tree responds to spring by blooming, the speaker responds by _____

_____

Applying Skills

Using personification, write a paragraph or a short poem about a March wind, leaves falling in autumn, a rose blooming in spring, or some other aspect of nature.

_____

_____

_____

_____

_____

_____

_____

_____

Reader's Response

The tone of "A Pastoral" is rather sentimental. How did you feel about the speaker's annual ritual of saving the "wise old apple tree"? Have you ever been strongly attached to an object that others might consider to be of little value?

_____

_____

_____

_____

_____

_____

_____

_____

_____

_____

Personification and Humor

A **personification** may assign only a few human characteristics to an object, quality, or idea. Or the personification can make a fairly complete identification of the thing with a human being. "March 1st" does this with comic effect, as February is envisioned as an obese old woman.

Understanding Details of Personification

1. The left-hand column below lists literal details of February. The right-hand column lists these details as represented by the poet through personification. Complete the chart by supplying the missing items.

Literal Detail	Detail in Personification
a. _____	a body draped with powder
b. dirty piles of snow	_____
c. _____	indentation of a huge body on piled-up sheets

2. The poet uses laundry images throughout the poem. Explain in your own words the idea conveyed by each of the following images:

   a. "February still meandering around/like laundry caught in a Bendix"

   _____

   _____

   b. "Stray shreds/of cloud, like pillow slips, were rent from/her large endlessness"

   _____

   _____

   c. "Winter, you /old clothes hamper, what mildew/still molders inside you"

   _____

   _____

   _____

   _____

Applying Skills

Describe a person that might be used to personify each of the following:

1. Changeable weather in April

_____

_____

2. Hot, sultry days in August

_____

_____

3. Brisk October weather

_____

_____

Workbook: Elements of Literature, Third Course

HRW material copyrighted under notice appearing earlier in this work.

79

Personification and Theme

Personification is a special kind of metaphor in which a nonhuman thing or quality is talked about as if it were human. Personification may be used by a writer to reveal a **theme,** or central idea, of a story or poem. Through the use of personification and other literary devices, the writer can illustrate or illuminate the overall theme of a work.

Understanding Theme Through Personification

Answer the following questions about the images in the poem.

1. What images does the speaker have in mind when she says, "And when the car stopped at the foot of our hill,/the bell rang twice, the flu got off"?

   _____

   _____

2. How does she continue the image in lines 29–34? _____

   _____

   _____

3. What does this image suggest about how the speaker views the flu? _____

   _____

4. What image is suggested by the mother's theory that the two young uncles had brought the flu back from France in the fan:
   "hidden in the silk webbing
   that stretched between the carved ivory fingers"?

   _____

   _____

   _____

5. What effect does attributing the flu to these humanized sources have on the victim's suffering?

   _____

   _____

Applying Skills

Consider not only the images discussed above but all the images in the poem. What overall theme is revealed through the use of these images?

_____

_____

_____

_____

_____

_____

Reader's Response

The flu epidemic of 1918-1919 mentioned in "My Mother Remembers Spanish Influenza" caused many deaths and was, naturally, very dreaded. What feelings would you have if you became sick with such a dangerous, contagious illness? Would you also think of the illness as a living being intent on inflicting harm as did the speaker in this poem?

_____

_____

_____

_____

_____

_____

_____

Workbook: Elements of Literature, Third Course

HRW material copyrighted under notice appearing earlier in this work.

81

Personifying a Machine

Personification is a kind of metaphor in which an inanimate object or an idea or quality is spoken of as though it were human. In "Fifteen," a shiny motorcycle seems to be an exciting companion offering an invitation to adventure.

Understanding Personification

Answer the following questions about the poem in the spaces provided.

1. Which details in lines 6-10 suggest the qualities of a living creature rather than those of a machine?

_____

_____

_____

_____

2. Which words or expressions in lines 11-15 suggest that the motorcycle is a responsive living being?

_____

_____

_____

_____

3. Reread lines 16-20 of the poem. How does this stanza depart from the personification found earlier in the poem?

_____

_____

_____

_____

Applying Skills

Using personification, write a few descriptive details for each of the following machines:

1. A computer

_____

_____

2. A sleek sports car

_____

_____

3. A reliable washing machine

_____

_____

Reader's Response

The speaker in the poem mentions his age four times in the poem. Three times, the sentence "I was fifteen" ends the last line of a stanza. At the end of the poem, the reference to his age is set off as a separate line. Why do you think the poet did that? What effect does setting off this last line have?

_____

_____

_____

_____

_____

_____

_____

_____

Analyzing Personification

When you analyze **personification**, you examine the kinds of insights the use of the device brings to a poem or story. In "Slumnight," television, war, and the moon perform human functions in images that sketch a vivid picture of children's lives in the slums.

Understanding Personification

Study the following three personifications in "Slumnight" and answer the questions.

1. TV as sheriff
   a. What kind of television shows are suggested by the images in the poem?

   _____

   b. How do the children feel about the shows they watch?

   _____

   c. How does the personification of the TV as sheriff suggest that no parents are home?

   _____

   _____

2. Wars sign an armistice
   a. Who is fighting on the vacant lots?

   _____

   b. What kinds of weapons are used?

   _____

   c. When do the "wars" end?

   _____

3. The moon as a police officer
   a. What does this personification of the moon say about violence in the neighborhood?

   _____

   b. What is the function of the moon in the poem?

   _____

   _____

Applying Skills

List a human function, quality, or trait that might be used to personify each of the following items. The first one has been done for you.

1. a computer   the work or duties of an accountant

2. a burglar alarm   _____

3. a stop light   _____

4. a drum   _____

Reader's Response

Did you find the image of the moon pulling up in a squadcar an effective one? Explain how you feel about it in a sentence or two.

_____

_____

_____

_____

_____

_____

_____

_____

_____

_____

Imagery and Meter

Both the imagery and the meter of "Flannan Isle" are used to create a feeling of mystery or suspense. The **imagery**, or language that appeals to the senses, tells of strange or unnatural sights and sounds. The very regular **meter**, or pattern of stressed and unstressed syllables, moves the reader steadily on toward the disaster just as the rise and fall of the sea moves the rescue party steadily closer.

Understanding Imagery and Meter

Below are images from "Flannan Isle." For each image, circle the letter of the item that best describes it. (To check for stressed syllables, say the line out loud while tapping out its meter with your finger.)

1. "The winter day broke blue and bright"

  a. This sight image is an omen of danger. Both syllables in *winter* are stressed.

  b. This sound image is an omen of danger. Both *day* and *and* are stressed.

  c. This sight image does not predict danger. Both *blue* and *bright* are stressed.

2. "We saw three queer, black, ugly birds—"

  a. This sight image contributes to the feeling of suspense. Only one syllable of *ugly* is stressed.

  b. This sight image contributes to the feeling of suspense. Both syllables of *ugly* are stressed.

  c. This sound image contributes to the feeling of suspense. The second syllable of *ugly* is stressed.

3. "The black, sun-blistered lighthouse door, / That gaped for us ajar"

  a. Suspense builds with this image that appeals to sight. The final syllables of *blistered* and *lighthouse* are stressed.

  b. There is no suspense in this image that appeals to sight. *Gaped* and the first syllable of *ajar* are stressed.

  c. Suspense builds with this sight image. In the phrase *lighthouse door*, both *light* and *door* are stressed.

4. "The feeble chirping of a bird / That starved upon its perch"

  a. This sight image builds the feeling of suspense. *Starved* and *perch* are unstressed.

  b. This sight and sound image builds the feeling of suspense. *Starved* and *perch* are stressed.

  c. This sight and sound image lessens the feeling of suspense. The first syllable in *chirping*

Workbook: Elements of Literature, Third Course

86

HRW material copyrighted under notice appearing earlier in this work.

Applying Skills

Each of the images below creates a certain mood. For each image given, write an original image that creates the opposite mood.

1. Lonely night in a city: The neon sign of the cafe flashed on and off, lighting the face of the lone customer who sat with bowed back and folded arms at the counter.

   Pleasant day in the country: _____

   _____

   _____

   _____

2. Boredom: As the adult voices droned on, the little boy's eyes traced the spider web that draped itself across the windowsill.

   Excitement: _____

   _____

   _____

   _____

Reader's Response

Below are images from "Flannan Isle." Place a check mark next to the image that caused you to feel the most suspense. Then, on the blanks provided, write a suspenseful image of your own involving a lighthouse or a bird.

_____ "And saw the lighthouse towering white, / With blinded lantern that all night / Had never shot a spark"

_____ "But as we neared, they plunged from sight / Without a sound or spurt of white / And still too mazed to speak"

_____ "The feeble chirping of a bird / That starved upon its perch"

_____

_____

_____

_____

THE PEAR TREE   Edna St. Vincent Millay   (page 297)

Theme and Meter

The **theme**, or central idea, of "The Pear Tree" is that beauty may exist even in ugly surroundings. In only forty-three words, the poet conveys both the beauty of the pear tree and the ugliness of its surroundings. In the poem, these words are carefully arranged to create a **meter**, or pattern of stressed and unstressed syllables, that, like nature, is natural rather than mechanical.

Understanding Theme and Meter

I. Below is a list of words about the pear tree. If the word or a form of it was used or might have been used to describe the pear tree, leave it alone. If you think the poet would not use the word to describe the pear tree, cross it out.

1. pure

2. white

3. incredible

4. strange

5. holy

6. light

7. unaware

8. proud

9. clean

10. innocent

11. hidden

12. plain

13. fresh

14. wondrous

15. insignificant

On the blanks provided, write four new phrases that describe the pear tree. For each phrase, use words that you did not cross out in the list above. Say the phrases aloud to yourself until you hear the meter. Then above each stressed syllable write the mark ´ . Above each unstressed syllable write the mark ˘ .

1. _____

_____

2. _____

_____

3. _____

_____

4. _____

_____

Applying Skills

Write several phrases that describe something beautiful found in nature. Select words that reveal the beauty of nature's handiwork. Repeat the phrases aloud until you hear the meter. Above each stressed syllable write the mark ´ . Above each unstressed syllable write the mark ˘ .

Object in nature ______________________________

1. ______________________________

2. ______________________________

3. ______________________________

Reader's Response

Write a brief description of something beautiful that stands apart in ugly surroundings. Choose descriptive words carefully.

Diction and Meter

The **diction**, or word choice, and the **meter**, or pattern of stressed and unstressed syllables, of a poem work together to create an overall effect on the reader. To indicate the metrical pattern of a poem, the stressed or accented syllables are marked with the symbol ´ and the unstressed syllables with the symbol ˘ .

Understanding Diction and Meter

I. On the blanks provided, answer the following questions about the diction and meter of "Woman Work."

1. In the first fourteen lines of the poem, the speaker mentions fourteen things that require her attention. Name those things. If the word is one syllable, indicate that it is stressed with the mark ´ . If the word is two or three syllables, indicate the stressed syllable with the mark ´ and the unstressed syllable or syllables with the mark ˘ . Use your dictionary if you need help.

_____

_____

_____

2. In the first ten lines of the poem, the poet creates ten similar phrases by following the name of a thing with the word *to* and a verb. Write the phrases. Then add the marks for stressed ´ and unstressed ˘ syllables. The first one has been done for you.

chíldrĕn tŏ ténd, _____

_____

_____

3. In the last four stanzas of the poem, the poet mentions fourteen things of nature. Name those things. Then add the marks for stressed ´ and unstressed ˘ syllables. The first one has been done for you.

súnshĭne, _____

_____

_____

II. Below are pairs of sentences about the diction and meter of "Woman Work." Circle the letter of the sentence in each pair that best describes the diction and meter.

1. **a.** The simple diction and the many stressed words sound like they belong to a simple but strong woman used to much work.

   b. The complicated diction and the few stressed words sound like they belong to a simple woman used to much work.

2. **a.** No words in the poem indicate that the speaker is a woman of feeling.

   b. Words like *fiercest wind* and *cold icy kisses* indicate that the speaker is a woman of feeling.

3. **a.** The diction indicates that the speaker likely lives in the rural South.

   b. The diction indicates that the speaker likely lives in the Pacific Northwest.

Applying Skills

Create your own "Student (or Son/Daughter) Work" poem by supplying words for the blanks. As you write, think about the effect you create through your diction.

I've got _____

The _____ to _____

The _____ to _____

The _____ to _____

Then the _____ to _____

I got _____

Then see about _____

And the _____ to _____

Workbook: Elements of Literature, Third Course

HRW material copyrighted under notice appearing earlier in this work.

91

THE FURY OF OVERSHOES   Anne Sexton   (page 300)

Analyzing Theme

Analyzing the **theme**, or central idea, of a poem means looking at the separate elements that combine to create it. In "The Fury of Overshoes," the theme is child versus adult perceptions of life and the insecurities of life. Elements that contribute to this theme include **visual imagery**, language that appeals to the sense of sight, and **diction**, or word choice. "The Fury of Overshoes" is written in **free verse**—that is, without regular rhyme and meter. In free verse, lines are arranged according to meaning or sound rather than meter.

Understanding a Poem's Theme

Below are phrases and lines from "The Fury of Overshoes." For each set of phrases or lines, circle the letter of the statement that best explains its meaning.

1. "They sit in a row / . . .
   . . . black, red, brown"
   a. These lines picture the overshoes lined up outside a kindergarten room door.
   b. These lines picture the overshoes stacked up outside a kindergarten room door.

2. "tears / running down like mud"
   a. Children's tears tend to be thicker than those of adults.
   b. Children are hurt more easily than adults.

3. "Big fish" and "stone frog"
   a. These phrases recreate the loss of innocence by adults.
   b. These phrases compare and contrast adults and children.

4. "Under your bed / sat the wolf / and he made a shadow / when cars passed by / at night"
   a. The wolf is the child's stuffed animal that stays under the bed.
   b. The wolf is the fear of the unknown that all children live with.

5. "Oh, overshoes, / don't you / remember me, /
   pushing you up and down / in the winter snow?"
   a. This image suggests a child wearing overshoes running and jumping and playing in the snow.
   b. This image suggests a child pushing a pair of overshoes up and down the block.

6. "Oh, thumb, / I want a drink, / it is dark"
   a. The poet's purpose in these sentences is probably to recreate the way small children talk.
   b. The poet's purpose in these sentences is probably to personify a part of the body.

7. "where are the big people"
   a. The image "the big people" suggests adults who tower over small children.
   b. The image "the big people" suggests people who are overweight.

8. "when will I get there, / taking giant steps / all day / each day / and thinking / nothing of it?"
   a. By adding the words "each day," the poet balances long and short lines.
   b. By adding the words "each day," the poet makes adulthood seem far away to the child yet somewhat desirable.

Applying Skills

Common objects or experiences often trigger childhood memories and the feelings associated with such memories. For each of the following objects or experiences, briefly describe the childhood memories or feelings you associate with each one.

roller skates _____

_____

the first day of school _____

_____

a teddy bear _____

_____

Halloween _____

_____

a kite _____

_____

Workbook: Elements of Literature, Third Course

HRW material copyrighted under notice appearing earlier in this work.

93

CLEMENTINE   Percy Montross   (page 307)

Rhyme and Alliteration

Repetition contributes to a poem's rhythm. **Rhyme** is the repetition of the sound of a stressed syllable and any syllables that follow. **Alliteration** is another form of repetition often found in poetry. Alliteration is the repetition of the same consonant sound in several words.

As the following example shows, alliteration is not necessarily limited to beginning sounds.

You are lost and gone forever, dreadful sorry, Clementine.

Understanding Rhyme and Alliteration

Identify the alliterations in each of the following lines and tell how each sound contributes to the poem. The number in parenthesis tells you how many different consonant sounds you can expect to find repeated. The first one has been done for you.

1. "Light she was and like a fairy, and her shoes were number nine." (2)

   light, like—suggests light, graceful movement
   _____

   number nine—Like the meaning, it suggests a plodding quality.
   _____

2. "Hit her foot against a splinter, fell into the foaming brine." (2)

   _____

   _____

3. "Ruby lips above the water, blowing bubbles soft and fine," (3)

   _____

   _____

   _____

4. "Alas, for me! I was no swimmer, so I lost my Clementine." (2)

   _____

   _____

5. "In my dreams she still doth haunt me, robed in garments soaked in brine." (3)

   _____

   _____

   _____

Applying Skills

1. Each line of "Clementine" ends with the rhyming sound /īn/. What verb with a sad, complaining sound also rhymes with each line? _____

2. How is this long, complaining sound an appropriate rhyme for the poem and why is it more appropriate than, for instance, a rhyme for *grieve* or *mourn*?

   _____

   _____

3. When the poem is sung as a song, the refrain is repeated after each verse. How does this affect the sound and meaning of the poem?

   _____

   _____

Rhythm and Rhyme

A poem's **rhythm** is the musical quality produced by the repetition of stressed (accented) and unstressed (unaccented) syllables, or by the repetition of other sound patterns. Rhythm may also be created by the use of **rhymes**. A poem's rhythm, along with its rhyme scheme, may create a special feeling or mood, such as humor, melancholy, or joy.

Understanding Rhythm and Rhyme

Compare these two versions of the first stanza of the poem. Then answer the questions that follow.

"The night was thick and hazy   [original]
   When the 'Piccadilly Daisy'
Carried down the crew and captain in the sea;
   And I think the water drowned 'em
5   For they never, never found 'em.
And I know they didn't come ashore with me."

The night was thick and dark   [revision]
   When our old sea-worthy bark
Carried down the crew and captain in the sea;
   And I think they must have drowned
5   For they were never, never found.
And I know they didn't come ashore with me.

1. Write the numbers of the lines that rhyme in each poem.

   original _____

   revision _____

2. What is the syllable pattern for the rhyming words in lines 1 and 2 and lines 4 and 5 in each poem?

   original _____

   _____

   revision _____

3. How does the difference in the syllable pattern of the rhymes affect the tone of each poem?

   original _____

   _____

   revision _____

   _____

Applying Skills

Write at least one humorous stanza of your own following the rhyme and rhythmic pattern of the original poem. You may want to make it a satiric verse about a humorous person, situation, or event.

_____

_____

_____

_____

_____

_____

_____

_____

_____

_____

_____

_____

_____

Exact and Slant Rhymes

Slant rhymes are words that sound alike in some ways, but do not rhyme exactly. They are also called **approximate rhymes**. Instead of a chiming sound, a slant rhyme is a partial echo: "flush" and "flash" or "pain" and "again." **Exact rhymes** are words that repeat the sound of a stressed syllable: "dark" and "bark" or "mind" and "behind."

Understanding Exact and Slant Rhyme Schemes

Find the pairs of rhyming words in the list below and write each pair in the appropriate column. One pair has been done for you.

alive	erase	~~heaven~~	savior
amaze	ever	labor	several
assign	favor	level	shoved
contrive	furrow	loved	sorrow
design	~~given~~	neighbor	weather

EXACT RHYMES	SLANT RHYMES
	heaven, given

Applying Skills

1. In stanza 1 of "I Never Saw a Moor," what are the pairs of slant rhymes used?

_____

What are the exact rhymes in this stanza? _____

2. In stanza 2, what are some examples of slant rhymes used?

_____

What are the exact rhymes in this stanza? _____

Workbook: Elements of Literature, Third Course

98   HRW material copyrighted under notice appearing earlier in this work.

Reader's Response

Emily Dickinson's poem "I Never Saw a Moor" expresses the notion that one can have knowledge of something without ever having experienced it. Describe some experience or belief you hold to be true even though you have never directly experienced it.

_____

_____

_____

_____

_____

_____

_____

_____

_____

_____

_____

_____

_____

_____

Rhyme

Rhyme, the repetition of accented vowel sounds and all sounds following them, plays an important role in a poem. A poet often chooses words for the effects of their sounds. Repeating those sounds within a line (**internal rhyme**) or at the end of lines (**end rhyme**) heightens those effects. Also, the rhyming words tie together parts of the poem.

Understanding Rhyme

I. Below is the first stanza of "Boy at the Window" with blanks for some of the rhyming words. On each blank, write a word (or phrase) that means the same as the word in your text but doesn't rhyme. When you finish, read the stanza aloud to yourself to judge the effect of removing the rhyme. The first one has been done for you.

Seeing the snowman standing all _by himself_ _____

In dusk and cold is more than he can _____ .

The small boy weeps to hear the wind _____

A night of gnashings and enormous _____ .

His tearful _____ can hardly reach to where

The pale-faced figure with bitumen eyes

Returns him such a god-forsaken _____

As outcast Adam gave to _____ .

II. Use the blanks provided to answer the following questions about your version of the poem.

1. In the original version of the poem, the rhyming words *alone* and *moan* heighten the isolation of the snowman. Does your version help readers to feel this isolation? Why or why not?

_____

_____

2. In the original version, the internal rhymes *night* and *sight* (lines 4 and 5) tie together the small boy's listening to the wind in line 4 and his looking at the snowman in line 5. Does your version show that these two sentences are related? Why or why not?

_____

_____

3. In the original version, the internal rhymes *night* and *sight* in the first stanza and *bright* and *light* in the second stanza heighten the contrast between the terrible night for the snowman and the bright light for the boy. Does your version also make you think of the terrible night? Does your version lessen the intensity of the terrible night or does it produce the same effect?

_____

_____

Applying Skills

Below are two limericks with blanks for the rhyming words. Fill in the blanks with the rhyming words that you think complete the limerick.

I set next to the Duchess at tea.

It was just as I feared it would _____ :

    Her rumblings abdominal

    Were simply _____ .

And everyone thought it was _____ .

There was an old man of Peru

Who dreamt he was eating his _____ .

    He awoke in the night

    In a terrible _____ .

And found it was perfectly _____ .

Workbook: Elements of Literature, Third Course

HRW material copyrighted under notice appearing earlier in this work.

101

FIRE AND ICE   Robert Frost   (page 315)

Rhyme and Theme

Rhyme, the repetition of accented vowel sounds, may reveal a poem's **theme,** or central idea, by making the most important words chime in the reader's ear. In "Fire and Ice," the rhyming words are short but powerful and help "sound out" the theme of the poem.

Understanding Rhyme and Theme

Answer the following questions about the poem.

1. Which word has more rhyming lines, *fire* or *ice*? _____

   Do you think this difference is significant to the meaning of the poem? Why or why not?

   _____

   _____

2. How are the sounds of the rhymes for each word appropriate to the meaning the poet assigns to them?
   (HINT: Try saying the words aloud and slightly exaggerating the ending sounds to better understand the relationship between sound and meaning.)
   fire: _____

   ice: _____

3. In which lines of the poem does the poet introduce a new pair of end rhymes?

   _____

4. How do the new rhyming words fit within the tone of the poem?

   _____

   _____

Applying Skills

1. How would you state the theme of the poem?

_____

_____

_____

2. How are the rhymes in the poem suited to the theme?

_____

_____

_____

Reader's Response

Explain what you think the poet means in line 5. Give reasons for your answer.

_____

_____

_____

_____

_____

_____

_____

Analyzing Sound Effects

Poets use sound effects to enhance the music of a poem. **Rhyme**, the repetition of a sound of a stressed syllable and any syllables that follow, is the most commonly used sound effect. Rhymes that sound exactly alike are called **exact rhymes**. Two words that sound alike in some sounds but do not rhyme exactly are called **slant rhymes** (also called **approximate rhymes**). **Internal rhymes** occur inside lines of poetry rather than at the end of lines.

Other sound effects include onomatopoeia and alliteration. **Onomatopoeia** is the use of a word whose sound echoes or imitates a sound—bang, pop, sizzle, slap, etc. **Alliteration** is the repetition of the same consonant sounds in words that are close together, as in, for example: Sally gathers sea shells by the sea shore.

Understanding Sound Effects

Answer the following questions about sound effects in "The Shell."

1. What slant rhyme occurs in stanzas 3 and 4?

   _____

2. What internal rhyme or rhymes occur in stanza 2? _____

   in stanza 10? _____

3. What consonant sound dominates in line 6? _____

   How does this sound relate to the poem's content and meaning?

   _____

   _____

4. What exact rhyme occurs in stanza 5? _____

5. What word in stanza 2 acts as an onomatopoeia? _____

   in stanza 7? _____

6. The rhythm of the poem appears at first irregular, with lines of different lengths. How does the rhythm, in fact, relate to the poem's content and meaning? [Hint: Read at least the first four stanzas aloud to try to capture the movement of the lines.]

   _____

   _____

   _____

7. How does the carry-over of rhyme from one stanza to another relate to the content and movement of the poem?

_____

_____

_____

Applying Skills

Think of a simple object that you strongly associate with a particular place. Write down the feeling that you associate with that object and place, and list sound effects that capture both the setting and your feelings. If you wish, you may use your ideas to create a short poem.

_____

_____

_____

_____

_____

_____

_____

_____

_____

_____

_____

_____

Workbook: Elements of Literature, Third Course

HRW material copyrighted under notice appearing earlier in this work.

105

Ranges of Tone

Tone is the attitude of the speaker toward his or her subject or audience. In real life, we can hear a speaker's tone in the words the speaker chooses and in the sound of his or her voice. In poems we judge the speaker's attitude through the words chosen and the details revealed.

Understanding Ranges of Tone

The attitude of the speaker in "Dear Mrs. McKinney of the Sixth Grade:" toward Mrs. McKinney is alternately admiring, nostalgic, regretful, and sad. The following lines are from the poem. In the blank provided, write the word that best describes the tone of each line: **admiring**, **nostalgic**, **regretful**, or **sad**.

1. "the patient way you taught,
    out of a deep belief and respect
    for learning"

_____

2. "Why didn't I stop, as I could
    see you wanted me to?"

_____

3. ". . . this poem,
    in which only time and loss, not
    you and I, are the subject to be held"

_____

4. "Long after I left that place
    I saw you once"

_____

5. "Hands down, you were my favorite
    teacher"

_____

Applying Skills

Below are some lines of ordinary conversation. For each one, indicate the tone of voice the speaker is likely to use, such as sad, regretful, happy, insincere, sarcastic, and so on. Remember that a line can be spoken with more than one tone; identify all the different tones in which the line of dialogue could be spoken.

1. A teacher says to the class, "Well, I know without asking that all of you have brought in your homework."

_____

2. The question "How are you?" is asked.

_____

Workbook: Elements of Literature, Third Course

106

HRW material copyrighted under notice appearing earlier in this work.

3. A teenager says, "Sure, I'll be glad to wash the car. By the way, could I borrow three dollars?"

_____

4. One friend says to another, "Jane, I'm so sorry that your canary died."

_____

5. As the National Anthem plays, the Olympic Gold Medal winner stands with his or her new medal and silently mouths to the crowd, "Thank you."

_____

6. The late-night disk jockey on the rock station signs on as usual, "All right, you out there in radio land, let's start rocking!"

_____

Tone and Meaning

Tone is the speaker's attitude toward the audience, a subject, or a character. In everyday speech, a speaker's tone helps the listener to determine the meaning of what is said. In a poem, tone also shapes meaning.

Understanding Tone and Meaning

The following lines are from "Out, Out—." Think about the tone of each of the lines within the context of the poem. Then circle the letter of the item that most appropriately conveys the meaning of the line.

1. "And the saw snarled and rattled, snarled and rattled"

   a. The saw was in bad condition.

   b. The sound of the saw foreshadows a tragedy.

2. "Call it a day, I wish they might have said"

   a. The speaker is exhausted by the events of the day.

   b. The speaker wishes the workers had stopped before the accident occurred.

3. " 'Don't let him cut my hand off— / . . . Don't let him, sister!' "

   a. The boy exhibits the strength of someone who refuses to be disabled.

   b. The boy whines helplessly.

4. "He must have given the hand."

   a. The boy allowed his hand to get in the way of the saw.

   b. The saw intentionally cut off the boy's hand.

5. "No more to build on there"

   a. The speaker is cold and indifferent to the loss.

   b. The speaker states the facts simply and directly.

Applying Skills

Imagine that the doctor saved the boy's hand and that the boy, after a long recovery, returned to farm work. Briefly describe how you think the tone of a poem with such an ending might differ from the tone of "Out, Out—."

_____

_____

_____

_____

_____

_____

_____

_____

_____

_____

THE LESSON OF THE MOTH   Don Marquis   (page 330)

Tone in Poetry

"The Lesson of the Moth" consists mostly of a dialogue between two characters: a cockroach and a moth. As it speaks, each character reveals its own attitude, or **tone**, toward its subject and its audience. The cockroach's tone is sarcastic and cynical. The moth's tone is more poetic and philosophical.

Understanding Tone in Poetry

Use the tone of each of the following lines from "The Lesson of the Moth" to determine whether the line is spoken by the cockroach or the moth. On the blank provided, write **cockroach** or **moth**.

_____ 1. "trying to break into / an electric light bulb"

_____ 2. "at times we get tired / . . . we get bored with the routine"

_____ 3. "it is better to be a part of beauty"

_____ 4. "come easy go easy"

_____ 5. "why do you fellows / pull this stunt"

_____ 6. "i wish / there was something i wanted"

Applying Skills

Imagine what the views of life of other animals might be, and what tones of speech they might use to express them. In the spaces below, write brief, first-person statements of the philosophies of the animals listed.

1. Tiger

_____

_____

2. Canary

_____

_____

3. Dolphin

_____

_____

Workbook: Elements of Literature, Third Course

110

HRW material copyrighted under notice appearing earlier in this work.

Reader's Response

Two philosophies of life are expressed in "The Lesson of the Moth." In your own words, express your personal philosophy of life. Do you *always* follow this philosophy?

_____

_____

_____

_____

_____

_____

_____

_____

_____

_____

_____

_____

_____

_____

_____

_____

_____

_____

_____

_____

_____

Tone and Diction

Tone is the speaker's attitude toward a character, subject, or audience. **Diction** is a writer's or speaker's choice of words. A writer's use of diction often helps to define and reinforce the tone of a work.

Understanding Tone and Diction

On the blanks provided, answer the following questions about the poem.

1. Count the words in this poem. How many are there?

_____

2. How many words of one syllable are there?

_____

3. How many words of two syllables are there?

_____

4. How many words of three syllables are there?

_____

5. Which words in the poem are not part of most people's everyday vocabulary?

_____

6. Considering your answers to the questions above, how would you describe the diction of this poem? How does the diction reinforce the poem's tone?

_____

_____

Applying Skills

Think about the characters in this poem. Think about who they might be and what their lives might have been like. Use your imagination freely, but remember the tone and content of the poem.

1. Briefly describe the two characters.

_____

_____

_____

2. Briefly describe what kinds of lives the characters might have led.

_____

_____

_____

_____

3. In a sentence or two, state what you think each character loves about the other.

_____

_____

_____

_____

Reader's Response

1. What did you like about this poem? What did you dislike about the poem?

_____

_____

_____

2. How do you feel about the couple in the poem?

_____

_____

_____

_____

Tone and Meaning

In a poem, **tone** is the speaker's attitude toward a character, subject, or the audience. "Every Good Boy Does Fine," for example, is about the speaker's painful experiences in youth and the insights he gained from them. The pain and the insight are clear in the tone of the poem.

Understanding Tone and Meaning

After each quotation below, circle the letter of the choice that best states the tone *and* meaning of the lines.

1. ". . . playing a wobbly solo,
   I blew up in the coda"
   a. In a self-mocking tone, the speaker tells how much fun he had at the contest.
   b. In a self-mocking tone, the speaker tells how he failed in the contest.
   c. In a nostalgic tone, the speaker tells how he won the contest.

2. "Under the showering voice of the coach, I stood in a towel"
   a. In a sad tone, the speaker confesses how he fooled the coach.
   b. In a happy tone, the speaker confesses how he fooled the coach.
   c. In a witty tone, the speaker tells how the coach scolded him.

3. "tossed free throws till I couldn't move my thumbs"
   a. The speaker describes basketball practice in a somewhat bitter tone.
   b. The speaker describes basketball practice in a grateful tone.
   c. The speaker describes basketball practice in an impersonal tone.

4. "I saw the bald judge slumped in the front row,
   The coach and team at the doorway, the safety man
   Galloping loud at my heels"
   a. In a happy tone, the speaker describes his dreams of success.
   b. In a haunted tone, the speaker describes his dreams of failure.
   c. In a rebellious tone, the speaker expresses his resolve not to fail again.

5. "You who have always horned your way through passages"
   a. In a matter-of-fact tone, the speaker addresses successful people.
   b. In an envious tone, the speaker addresses successful people.
   c. In a loving tone, the speaker addresses unsuccessful people.

6. "They watch me now"
   a. In a serious tone, the speaker says that his youthful experiences have stayed with him.
   b. In a playful tone, the speaker says that his youthful experiences have stayed with him.
   c. In a melancholy tone, the speaker says that he no longer cares about the past.

Applying Skills

1. On the blanks provided, write words that convey the tone of a painful experience (for example, *red* or *blaring*). Write as many words as you can think of quickly.

_____

_____

_____

2. Do the same for a happy experience (for example, *yellow* or *gentle*).

_____

_____

_____

Reader's Response

Describe a situation in which you feel you failed to perform to the best of your abilities. What lessons did you learn from your failure?

_____

_____

_____

_____

_____

_____

_____

_____

_____

_____

_____

_____

_____

Workbook: Elements of Literature, Third Course

CONQUERORS   Henry Treece   (page 336)

Tone and Imagery

In "Conquerors," Henry Treece creates a series of very vivid **images**—that is, pictures, sounds, sense impressions—that convey a somber tone of grief and compassion. He has carefully chosen words whose imagery and whose sounds enhance the somber **tone**, or attitude, of the poem.

Understanding Tone and Imagery

Some images from the poem are quoted below. For each one, answer the question in a way that explains the meaning of the image.

1. "blackened trees"—Why are the trees blackened?

_____

_____

2. "broken pane"—How do you think the pane of glass was broken?

_____

_____

_____

3. "rusting cage"—Why was the cage allowed to rust?

_____

_____

4. "his thin tattered breast . . . / His beak wide open"—What do his thinness and open beak tell you about the dead bird?

_____

_____

5. "weed-grown street"—Why have weeds grown in the street?

_____

_____

6. "gaunt dog"—Why is the dog so thin?

_____

_____

7. "There was not one who did not think of home."—Why?

_____

_____

_____

Applying Skills

Below is a list of objects Treece did *not* include in "Conquerors." Imagine how each one would look if it were found in the village by the soldiers of the poem. Describe each one very briefly, using words that fit the tone of the poem.

1. An automobile

_____

_____

2. A garden in the yard of a house

_____

_____

3. A child's toy

_____

_____

Workbook: Elements of Literature, Third Course

HRW material copyrighted under notice appearing earlier in this work.

117

Tone and Sound Effects

In "Needs," A. R. Ammons takes the language of advertising and turns it into poetry by adding a comic **tone**, or attitude toward his subject. He uses poetic devices to add an extra layer of meaning, by making us think about the words of the ad in a new way. These devices include sound effects such as **rhyme**, **alliteration**, **repetition**, and the use of colorful **adjectives**.

Understanding Tone and Sound Effects

Below is a list of phrases from the poem. Next to each one, put the letter of the poetic device used. (More than one poetic device may be used for each line.)

A – Rhyme   **C** – Repetition

B – Alliteration   **D** – Colorful adjectives

_____ **1.** "mow, throw snow, tow and sow" (line 4)

_____ **2.** "year round use / year after year" (line 2)

_____ **3.** "I want" (at the beginning of each of the first ten lines)

_____ **4.** "an easy spintype recoil starter" (line 7)

_____ **5.** "something suited to my special needs" (line 1)

_____ **6.** "pivoting front axle and extrawide turf tires" (line 9)

_____ **7.** "dozer blade and snowblade & deluxe steering wheel" (line 3)

_____ **8.** "if it's not too much, if I can deserve it, even if I
          can't pay for it I want to mow while riding" (line 11)

_____ **9.** "a console styled dashboard" (line 6)

Workbook: Elements of Literature, Third Course

118   HRW material copyrighted under notice appearing earlier in this work.

Applying Skills

On the blanks provided, rewrite each of the following lines from "Needs" in ordinary prose, without the poetic devices. Notice the difference in the effect.

1. "I want something suited to my special needs"

   _____

   _____

2. "I want something to mow, throw snow, tow and sow with"

   _____

   _____

3. "year round use year after year"

   _____

   _____

Reader's Response

In the space below, write a few lines of magazine advertising copy for a riding mower. Which do you prefer—your copy or the poem?

_____

_____

_____

_____

_____

_____

Workbook: Elements of Literature, Third Course

HRW material copyrighted under notice appearing earlier in this work.

119

Analyzing Tone

The **tone** of a poem—the speaker's attitude toward the character, subject or audience—can be analyzed by looking at individual elements within the poem. These elements include the poet's choice of *details*—what the poet describes—and choice of *wording*—how the poet describes details and images.

Understanding Tone

Some lines from "Highway: Michigan" are printed below. Along with each of the lines is a rewording that changes its tone. As directed, answer the questions about the changes on the blanks provided.

1. Original: "Here from the field's edge we survey
       The progress of the jaded"
   Revised: "We're at the edge of the field, looking at
       The progress of the jaded"

   a. Are any details different in the revised passage, or just the wording?

   _____

   b. Is the tone of the revised passage more casual or more formal than the original passage?

   _____

2. Original: "The drivers from production lines"
   Revised: "The drivers—from production lines, cubicles, and academies"

   a. What details have been added in the revised line?

   _____

   b. Which line seems livelier—the original or the revised?

   _____

3. Original: "They toy with death and traffic fines"
   Revised: "They flirt with speeding tickets"

   a. Have any details been changed in the revised line? Which ones?

   _____

   b. Which version sounds more serious—the original line or the revised one?

   _____

4. Original: "Acceleration is their need"
   Revised: "They've got to go fast"

   a. Have any details been changed in the revised line? Which ones?

   _____

   b. Which version sounds more approving of speeding—the original or the revised line?

   _____

5. Original: "We shiver at the siren's blast"
   Revised: "We listen to the siren's blast"

   a. What one detail has been changed in the revised version?

   _____

   b. In which version does the speaker seem more moved about the accident—the original or the revised line?

   _____

Applying Skills

Suppose you were asked to rewrite "Highway: Michigan" in order to give the poem a lighthearted or jocular tone. Take one stanza from the poem and rewrite it to convey a sense of humor or a much less somber tone.

_____

_____

_____

_____

_____

_____

_____

_____

_____

_____

Workbook: Elements of Literature, Third Course

HRW material copyrighted under notice appearing earlier in this work.

121

Tone

Tone reveals the speaker's attitude toward a character, subject, or the audience. In "Lucinda Matlock," the speaker is a woman who died at the age of ninety-six. As she looks back on her life, her tone is vigorous, defiant, nostalgic, and loving.

Understanding Tone

The following statements are ones that might be made by Lucinda Matlock. Based on her tone in the poem, decide whether Lucinda Matlock would be likely to make each of the statements. If you think that she would have made such a statement, write **yes** on the blank before the statement. If she would not be likely to make the statement, write **no** on the blank.

_____   **1.** "Listen to the wind as it whispers through those tall pines there."

_____   **2.** "Life is what you make of it."

_____   **3.** "I sit. I read. I watch soap operas on television."

_____   **4.** "The death of a child is painful, but life goes on."

_____   **5.** "I don't hold with this dating and flirting that goes on in these high schools today."

_____   **6.** "If we had had organ transplants back then, I might still be alive today."

_____   **7.** "Why, that mollusk shell we found was so thin that you could almost see the moon shine through it."

_____   **8.** "Nothing worthwhile comes easy."

_____   **9.** "After many years together, people often change and grow apart."

_____   **10.** "Life is for the strong of heart."

Applying Skills

Below is a list of adjectives that may or may not convey the tone of the poem "Lucinda Matlock." Circle the adjectives that you think describe the tone of the poem. Then write a sentence or two explaining why these adjectives fit the tone of the poem.

proud	wondrous	bitter
cynical	spiteful	fulfilled
regretful	contented	morose
romantic	joyful	passionate

_____

_____

_____

_____

_____

_____

_____

_____

Reader's Response

The last line of "Lucinda Matlock" states "It takes life to love Life." In your own words, explain the meaning of this line.

_____

_____

_____

_____

_____

Dialogue

Many **ballads** (songs that tell stories) are in the form of **dialogue,** a form of writing in which two or more characters engage in conversation. The reader or listener learns about the characters, the action of the story, the emotions, and even the setting from what the characters themselves say. Because ballads were originally meant to be sung, the dialogue usually contains many repeated lines or stanzas called **refrains.**

Understanding Dialogue

"The Unquiet Grave" contains the dialogue of two characters: a young man and the dead young woman for whom he grieves. In the blanks provided, identify the speaker of each of the following passages from the poem, and paraphrase its meaning in your own words.

1. " 'Oh who sits weeping on my grave,
        And will not let me sleep?' "

_____

_____

2. " 'my breath smells earthy strong' "

_____

_____

3. " 'The wind doth blow today, my love,
        And a few small drops of rain.' "

_____

_____

4. " 'The finest flower that e'er was seen
        Is withered to a stalk.' "

_____

_____

5. " 'So make yourself content, my love,
        Till God calls you away.' "

_____

Applying Skills

Think of a situation in which two characters from different books, movies, or television shows might meet. In the space below, write the dialogue the two might have. Write the dialogue so that a classmate who is not familiar with the two characters would learn about their backgrounds by reading it.

_____

_____

_____

_____

_____

_____

_____

_____

_____

_____

_____

_____

_____

Reader's Response

In "The Unquiet Grave," whose attitude do you feel more sympathy for—the young man's or his dead lover's? Why?

_____

_____

_____

_____

_____

Rhythm

Rhythm is the musical quality produced by the repetition of stressed and unstressed syllables. Ballads usually have strong rhythms because they were composed to be sung. In old ballads, the rhythm is usually much more regular and more strictly observed than in modern poems.

Understanding Rhythm in Poetry

Below are the first three stanzas of "The Demon Lover." In each stanza, the first and third lines have four strongly accented syllables, and the second and fourth lines have three. Put an accent mark above each strongly accented syllable in the stanzas below. The first two lines have been done for you.

" 'O whére have you béen, my lóng, long lóve,

    This lóng seven yeárs and maír?'

'O I'm come to seek my former vows

    Ye granted me before.'

'O hold your tongue of your former vows,

    For they will breed sad strife;

O hold your tongue of your former vows,

    For I am become a wife.'

He turned him right and round about,

    And the tear blinded his ee:

'I wad never hae trodden on Irish ground,

    If it had not been for thee.' "

Applying Skills

The first verse of Shakespeare's song "Spring" has a very regular pattern of stressed and unstressed syllables. Mark the strongly accented syllables as you did those for "The Demon Lover."

"When daisies pied and violets blue,

    And lady-smocks all silver-white,

And cuckoo-buds of yellow hue

    Do paint the meadows with delight,

The cuckoo then, on every tree,

    Mocks married men; for thus sings he,

              'Cuckoo!' "

Suspense and Dialogue

"Edward" builds a suspenseful, dramatic situation by using a question-and-answer format. The action—a murder—has already been committed when the ballad begins. The **suspense**, or anxiety we feel, is built from the way this information is revealed, one piece of information at a time. The fact that Edward sometimes gives false answers heightens the suspense.

Understanding Suspense and Dialogue

For each of the seven stanzas of the poem, state in your own words the question Edward's mother asks him and the answer he gives. (In stanzas 2 and 3, Edward's mother disputes his previous answer rather than asking a new question, but the mother-son dialogue pattern is unchanged.)

Stanza 1:

    Mother's Question: _____

    Edward's Answer: _____

Stanza 2:

    Mother's Question: _____

    Edward's Answer: _____

Stanza 3:

    Mother's Question: _____

    _____

    Edward's Answer: _____

Stanza 4:

    Mother's Question: _____

    Edward's Answer: _____

Stanza 5:

    Mother's Question: _____

    Edward's Answer: _____

Stanza 6:

    Mother's Question: _____

    Edward's Answer: _____

Stanza 7:

Mother's Question: _____

Edward's Answer: _____

Applying Skills

Assume that you are a detective investigating the murder of Edward's father. Write down a false answer Edward's mother might give to the question, "Why did you advise Edward to kill his father?" Write down an objection to this answer. Then write down Edward's mother's true answer. Use your imagination freely, but aim for believability as well.

You: Why did you advise Edward to kill his father? _____

Mother's False Answer: _____

_____

Your Objection: _____

_____

Mother's True Answer: _____

_____

Workbook: Elements of Literature, Third Course

HRW material copyrighted under notice appearing earlier in this work.

129

OLD CHRISTMAS   Roy Helton   (page 361)

Ballads

Ballads contain several literary elements. **Rhythm**, the regular repetition of stressed and unstressed syllables, is always an important element of ballads. The **characters** often reveal anxiety about what will happen in the story. This is known as **suspense**. In addition, conversation between two people, known as **dialogue**, often takes place.

Understanding Ballads

A four-line stanza from "Old Christmas" is reprinted below. Reread the stanza, and answer the questions about the literary elements in the blanks provided.

" 'Now where you been so airly this morning?'

    'Graveyard, Sally Anne.

Up by the trace in the salt-lick meadows

    Where Taulbe kilt my man.' " (p. 361)

1. This stanza contains two speaking characters and two characters who are spoken about. Who are the four characters and what are their relationships?

2. The dialogue is in the form of Appalachian dialect. What three dialect words are in this stanza, and what do they mean?

3. In this stanza a question is both asked and answered. What is the question? What is the answer? How do the question and answer create suspense?

4. a. This stanza contains rhyme and rhythm. What are the rhyming words?

_____

b. How many strong accents are there in the first and third lines? In the second and fourth lines?

_____

5. The stanza describes a scene, using vivid, imagistic language. What is the scene?

_____

6. Repetition is very important in ballads. What are some of the key words in this stanza that are repeated in other parts of the poem? What entire line is repeated in another stanza?

_____

_____

_____

7. What crucial, suspenseful piece of information is not revealed in this stanza or in the rest of the ballad?

_____

Applying Skills

Select another stanza from "Old Christmas" and answer the following questions about the ballad.

1. Which character or characters are speaking?

_____

2. Does the dialogue create suspense? If so, what suspenseful piece of information is revealed?

_____

_____

3. How many strong accents are found in each line of the stanza?

_____

4. What dialect words are in the stanza, and what do they mean?

_____

Workbook: Elements of Literature, Third Course

HRW material copyrighted under notice appearing earlier in this work.

131

Lyric Poetry

A **lyric poem** expresses a speaker's personal emotions or thoughts. It does not necessarily tell a story. Lyric poems are usually short, and they usually tell us more about the speaker than about characters or events.

Understanding Lyric Poetry

I. Listed below are the three people that the speaker in "whom do you visualize as your reader?" imagines as her readers. On the blanks provided, tell what the speaker probably realizes about each person.

1. "the humanities 5 section man"

_____

_____

_____

_____

_____

2. "my mother"

_____

_____

_____

_____

_____

3. "the running back"

_____

_____

_____

_____

_____

Applying Skills

In the space below, name someone whom you might visualize as a reader for a lyric poem of your own. In your own words, explain what you know about your reader and how he or she might react to your poetry. You may want your response to take the form of a lyric poem of your own.

_____

_____

_____

_____

_____

_____

_____

_____

Reader's Response

Do you think poets or writers in general visualize their readers as they are creating a work of literature? What purpose would visualizing one's readers serve?

_____

_____

_____

_____

_____

Theme

The **theme** of a poem is its central idea. It is the statement the poem makes about its subject. The subject of "Success Is Counted Sweetest" is success. Its theme is that success is most appreciated by those who have failed.

Understanding Theme

Based on the **theme** of this poem, consider whether the poet would be likely to agree or disagree with the following statements. Write **agree** or **disagree** in the space provided.

_____ **1.** Those who have succeeded don't think as highly of success because they have experienced its drawbacks.

_____ **2.** When we need or desire something, we don't think about it very much or imagine what it would be like to have it.

_____ **3.** Being denied something we desire makes us want it even more so.

_____ **4.** Most people think that the definition of victory or success is very clear, but it actually isn't.

_____ **5.** We always view victory and defeat clearly.

Applying Skills

Write an imaginary dialogue between someone who has succeeded in some way and someone who has failed. In the dialogue, include the feelings of the individuals about themselves and about each other. Include, also, their feelings about success and about failure.

_____

_____

_____

_____

_____

_____

_____

_____

_____

Workbook: Elements of Literature, Third Course

134

HRW material copyrighted under notice appearing earlier in this work.

Reader's Response

Emily Dickinson is one of the most well-known and loved of all American poets. Yet some of her imagery can be, at times, difficult to grasp. Did you have any problems following Dickinson's lines in "Success Is Counted Sweetest"? Based on your exposure to Dickinson, what is your overall feeling about the poet?

_____

_____

_____

_____

_____

_____

_____

_____

Analyzing Lyric Poetry

When we analyze a **lyric poem**, we take apart its elements of sound and meaning, to see how they work together to express the speaker's personal emotions or thoughts. Important elements in "Those Winter Sundays" include **imagery** (sense impressions), **tone** (attitude), **alliteration** (repeated consonant sounds), and **assonance** (similar vowel sounds).

Understanding Lyric Poetry

Answer the following questions about "Those Winter Sundays" on the blanks provided.

1. Line 6 contains the image "I'd wake and hear the cold splintering, breaking."
   Explain this image in your own words.

   _____

   _____

2. How does the description of the cold in line 6 resemble the description of the father's hands in line 3?

   _____

   _____

3. Line 13 reads, "What did I know, what did I know."
   What is the tone of that line?

   _____

   _____

4. How does the repetition in line 13 help to create that tone?

   _____

   _____

5. Three words in this poem begin with the letter *l*. What are they?

   _____

6. How are all three *l* words connected in similar ways to the father's actions?

_____

_____

7. List as many words as you can find in the first six lines of the poem that have the long *a* sound.

_____

_____

8. List as many words as you can find in the first six lines of the poem that have the *k* or *ck* sound.

_____

_____

Applying Skills

The following stanza of poetry is from "Sea Fever" by John Masefield. Read the excerpt and then identify the literary elements used in the lines of poetry.

> "I must go down to the seas again, for the call of the running tide
> Is a wild call and a clear call that may not be denied;
> And all I ask is a windy day with the white clouds flying,
> And the flying spray and the brown spume, and the sea gulls crying."

1. Describe an image revealed in this stanza.

_____

_____

2. What is the overall tone of these lines of poetry?

_____

_____

3. Give an example of alliteration found in this stanza.

_____

_____

4. List as many words as you can find in these four lines of the poem that have the long *i* sound.

_____

_____

THE GIANT WATER BUG   Annie Dillard   (page 377)

Using Details

Well-chosen details help to strengthen a description. In "The Giant Water Bug," Annie Dillard focuses on a small-scale event, the death of a frog, and describes it in such detail that readers seem to see it through a magnifying glass.

Understanding Details

On the blanks below, answer the following questions about specific details from "The Giant Water Bug."

1. What creatures took off from hiding places "just ahead of your feet, in dire panic"?

_____

_____

2. To the narrator, what detail was most puzzling about the frog who was half in and half out of the water?

_____

_____

3. What part of the frog lay on top of the water after he died?

_____

_____

4. What is the shape of the water bug's forelegs?

_____

_____

5. How does the giant water bug kill its victims?

_____

_____

_____

Applying Skills

Based on the photograph on page 377, write your own detailed description of the conflict between a frog and a giant water bug.

_____

_____

_____

_____

_____

_____

_____

_____

_____

_____

_____

Reader's Response

Annie Dillard is considered a good writer because she is able to make readers visualize, through the use of details, the subjects she describes. In the following passage, underline the details that help you to form a mental image of the frog as it is being attacked by the water bug.

"The spirit vanished from its eyes as if snuffed. His skin emptied and drooped; his very skull seemed to collapse and settle like a kicked tent. He was shrinking before my eyes like a deflating balloon."

Workbook: Elements of Literature, Third Course

HRW material copyrighted under notice appearing earlier in this work.

139

The Humorous Essay

To create his humorous essay, Thurber uses all four kinds of writing: **narration** (telling a story), **description** (creating a mood or emotion, or recreating a person, place, thing, event, or experience), **exposition** (informing, defining, or clarifying), and **persuasion** (aiming to convince the reader of something).

Understanding the Humorous Essay

Below are five passages from "The Night The Bed Fell." On the blanks provided, write down which of the kinds of writing Thurber uses for comic effect: **narration**, **description**, **exposition**, or **persuasion**.

1. "It happened, then, that my father had decided to sleep in the attic one night, to be away where he could think." (p. 379)

   _____

2. "My mother opposed the notion strongly because, she said, the old wooden bed up there was unsafe; it was wobbly and the heavy headboard would crash down on father's head in case the bed fell, and kill him." (p. 379)

   _____

3. "It makes a better recitation . . . than it does a piece of writing . . . . Still it did take place." (p. 379)

   _____

4. "It left me still warmly bundled up and unhurt, for the bed rested above me like a canopy." (p. 380)

   _____

5. "The layout of the rooms and the disposition of their occupants is important to an understanding of what later occurred." (p. 380)

   _____

Applying Skills

Create another character who is a member of the family in Thurber's essay. In the space provided, describe what he or she did on the night the bed fell. Use at least two kinds of writing in your account.

_____

_____

_____

_____

_____

_____

_____

_____

_____

_____

_____

_____

Reader's Response

Would you like to have been a member of the Thurber family? Why or why not?

_____

_____

_____

_____

_____

_____

Workbook: Elements of Literature, Third Course

Description

Description is a kind of writing whose purpose is to create a mood or emotion, or to recreate a person, a place, a thing, an event, or an experience.

Understanding Description

Below is a series of descriptions from "The Washwoman." Answer the question about each one on the space provided.

1. "Every piece of linen sparkled like polished silver. Every piece was neatly ironed." (p. 384)
   What is Singer telling us about the washwoman?

   _____

   _____

2. ". . . the snow was dry as salt and the air was filled with dusty white whirlwinds, like goblins dancing in the cold." (pp. 386-387)
   What mood do you think the author creates by describing the cold this way?

   _____

   _____

3. "Under the bundle tottered the old woman, her face as white as a linen sheet." (p. 387)
   What is the author telling us about the woman's physical condition?

   _____

   _____

4. "The branches of the trees looked like glass." (p. 387)
   How can tree branches look like glass?

   _____

   _____

5. "If one of us had something in his eye, Mother would lick the eye clean with her tongue." (p. 386)
   What is the author telling the reader about his mother?

   _____

   _____

Applying Skills

Good descriptions create vivid pictures in the reader's mind. However, no two readers see exactly the same mental picture, nor do they recreate exactly the same picture that was in the writer's mind. Without referring to the essay again, describe in your own words the washwoman as you see her in your mind. Use the space provided.

_____

_____

_____

_____

Reader's Response

The author describes the old washwoman with affection and admiration. What one detail about the washwoman did you find to be the most moving? Explain.

_____

_____

_____

_____

Workbook: Elements of Literature, Third Course

HRW material copyrighted under notice appearing earlier in this work.

143

CHARLEY IN YELLOWSTONE   John Steinbeck   (page 389)

Facts and Opinions

A **fact** is a statement of truth or of something that actually happened. An **opinion** is a statement expressing a personal reaction or belief. Writers of personal essays often have opinions they want to share with the reader. Opinions, however, are only convincing if they are supported by facts.

Understanding Facts and Opinions

Below is a series of passages from "Charley in Yellowstone." On the blanks provided, label each one **Fact** or **Opinion**.

1. "Yellowstone National Park is no more representative of America than is Disneyland."
   (p. 389)

   _____

2. ". . . I saw a bear beside the road, and it ambled out . . . ." (p. 391)

   _____

3. ". . . a well-favored bear can bat a dog like a tennis ball." (p. 391)

   _____

4. "He became a primitive killer lusting for the blood of his enemy . . . ." (p. 391)

   _____

5. "I am certain that if he were released he would have charged every bear we passed and found victory or death." (p. 391)

   _____

6. "He couldn't eat his dinner, he refused the evening walk, and once we were in he collapsed on the floor and went to sleep." (p. 391)

   _____

7. ". . .we enclose and celebrate the freaks of our nation and of our civilization." (p. 389)

   _____

Applying Skills

In the space provided, briefly tell the story of Charley in Yellowstone from Charley's first-person point of view. Include both facts about the experience and Charley's opinions about the bears, Yellowstone Park, and Steinbeck. Underline each fact and each opinion in your account of the story, and label it **F** (fact) or **O** (opinion).

_____

_____

_____

_____

_____

_____

_____

_____

_____

_____

_____

_____

_____

_____

_____

_____

_____

_____

_____

Purposes for Reports

In writing *Coming into the Country*, John McPhee has three separate purposes: (**1**) to establish his own credibility as a writer and researcher, (**2**) to make the report interesting through the use of suspenseful details, and (**3**) to make the survival of Leon Crane believable.

Understanding Purposes for Reports

Below are sets of details from *Coming into the Country*. In the space before each set of details, write the number given above that corresponds to McPhee's purpose. (For example, write **1** if the purpose is to establish the writer's credibility, etc.)

____ **1.** "At length, I was given the name of Gerard Hasselwander, a historian at the Albert F. Simpson Historical Research Center, Maxwell Air Force Base, Alabama." (p. 399)

____ **2.** "Since the plane was falling like a swirling leaf, he had to drag himself against heavy centrifugal force toward the open bomb bay. He had never used a parachute. The outside air temperature was at least thirty degrees below zero. When he jumped, he forgot his mittens." (p. 400)

____ **3.** "He was telling me some of this on a sidewalk in Philadelphia when I asked him how he had dealt with fear." (p. 400)

____ **4.** "It was Alaskan custom always to leave a cabin open and stocked for anyone in need. Split firewood was there, and matches, and a pile of prepared shavings. On a table were sacks of dried raisins, sugar, cocoa, and powdered milk." (p. 401)

____ **5.** "He scraped together some twigs, but his cut and bare hands were shaking so—at roughly fifty below zero—that he failed repeatedly to ignite a match. He abandoned the effort, and moved on through the snow. He kept hitting boulders." (p. 401)

____ **6.** "He developed a routine, with meals twice a day, a time for hunting, a fresh well chopped daily through the four-foot river ice. He slept eighteen hours a day, like a wintering bear. . . ." (p. 402)

____ **7.** "He came to a lead one day, a patch of open water, and, trying to use some boulders as stepping stones, he fell in up to his armpits. Coming out, barging through snowdrifts, he was the center of a fast-forming block of ice." (p. 402)

____ **8.** "If he stayed, he would starve. He felt panic now. . . ." (p. 402)

Applying Skills

Think of a real or imaginary person who has been in an unusual or difficult situation. In the space provided, write a brief report about the person and the situation. Details in the report should establish your credibility and should make the report interesting and believable.

_____

_____

_____

_____

_____

_____

_____

_____

_____

_____

_____

_____

_____

_____

_____

_____

_____

_____

_____

_____

Objectivity vs. Subjectivity

An **objective** report emphasizes the facts of a subject without personal comment by the author. In **subjective** reporting, the author's personal feelings become part of the report. Both objectivity and subjectivity have their place in reporting. What is important is for readers to learn the difference between the two.

Understanding Objectivity vs. Subjectivity

Below are quotations from *Everything in Its Path*. On the blanks provided, label each one **Subjective** or **Objective**.

1. "At one minute before 8:00, the dam simply collapsed." (p. 409)

   _____

2. "I cannot explain that water as being water . . . . The water seemed like the demon itself."
   (p. 411)

   _____

3. "I was about a hundred and fifty feet above where the water came out. It was burning there, and when the water hit the fire, it shot right through the air about two hundred feet . . . ."
   (p. 410)

   _____

4. "The wreckage of hundreds of homes and other buildings was strewn all over the landscape . . . ." (p. 415)

   _____

5. ". . . . soft flakes of snow curled into the valley, as if to accentuate the blackness below and to mock their misery." (p. 415)

   _____

6. "The idea itself was sound in principle, and the agency did a remarkable job of administering it." (p. 419)

   _____

Workbook: Elements of Literature, Third Course

148   HRW material copyrighted under notice appearing earlier in this work.

Applying Skills

Below are some passages from the essay, labeled either *Subjective* or *Objective*. Rewrite the subjective ones so that they become objective. Rewrite the objective ones so that they become subjective. The first one has been done for you.

1. Subjective: " 'We were like a litter of puppies .... wet and cold, with no place to go.' " (p. 415)
   Objective: "We were wet and cold and felt that we had no place to go." _____

2. Subjective: " 'He just looked like a walking piece of dirt.' " (p. 416)
   Objective: _____

3. Objective: " 'I went into the bathroom and stepped on a body at the door, so I just got out of there.' " (p. 419)
   Subjective: _____

   _____

4. Objective: "Middle Fork was full of slag." (p. 408)
   Subjective: _____

Reader's Response

What one image of the disaster at Buffalo Creek sticks in your mind most powerfully?

_____

_____

Is the image described subjectively or objectively in the text? Explain.

_____

_____

_____

_____

Workbook: Elements of Literature, Third Course

HRW material copyrighted under notice appearing earlier in this work.

149

Analyzing Reports

When we analyze a report, we break it into its elements. In "Annapurna," these literary elements include the use of figurative language, including **similes** and **metaphors**, and images to heighten suspense. They also include **characterization** and **conflict**.

Understanding Reports

On the blanks provided answer the following questions about the literary elements of "Annapurna."

I. Each of the following passages from "Annapurna" helps build suspense. Identify the device used in each passage by Herzog to build this suspense: **simile, metaphor,** or **descriptive imagery.**

1. ". . . my wooden feet kept slipping on the ice wall . . . ." (p. 426)

_____

2. "I turned round and round like a puppet." (p. 424)

_____

3. "Through the swirling mist I sometimes caught glimpses of the two Sherpas . . . ." (p. 427)

_____

4. "I heard a queer crack and supposed I must have broken something . . . ." (p. 426)

_____

II. On the blank provided, write whether you think Herzog views each of the following characters as **heroic** or **unheroic.**

1. Lachenal: ". . . he frequently stopped and moaned about his feet." (p. 424)

_____

2. Sarki: ". . . without a second's hesitation Sarki gave his own [sunglasses] to Rébuffat." (p. 426)

_____

3. Herzog: " . . . if I let go, we should all fall to the bottom: if I held on, what would remain of my hands? I decided to hold on." (p. 426)

_____

III. On the blank provided, write whether each of the following passages describes an **internal conflict** (within a character's mind) or an **external conflict** (between a character and some outside force).

1. "Every minute I felt like giving up; and why, anyway, should I go on when for me everything was over?" (p. 426)

_____

2. "We now come to the first wall. How on earth should we get down?" (p. 426)

_____

3. "Every inch was a torture I was resolved to ignore." (p. 426)

_____

Applying Skills

Identify the literary element revealed in each of the following passages from "Annapurna." Write **figurative language, characterization**, or **conflict** on the blank to identify each excerpt.

1. "I crashed into solid ice as I went hurtling from one serac to another, and the snow crushed me down." (p. 424)

_____

2. "Seeing him walk like this made my heart ache . . . ." (p. 426)

_____

3. "The sun was at its height, the weather brilliant and the colors magnificent." (p. 424)

_____

4. "With infinite sorrow, he whispered: 'Poor Bara Sahib—Ah . . .' " (p. 428)

_____

Workbook: Elements of Literature, Third Course

HRW material copyrighted under notice appearing earlier in this work.

151

Attitude

The writer's **attitude**, or viewpoint toward the subject, is usually apparent. Biographers, for example, sometimes admire the people about whose lives they write and sometimes do not. Often they have mixed feelings about their subjects.

Understanding Attitude

Joseph P. Lash regards his subject, Annie Sullivan, as a woman of great courage who overcame enormous obstacles in her life. Below are details from "Annie." Circle the numbers of the sentences which contain details that make Lash's attitude toward his subject apparent.

1. "For Annie there was only one event in history, the Great Famine in Ireland of 1847 that had subsequently driven her impoverished young parents, like thousands of others, to the United States." (p. 437)

2. "Annie was born in April 1866 in Feeding Hills, a village outside of Springfield, Massachusetts, in circumstances of poverty that were not uncommon among Irish immigrants." (p. 437)

3. "She awoke suddenly in the middle of the night and, sensing the empty space next to her, knew immediately what had happened. She began to tremble. She crept to the dead room and, feeling his cold body under the sheets, began to scream, waking everyone." (p. 441)

4. " 'Very much of what I remember about Tewksbury is indecent, cruel, melancholy,' she told Nella Braddy fifty years later, 'gruesome in the light of grown-up experience . . . .' " (p. 442)

5. "Not long after Jimmy's death, an estrangement from the Church began." (p. 441)

6. "A sense that she was different, that she wanted something more from life than these women did, was always with her." (p. 442)

7. "That day—October 7, 1880—she entered the Perkins Institution for the Blind." (p. 444)

Workbook: Elements of Literature, Third Course

152   HRW material copyrighted under notice appearing earlier in this work.

Applying Skills

Think of person, from real life or from a book, movie, or television, whom you admire. On the blanks below, write a paragraph about that person, using details that make your attitude toward the person apparent.

_____

_____

_____

_____

_____

_____

_____

_____

Reader's Response

What effect has reading "Annie" had on your own attitude toward Annie Sullivan? In the space below, jot down at least four adjectives describing Annie Sullivan that reveal your attitude toward Lash's subject.

_____

_____

_____

_____

BARRIO BOY   Ernesto Galarza   (page 446)

Narration in Autobiography

There are four major modes, or techniques of writing: **narration** (tells what happened), **description** (creates a mood or emotion), **exposition** (explains or gives information), and **persuasion** (seeks to convince the reader of something). Each of these modes has a separate purpose although writers usually blend the modes together in their writing. For example, an **autobiography**, an account of the writer's own life, would make frequent use of the mode of narration, though it may contain examples of the other modes as well.

Understanding Narration in Autobiography

Below is a list of sentences from "Barrio Boy." Circle the numbers of those sentences that are *not* primarily narrative. (For example, number 1 is circled because it is mainly description, not narration.)

1. "It was a new building, painted yellow, with a shingled roof. . . ." (p. 446)

2. "Matti told the class about his mother's down quilt. . . ." (p. 449)

3. "Off the school grounds we traded the same insults we hear from our elders." (p. 449)

4. "Now it was my turn to be excused from class to interpret for a parent enrolling a new student fresh from Mexico." (p. 450)

5. "Homer was a chunky Irishman who dressed as if every day was Sunday." (p. 449)

6. "He was brown like us, a plump kid with shiny black hair combed straight back, neat, cool, and faintly obnoxious." (p. 448)

7. "I astounded the third grade with the story of my travels on a stagecoach. . . ." (p. 449)

8. ". . . La Leen-Con. . . became a benchmark in our lives, like the purple light of the Lyric Theater and the golden dome of the Palacio de Gobierno. . . ." (p. 450)

9. "The entire school witnessed sizzling Americanism in its awful majesty one morning at flag salute." (p. 450)

10. "At Lincoln, making us into Americans did not mean scrubbing away what made us originally foreign." (p. 449)

11. "She strode to a door in the far corner of the office, opened it , and called a name." (p. 448)

12. "Her radiant, no-nonsense character made us either afraid not to love her or love her so we would not be afraid." (p. 449)

Applying Skills

I. On the blanks provided, write down the story of how you got to school this morning and what happened to you on the way. Use mainly the mode of narration, with no unnecessary descriptions.

_____

_____

_____

_____

_____

_____

_____

_____

_____

_____

II. Choose one detail from your narrative account and, on the blank lines below, write a sentence or two describing it more fully by recreating the mood or emotion involved. Decide where it would fit in the narrative. Would it add to or detract from the story?

_____

_____

_____

_____

_____

_____

_____

_____

_____

_____

THE PHANTOM OF YAZOO   Willie Morris   (page 452)

Combining Modes in Nonfiction

The four modes of writing are **narration** (storytelling), **description** (creating a mood or recreating someone or something through physical details), **exposition** (explaining, giving information, or defining ideas), and **persuasion** (trying to convince the reader to think or act in a certain way). These modes of writing apply to both works of fiction and works of nonfiction.

Understanding Modes of Nonfiction

Below are three groups of sentences from "The Phantom of Yazoo." All the sentences in each group are examples of one mode of writing. On the blanks provided, identify the mode for each group.

Group I

1. "If there was no winner, the next day's pot would go up a dollar." (p. 453)

2. "I learned that I was listening to the Armed Forces Radio Service, which broadcast games played in New York." (p. 455)

3. "At Bozo's grocery store I was a full-scale oracle." (p. 458)

4. "My main concern that earlier summer, however, lay in the more academic aspects of the game." (p. 452)

_____

Group II

1. "I can see the town now on some hot, still weekday afternoon in midsummer: ten thousand souls and nothing doing." (p. 453)

2. "In his simian posture he would catch the ball and toss it lightly into the air and then whip his mitt off and catch the ball in his bare left hand. . . ." (p. 453)

3. "The one o'clock whistle at the sawmill would send out its loud bellow, reverberating up the streets to the bend in the Yazoo River, hardly making a ripple in the heavy somnolence." (p. 455)

4. "Some of the old crowd was there, but the atmosphere was grim." (p. 459)

_____

Group III

1. "Then a curious thing happened." (p. 455)

2. "One day, when the jackpot was a mere two dollars, the announcer tried to confuse me." (p. 453)

3. "I decided not to try out for the American Legion Junior Baseball team that summer." (p. 452)

4. "Then I went back home and took more notes from the shortwave." (p. 457)

_____

Applying Skills

Identify the mode of writing for each of the sentences below.

1. There are four modes of writing. _____

2. Every educated person must be able to recognize the four modes of writing.

_____

3. The lyrical, flowing quality of her prose gave the description a nostalgic tone.

_____

4. Then the writer decided to add some description to his narration.

_____

Workbook: Elements of Literature, Third Course

HRW material copyrighted under notice appearing earlier in this work.

157

Figurative Language

Maya Angelou uses both figurative language and vivid, unusual adjectives to make her story more compelling. The figurative language that she uses includes **personification**, a kind of metaphor in which a nonhuman thing or quality is given human characteristics, and **simile**, a figure of speech that makes a comparison between two unlike things, using an explicit word such as *like*, *as*, *resembles*, or *than*.

Understanding Figurative Language

I.   Answer the questions about the following examples of personification.

1.   "the noon sun called the workers to rest" (p. 463):
How can the sun call people? _____

_____

2.   "the early morning air forced its way in" (p. 463):
How can the air force its way in? _____

_____

3.   " I had seen the fingers cut by the mean little cotton bolls. . . ." (p. 464)
What impression is created by describing the cotton bolls as "mean"?

_____

_____

II.   Here are some unusual adjectives Maya Angelou uses to describe things: "sleep-filled voice," "caterpillar green," "tender mornings," "heavy knowledge." Explain each of them in your own words on the blanks below. The first one has been done for you.

1.   "caterpillar green" (p. 463):   a pale, yellowish green

2.   "sleep-filled voice" (p. 463): _____

_____

3.   "tender mornings" (p. 463): _____

_____

4.   "heavy knowledge"(p. 464): _____

III. Answer the questions about the following similes in the space provided.

1. "I sensed a wrongness around me, like an alarm clock that had gone off without being set." (p. 467) Do you think this is an effective simile? Why or why not?

_____

_____

_____

2. ". . . hand over hand, like a man climbing out of a dream." (p. 467) How can a person climb out of a dream?

_____

_____

Applying Skills

On the blanks provided, write down the most unusual adjectives you can think of for the following nouns. Then explain what the image means to you.

1. a _____ evening

_____

2. a _____ song

_____

3. a _____ friend

_____

4. a _____ house

_____

5. a _____ hamburger

_____

Workbook: Elements of Literature, Third Course

HRW material copyrighted under notice appearing earlier in this work.

159

Elements of Autobiography

An **autobiography** is a factual recollection or an account of a writer's own life. Yet it often shares many of the same elements of a fictional story, such as **plot**, **characterization**, and **point of view**. To analyze an autobiography, one should be aware of how these elements work together to tell a story.

Understanding Elements of Autobiography

As directed, answer the following questions about the literary elements of *Life on the Mississippi*.

I. Plot is the series of related events that make up the story. Number the following events 1-4 to show the order in which they happen.

_____ "The boy started out and even had his foot on the upper step outside the door, when Brown, with a sudden access of fury, picked up a ten-pound lump of coal and sprang after him . . . ."

_____ "On the evening of the sixth day his wandering mind busied itself with matters far away, and his nerveless fingers 'picked at his coverlet.' His hour had struck; we bore him to the death room, poor boy."

_____ "I still remember the first time I ever entered the presence of that man [Brown]."

_____ "When Mr. Wood and Henry fell in the water they struck out for shore, which was only a few hundred yards away; but Henry presently said he believed he was not hurt . . . ."

II. Characterization, the process of revealing a character's personality, is important in autobiography. Circle the numbers of adjectives that describe each of the following characters.

Brown	Henry
1. hateful	1. inoffensive
2. incompetent	2. selfish
3. horse-faced	3. vain
4. unreasonable	4. brave
5. abusive	5. ill-fated

III. Point of view is the vantage point from which the writer tells the story. *Life on the Mississippi* is written from the first-person point of view of Mark Twain. Think how the story might differ from another character's viewpoint. On the space below, write Brown's first-person account of why he left the *Pennsylvania*.

_____

_____

_____

_____

_____

Applying Skills

Explain in your own words why an autobiography, which is supposed to be a true account of the writer's life, should contain the basic literary elements—plot, characterization, and point of view—of a work of fiction.

_____

_____

_____

_____

_____

_____

Workbook: Elements of Literature, Third Course

HRW material copyrighted under notice appearing earlier in this work.

161

THE MIRACLE WORKER, Act One   William Gibson   (page 494)

Exposition in Drama

Exposition in a drama is the part of a play that gives the audience information about the characters, their situation, and their basic conflicts.

Understanding Exposition

On the blanks provided, tell what important information about characters, situations, or conflicts each of the following speeches from *The Miracle Worker* gives us.

1. **Doctor**. She'll live. (p. 495)

_____

_____

2. **James** (*blandly*). She only dug Martha's eyes out. Almost dug. It's always almost, no point worrying till it happens, is there? (p. 497)

Information about Helen: _____

_____

Information about James: _____

_____

3. **Anagnos**. Annie, be—humble. It is not as if you have so many offers to pick and choose. (p. 500)

_____

_____

4. **Aunt Ev**. Well, if it's just a question of money, Arthur, now you're marshal you have this Yankee money. Might as well— (p. 497)

_____

_____

5. **Annie**. Well. I suppose I can wait one more mile. But don't be surprised if I get out to push the horse! (p. 504)

_____

_____

Workbook: Elements of Literature, Third Course

162   HRW material copyrighted under notice appearing earlier in this work.

Applying Skills

Imagine that you are eating in a fast-food restaurant and you overhear two teenagers at another table having the following conversation:

First teenager: You mean he asked her to the dance? But I thought he was going with Kimberly.

Second teenager: That's what Kimberly thought, too.

First teenager: Uh-oh. And Dawn said yes? I thought she didn't like him.

Second teenager: Well, she changed her mind, all right?

First teenager: But didn't Daniel ask her?

Second teenager: He thought he didn't *have* to ask her. He thought it was like *assumed* that she would go with him.

First teenager: Uh-oh. What do you think's gonna happen?

1. In the space below, list every piece of information you have learned from your eavesdropping.

_____

_____

_____

_____

_____

_____

2. In the space below, tell what you haven't learned that you are still curious about.

_____

_____

_____

_____

_____

Workbook: Elements of Literature, Third Course

HRW material copyrighted under notice appearing earlier in this work.

163

Conflict in Drama

Conflict is the struggle between characters or opposing forces. In an **external conflict** one character struggles against another, or against something in the environment. An **internal conflict**, on the other hand, takes place entirely within the character's mind.

Understanding Conflict

Each of the speeches below highlights one of the major conflicts in *The Miracle Worker*. The characters involved in the conflict have been identified for you (for example, "*Annie* vs. *Helen*"). On the blanks provided, explain the conflict as it is revealed in the dialogue.

1. *Annie* vs. *Helen*
   Annie. But, I, shall, insist, on, reasonable, obedience, from the start— (p. 514)

   _____

   _____

2. *Annie* vs. *Captain Keller*
   Annie. I can't *un*teach her six years of pity if you can't stand up to one tantrum! Old Stonewall, indeed. (p. 518)

   _____

   _____

   _____

   _____

3. *Kate* vs. *Captain Keller*
   Kate. She did fold her napkin. She learns, she learns, do you know she began talking when she was six months old? (p. 527)

   _____

   _____

4. *Captain Keller* vs. *James Keller*
   Keller. He can't bear me, you'd think I treat him as hard as this girl does Helen— (p. 531)

   _____

   _____

Applying Skills

Imagine that you have been shipwrecked on a desert island with one other person. No one has come to your rescue, and there is no land within hundreds of miles. Now imagine a conflict that might develop. Perhaps it is an internal conflict that you alone experience. Or perhaps it is an external conflict between you and the other person or between you and forces in your environment. On the space below, write a dialogue that reveals something of the conflict.

_____

_____

_____

_____

_____

_____

_____

_____

_____

_____

_____

_____

_____

_____

Characterization and Dialogue

In drama, the characters often reveal something about themselves by the way they look and dress on stage. The personalities of characters are mostly revealed, however, through **dialogue,** or the words that they speak.

Understanding Characterization and Dialogue

Below are excerpts of dialogue of major characters in *The Miracle Worker*. On the blanks provided, answer the questions about what is revealed about the characters in these excerpts.

1. **Annie** (*presently*). I taught her one thing, no. Don't do this, don't do that— (p. 539)
   What does this excerpt tell us about Annie?

   _____

   _____

2. **Aunt Ev.** Oh, let her stay, my goodness, she's only a child, she doesn't have to wear a napkin if she doesn't want to her first evening—
   Annie (*level*). And ask outsiders not to interfere.
   What does this exchange tell us about Aunt Ev? (p. 541)

   _____

   _____

   What does it tell us about Annie?

   _____

   _____

3. **Keller** (*tolerant*). I'm afraid you're the difficulty, Miss Annie. Now I'll keep her to what she's learned, you're quite right there—but I don't see that we need send her from the table, after all, she's the guest of honor. Bring her plate back. (p. 541)
   What does this speech tell us about Captain Keller?

   _____

   _____

4. Helen. Wah. Wah. (*And again, with great effort.*) Wah. Wah. (p. 542)

What does this excerpt tell us about Helen?

_____

_____

_____

Applying Skills

Imagine that two people are waiting for a bus. One asks the other what time it is. They begin talking about the fact that the bus is late, expressing their feelings about waiting for buses. However, they do not tell each other anything specific about the rest of their lives. On the blanks below write their conversation so that readers can tell that they have two distinct personalities.

_____

_____

_____

_____

_____

_____

_____

_____

_____

_____

_____

_____

_____

Workbook: Elements of Literature, Third Course

VISITOR FROM FOREST HILLS   Neil Simon   (page 551)

Farce

Farce is a type of comedy in which the emphasis is on ridiculous situations and comical physical actions. The characters tend to be one-dimensional **stereotypes**. In *Visitor from Forest Hills* much of the dialogue is farcical, with outlandish exaggerations and comparisons.

Understanding Farce

Below are pairs of lines from *Visitor from Forest Hills*. In each pair, circle the letter of the line that is more farcical.

1. a. **Norma.** Now, I want you to come out of that bathroom and get married.
   b. **Norma.** If you want, I'll have it annulled next week, but please come out and get married! (p. 552)

2. a. **Roy.** I don't hear a peep out of her. Is there a window in there? Maybe she tried something crazy.
   b. **Norma.** That's right. Tell a woman who's having a heart attack that her daughter jumped out the window. (p. 554)

3. a. **Norma.** Wouldn't I have heard the water running?
   b. **Roy.** With that hat you couldn't hear Niagara Falls! (p. 555)

4. a. **Roy.** I think you know I'm not a violent man. I can be stern and strict, but I have never once been violent. Except when I'm angry.
   b. **Norma.** It's true, darling, your father is very angry. (p. 556)

5. a. **Roy.** I break every bone in my body and you come out for 'Cool it' ?
   b. **Roy.** *Now* you're ready? *Now* you come out? (p. 562)

Applying Skills

Each of the following lines from *Visitor from Forest Hills* is farcical. On the blanks provided, rewrite the line by removing or changing the outrageous tone but retain the overall meaning of the line. The first one has been done for you.

1. "Are you coming out or do we have the wedding in the bathroom?" (p. 554)

   Are you coming out or not?

   _____

2. "I'm not coming in, Mimsy, because I have a broken arm." (p. 555)

   _____

   _____

3. "I find it funny that I hired a photographer for three hundred dollars. I find it hysterical that the wedding pictures are going to be you and me in front of a locked bathroom!" (p. 557)

_____

_____

4. "You don't need me. You need a rhinoceros with a blowtorch—because no one else can get into that bathroom." (p. 560)

_____

_____

THE MOTHER   Paddy Chayefsky   (page 567)

Conflict, Complication, and Resolution

The **conflict** in a story is often a struggle or clash between opposing characters or opposing forces. The **complication** is the part of the story in which characters take some action to resolve the conflict and deal with the problem presented. The **resolution** is the way the problem or conflict is finally worked out.

Understanding Conflict, Complication, and Resolution

Below are speeches from different parts of *The Mother*. On the blanks provided, write **conflict**, **complication**, or **resolution** to indicate which part of the play is represented by the speech.

1. **Son-in-law.** Look, Annie, I don't wanna tell you how to treat your own mother, but why don't you leave her alone? It's obviously very important to her to get a job for herself. (p. 569)

   _____

2. **Daughter.** We'll move Tommy into the baby's room, and you can have Tommy's room. (p. 571)

   _____

3. **Old Lady.** Will you stop hovering over me like I was a cripple in a wheel chair? I can make my own coffee. . . . (p. 570)

   _____

4. **Boss.** Fire her! Fire her! Fire her! (p. 581)

   _____

5. **Daughter.** George, let's drop the kids at your sister's for a week or ten days and drive down to Virginia. You don't want to spend your one vacation a year sitting in New York, watching it rain. (p. 585)

   _____

Applying Skills

The dialogue below is from the resolution of an imaginary play. On the blanks provided, describe an imaginary conflict and complication for the resolution.

Edwin.   Don't look back, look forward. We'll never have to go back there again.

Marlana. The sun is shining. Evil has been conquered. And you and I . . .?

Edwin.   I misunderstood you. But now—and forever—I understand.

Conflict

_____

_____

_____

_____

Complication

_____

_____

_____

_____

Blank Verse, Rhymed Verse, and Prose

Shakespeare usually wrote in a form of poetry called **blank verse**, or unrhymed **iambic pentameter**. "Blank" means that the poetry is not rhymed. "Iambic pentameter" refers to the fact that each line contains five **iambs**, or metrical feet, consisting of a stressed syllable followed by an unstressed syllable. Sometimes, however, Shakespeare used **rhymed verse** especially for romantic or heroic speeches. At times he did not use verse at all, but instead wrote **prose** (ordinary written or spoken language), especially for servant roles and for comic scenes.

Understanding Blank Verse, Rhymed Verse, and Prose

Below are speeches from the first act of *Romeo and Juliet*. On the blanks provided write **blank verse**, **rhymed verse**, or **prose** to indicate the kind of language used in the speech.

1. "Oh, she doth teach the torches to burn bright!
   It seems she hangs upon the cheek of night
   As a rich jewel in an Ethiop's ear—
   Beauty too rich for use, for earth too dear!" (p. 624)

   _____

2. "Three civil brawls, bred of an airy word
   By thee, old Capulet, and Montague,
   Have thrice disturbed the quiet of our streets" (p. 607)

   _____

3. "From forth the fatal loins of these two foes
       A pair of star-crossed lovers take their life;
   Whose misadventured piteous overthrows
       Doth with their death bury their parents' strife." (p. 603)

   _____

4. "My naked weapon is out. Quarrel! I will back thee." (p. 604)

   _____

5. "Her mother is the lady of the house,
   And a good lady, and a wise and virtuous.
   I nursed her daughter that you talked withal." (p. 626)

   _____

Workbook: Elements of Literature, Third Course

172   HRW material copyrighted under notice appearing earlier in this work.

6. "Well, think of marriage now. Younger than you,
Here in Verona, ladies of esteem,
Are made already mothers. By my count,
I was your mother much upon these years
That you are now a maid." (pp. 617-618)

_____

Applying Skills

On the blanks provided, tell why you think Shakespeare chose the form he did—blank verse,
rhymed verse, or prose—for each of the following speeches.

1. "Madam, an hour before the worshiped sun
Peered forth the golden window of the East,
A troubled mind drave me to walk abroad" (p. 608)

_____

_____

2. "If I profane with my unworthiest hand
    This holy shrine, the gentle sin is this:
My lips, two blushing pilgrims, ready stand
    To smooth that rough touch with a tender kiss." (p. 625)

_____

_____

3. "Where's Potpan, that he helps not to take away? He shift a trencher! He scrape a trencher!"
(p. 622)

_____

_____

Workbook: Elements of Literature, Third Course

HRW material copyrighted under notice appearing earlier in this work.

173

Characterization

In drama, **characterization**, the process of revealing the personality of a character, occurs mainly through **dialogue**, or the spoken lines of the play. The characters reveal themselves to us in what they say. Often, too, we learn about characters from what the other players say about them.

Understanding Characterization

From the list of characters below, select the name of the character who is being described in each of the following speeches from Act II of *Romeo and Juliet*. Write the character's name on the blank provided.

Mercutio	Romeo	Nurse	Tybalt
Benvolio	Juliet	Friar	Capulet

1. "Blind is his love and best befits the dark."

   _____

2. "Though his face be better than any man's, yet his leg excels all men's; and for a hand and foot, and a body, though they be not to be talked on, yet they are past compare."

   _____

3. "He jests at scars that never felt a wound."

   _____

4. "O, speak again, bright angel, for thou art
   As glorious to this night, being o'er my head,
   As is a wingèd messenger of heaven"

   _____

5. "He fights as you sing pricksong—keeps time, distance, and proportion; he rests his minim rests, one, two and the third in your bosom! The very butcher of a silk button, a duelist, a duelist!"

   _____

6. "Had she affections and warm youthful blood,
  She would be as swift in motion as a ball;
  . . . But old folks, many feign as they were dead—
  Unwieldy, slow, heavy, and pale as lead."

_____

Applying Skills

Assume that the characters below have been transported to the present time. They have all applied for jobs, and you have been asked to describe each one for the prospective employer. On the blanks provided, write one or two sentences describing the personality of each character.

1. Juliet _____

_____

2. Romeo _____

_____

3. Mercutio _____

_____

Reader's Response

In the center of the cluster below, write the name of your favorite character so far. In the connecting ovals, write adjectives that describe that character's personality.

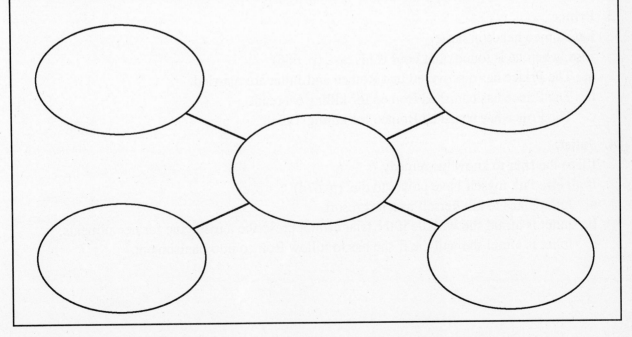

Workbook: Elements of Literature, Third Course

HRW material copyrighted under notice appearing earlier in this work.

175

THE TRAGEDY OF ROMEO AND JULIET, Act III
William Shakespeare   (page 650)

Suspense

Suspense, the uncertainty or anxiety that we feel about what will happen next, is as important in drama as in a story. Act III marks the turning point of *Romeo and Juliet*. Tybalt and Mercutio are killed, Romeo is banished, and Juliet is told she must wed Paris. These events heighten the suspense about the outcome.

Understanding Suspense

Below are suspenseful speeches from Act III of *Romeo and Juliet*, along with three possible explanations for each speech. Circle the letter of the sentence that best explains each speech.

1. Benvolio.

I pray thee, good Mercutio, let's retire.
The day is hot, the Capels are abroad,
And, if we meet, we shall not 'scape a brawl (p. 650)

a. Benvolio is tired of working for the Capulets and wants to retire.
b. Benvolio knows the Capulets are looking for a fight.
c. Benvolio wants to wait in ambush for the Capulets in order to kill Tybalt.

2. Romeo.

This day's black fate on more days doth depend;
This but begins the woe others must end. (p. 653)

a. Tybalt has killed Mercutio.
b. Mercutio has killed Tybalt.
c. Benvolio has killed Tybalt.

3. Prince.

Let Romeo hence in haste,
Else, when he is found, that hour is his last. (p. 656)

a. The Prince has discovered that Romeo and Juliet are married.
b. The Prince has banished Romeo for killing Mercutio.
c. The Prince has banished Romeo for killing Tybalt.

4. Juliet.

I'll to the friar to know his remedy.
If all else fail, myself have power to die. (p. 674)

a. Juliet plans to kill herself as a last resort.
b. Juliet is afraid she will die if the friar cannot prescribe a medicine for her ailments.
c. Juliet is afraid she will die if she has to follow Romeo into banishment.

Applying Skills

On the blanks provided, explain what you would predict would finally become of Juliet if you were each of the following characters.

1. Lord Capulet

_____

_____

_____

2. Friar Laurence

_____

_____

_____

3. Juliet

_____

_____

_____

Reader's Response

What, to you, is the single most suspenseful event in this act of *Romeo and Juliet*?
Explain your response.

_____

_____

_____

_____

_____

Workbook: Elements of Literature, Third Course

HRW material copyrighted under notice appearing earlier in this work.

177

Imagery

Imagery is language that appeals to the senses. Although most images are visual, they may also appeal to the senses of sound, touch, taste, or smell. Often, images appeal to two or more senses at once.

Understanding Imagery

On the blanks provided, write **sight, sound**, **touch**, **taste**, or **smell** to identify the sense appealed to by each of the following images. Remember that an image may appeal to more than one sense.

1. "She's cold,
   Her blood is settled, and her joints are stiff" (p. 685)

   _____

2. ". . . chain me with roaring bears,
   Or hide me nightly in a charnel house,
   O'ercovered quite with dead men's rattling bones" (p. 678)

   _____

3. "With reeky shanks and yellow chapless skulls" (p. 678)

   _____

4. "Death lies on her like an untimely frost
   Upon the sweetest flower of all the field." (p. 685)

   _____

5. "music with her silver sound" (p. 688)

   _____

6. ". . . with loathsome smells,
   And shrieks like mandrakes torn out of the earth" (p. 683)

   _____

7. ". . . bloody Tybalt, yet but green in earth,
   Lies fest'ring in his shroud" (p. 683)

   _____

8. "And this distilling liquor drink thou off;
   When presently through all thy veins shall run
   A cold and drowsy humor" (p. 678)

_____

Applying Skills

Think about the sights, sounds, textures, tastes, and smells that you associate with either the hottest or coldest day of the year. On the blanks below, write one or two sentences describing a sight, sound, touch, taste, and smell associated with either the hottest or the coldest day of the year.

1. sight _____

_____

_____

2. sound _____

_____

_____

3. touch _____

_____

_____

4. taste _____

_____

_____

5. smell _____

_____

_____

Analyzing Character

Analyzing a character involves examining the different aspects, or parts, of the character in order to draw a more complete picture of the overall personality of the character.

Understanding Character

Romeo is the most prominent character in Act V. In this act he shows more aspects of his personality than he has before. Below are some of the lines Romeo speaks in Act V, arranged into groups. Each group shows a different aspect of his character. In the box below each group of lines, write a brief statement of the character traits that are revealed by these lines from the play.

"By heaven, I will tear thee joint by joint
And strew this hungry churchyard with thy limbs." (p. 694)

"Wilt thou provoke me? Then have at thee, boy!" (p. 695)

"O mischief, thou art swift
To enter in the thoughts of desperate men!" (p. 691)

1.

"Good gentle youth, tempt not a desp'rate man.
Fly hence and leave me." (p. 695)

"O, give me thy hand,
One writ with me in sour misfortune's book!
I'll bury thee in a triumphant grave." (p. 695)

"Tybalt, liest thou there in the bloody sheet?
. . . Forgive me, cousin!" (p 696)

2.

"O my love, my wife!
Death, that hath sucked the honey of thy breath,
Hath had no power yet upon thy beauty." (p. 695)

"Ah me! How sweet is love itself possessed,
When but love's shadows are so rich in joy!" (p. 690)

"How fares my Juliet? That I ask again,
For nothing can be ill if she be well." (p. 690)

3.

"There is thy gold—worse poison to men's souls,
Doing more murder in this loathsome world,
Than these poor compounds that thou mayst not sell." (p. 692)

"O, here
Will I set up my everlasting rest
And shake the yoke of inauspicious stars
From this world-wearied flesh." (p. 696)

"Come, bitter conduct; come, unsavory guide!
Thou desperate pilot, now at once run on
The dashing rocks thy seasick weary bark!" (p. 696)

4.

Applying Skills

You should now have a fairly complete character sketch of Romeo. In a short paragraph describe Romeo's character as it is presented in the play. Use information from the previous exercise as well as the characterization found earlier in the play to describe his character.

_____

_____

_____

_____

_____

_____

_____

Workbook: Elements of Literature, Third Course

HRW material copyrighted under notice appearing earlier in this work.

181

Conflict

Conflict, a struggle between opposing forces or characters, may be external or internal. In an **external conflict**, a character struggles against some outside force. An **internal conflict** takes place within a character's own mind.

In *The Odyssey* there are external conflicts between gods and people and between people and people. The human characters also experience much internal conflict.

Understanding Conflict

Below are examples of conflicts in Part One of *The Odyssey*. On the blanks provided, explain each conflict in your own words.

1. *Gods* vs. *People*
   "for their own recklessness destroyed them all—/children and fools, they killed and feasted on /the cattle of Lord Helios, the Sun,/ and he who moves all day through heaven/ took from their eyes the dawn of their return." (p. 722)

   _____

   _____

2. *People* vs. *People*
   "Now here is the suitors' answer . . .
   . . . dismiss your mother from the house, or make her marry /the man her father names and she prefers./ Does she intend to keep us dangling forever?" (p. 726)

   _____

   _____

3. *People* vs. *People*
   " 'Ah, bitterly you need Odysseus, then!
   High time he came back to engage these upstarts.' " (p. 723)

   _____

   _____

4. *Gods* vs. *People*

[Telemachus replied:] " 'It could not be—even if the gods will it.'
At this gray-eyed Athena broke in, saying :
'What strange talk you permit yourself, Telemachus.
A god could save the man by simply wishing it—
from the farthest shore in the world.' " (p. 729)

_____

_____

5. *People* vs. *Themselves*

[Telemachus replied:] " '. . . how can I do it, how approach him?/ I have no practice in
elaborate speeches, and/ for a young man to interrogate an old man/ seems disrespectful—' "
(p. 728)

_____

_____

Applying Skills

Imagine that you are Telemachus listening to the following speech of King Nestor's:

"If gray-eyed Athena loved you
the way she did Odysseus in the old days,
in Troy country, where we all went through so much—
well, as I say, if she cared for you that way,
there would be those to quit this marriage game."

If you were Telemachus, what internal conflict might you experience as you listen to the speech?
On the space below, describe Telemachus's internal conflict.

_____

_____

_____

_____

_____

_____

_____

Homeric Similes

Homeric similes compare heroic or epic events to simple, everyday events—to people working, for instance, or to the behavior of animals. Homeric similes are usually longer and more detailed than modern similes.

Understanding Homeric Similes

In the left-hand column is a series of similes from Part Two of *The Odyssey*. In the right-hand column are explanations of the similes. For each simile, write the correct letter of its explanation in the blank before the simile.

_____ **1.** "A man surf-casting on a point of rock/ for bass or mackerel, whipping his long rod/ to drop the sinker and the bait far out,/ will hook a fish and rip it from the surface/ to dangle wriggling through the air: so these/ were borne aloft in spasms toward the cliff." (p. 767)

_____ **2.** ". . . all the sea was like a cauldron/ seething over intense fire, when the mixture/ suddenly heaves and rises." (p. 767)

_____ **3.** ". . . it was like a mast/ a lugger of twenty oars, broad in the beam—/ a deep-seagoing craft—might carry" (p. 749)

_____ **4.** ". . . he clutched at my companions/ and caught two in his hands like squirming puppies/ to beat their brains out, spattering the floor." (p. 748)

_____ **5.** "so came out rustling, like a mountain lion,/ rain-drenched, wind-buffeted, but in his might at ease,/ with burning eyes— who prowls among the herds" (p. 738)

a. The Cyclops killing Odysseus's men

b. Odysseus revealing himself to the girls doing the wash

c. Charybdis creating a maelstrom by vomiting

d. The stake that was used to blind the Cyclops

e. Scylla whisking Odysseus's men from the ship

Applying Skills

On the blanks provided, write the following comparisons as Homeric similes. Make sure each one is long enough so the comparison can be understood.

1. Compare a professional athlete or dancer in action with a graceful animal.

_____

_____

_____

_____

2. Compare someone's anger with a natural disaster such as a hurricane or tornado.

_____

_____

_____

_____

Analyzing Theme

The **theme** of a work of literature is the central idea expressed. A theme is not usually stated directly but is inferred through various elements of the work. A theme must be expressed in a statement or a sentence.

There are three major **themes**, or central ideas, of *The Odyssey*:

a. A boy must struggle to become a man.

b. A soldier must struggle to return home after a war.

c. A king must struggle to reclaim his kingdom.

Understanding Theme

On the blanks provided, write the letter of the appropriate theme for each of the following incidents from Part Three of *The Odyssey*. (For example, an incident revealing that a boy must struggle to become a man would be labeled **a**, etc.)

_____ **1.** Odysseus tries to hide his scar from his old nurse.

_____ **2.** Telemachus voyages to talk to Nestor and Menelaus.

_____ **3.** Odysseus has his men tie him to the mast so he can listen safely to the Sirens.

_____ **4.** Odysseus blinds the Cyclops.

_____ **5.** Odysseus easily strings the bow the suitors were unable to accomplish.

_____ **6.** Odysseus promises rewards to his servants for helping him.

_____ **7.** Odysseus descends into the underworld.

_____ **8.** Telemachus fights alongside his father.

_____ **9.** Penelope tests Odysseus before welcoming him back.

_____ **10.** Odysseus sails between Scylla and Charybdis.

_____ **11.** Odysseus kills Antinous.

_____ **12.** Odysseus begs Circe to let him go.

_____ **13.** Telemachus speaks to the suitors at the assembly.

Applying Skills

As directed, use the blanks provided to answer the following questions about the major themes of *The Odyssey*.

1. The theme of a return home from a perilous journey applies mostly to Odysseus.
   Explain how, in the following quote, it also applies to Telemachus:
   " 'Light of my days, Telemachus,
   you made it back! When·you took ship for Pylos
   I never thought to see you here again.' " (p. 771)

   _____

   _____

2. The theme of a boy becoming a man applies mostly to Telemachus. Explain how, in the
   following quote, it applies to Odysseus:
   " 'Oh, Father, I am he!
   Twenty years gone, and here I've come again
   to my own land!' " (p. 792)

   _____

   _____

   _____

3. The theme of a king claiming his kingdom applies mostly to Odysseus. Explain how it also
   applies to the gods, considering this fact: Poseidon wants to kill Odysseus, but Zeus lets him
   return home alive.

   _____

   _____

   _____

Workbook: Elements of Literature, Third Course

HRW material copyrighted under notice appearing earlier in this work.

187

He does as well as I do.

Characterization

Characterization is the process of revealing the personality of a character. One way that writers reveal character is by showing us what the character does—how he or she acts.

Understanding Characterization

Below are listed actions of several characters in *Animal Farm*. On the blanks provided, state what each action reveals about the character or characters who perform it. The first one has been done for you.

1. Major gathers the animals for a rebellious speech and teaches them to sing "Beasts of England."

   Major is the animals' leader. He has a strong personality and is an effective speaker.
   _____

2. Napoleon places himself in front of the milk buckets, but by that evening the milk has disappeared.

   _____

   _____

3. Mollie is found holding a blue ribbon against her shoulder and admiring herself in the mirror.

   _____

   _____

4. Benjamin spends his Sundays grazing beside Boxer but not speaking.

   _____

   _____

5. The pigs have secretly taught themselves to read and write.

   _____

   _____

6. The horse Clover protects the motherless ducklings with her foreleg.

_____

_____

7. Jones shoots his gun into the darkness when he hears a noise.

_____

_____

Applying Skills

Assume that an animal you are familiar with—your pet, a friend's pet, a farm animal, or an animal you've seen at the zoo—is participating in the Manor Farm rebellion. In the space below describe how the animal would behave. Then explain what this behavior reveals about the animal's personality.

_____

_____

_____

_____

_____

_____

_____

_____

_____

_____

_____

_____

_____

_____

Workbook: Elements of Literature, Third Course

Development

The **development** of a story occurs as readers continue to learn about the personality of the characters and the plot continues to unfold.

Understanding Development

Below are statements about the characters and plot of Chapters I and II of *Animal Farm*. For each statement, circle the letter of the choice that correctly explains how that aspect of characterization or plot develops in Chapters III and IV. The first one has been done for you.

1. Boxer was highly respected for his tremendous powers of work. [Characterization]
   a. Boxer's strength helps pull the farm through.
   b. Boxer regrets hurting the stable lad.

2. The pigs are recognized as the smartest animals. [Characterization]
   a. The pigs claim to require all the milk and apples.
   b. The pigs supervise the other animals.

3. Mr. Jones neglects his farm and the animals. [Plot]
   a. The animals attack Jones and the other men when they try to recapture the farm.
   b. Jones shoots and kills Snowball.

4. The rebellion occurs even more quickly than the animals had hoped. [Plot]
   a. Snowball reduces the seven commandments to a single slogan.
   b. News of the rebellion spreads like wildfire to neighboring farms.

5. Snowball is an especially inventive leader. [Characterization]
   a. Snowball plans the defense of the farm against the men.
   b. Snowball and Napoleon agree about the milk and apples.

6. Squealer, the animals said, could turn black into white. [Characterization]
   a. Squealer does not play a notable part in the Battle of the Cowshed.
   b. Squealer convinces the other animals that the pigs deserve all the milk and apples.

Applying Skills

Below are summaries of incidents from Chapters III and IV of *Animal Farm*. Read the summaries carefully. On the blanks provided, explain what you already know about the animal(s) and describe an event from Chapters I and II that foreshadows this incident.

1. The cat briefly becomes involved in the activity of the Re-education Committee. At one point she is seen in conversation with some sparrows who are a little beyond her reach. She is attempting to convince them that all animals are now comrades and that a sparrow could safely come and perch on her paw. (p. 819)

_____

_____

_____

2. Instead of doing a share of the work, the pigs take on the role of supervising the other animals. The role of leadership seems natural for them, given their superior knowledge. (p. 818)

_____

_____

_____

3. After the driving off the human beings who attempt to retake the farm, the animals notice that Mollie is missing. At first they are afraid that she has been harmed or captured. However, they find her in her stall with her head buried in the hay. (p. 822)

_____

_____

_____

Workbook: Elements of Literature, Third Course

HRW material copyrighted under notice appearing earlier in this work.

191

Satire

Satire is the kind of writing that ridicules something—a person, a group of people, humanity at large, an attitude or feeling, a social institution—in order to reveal a weakness. Satire often ridicules a point of view or action in order to convince the reader to adopt the opposite point of view or follow a different course of action.

Understanding Satire

In the left-hand column are summaries of a series of incidents from *Animal Farm*, Chapters V, VI, and VII. In the right-hand column are human characteristics or weaknesses. For each summary write the correct letter of the human characteristic that is being satirized in the incident. Use your dictionary to look up any unfamiliar words.

1. _____ Napoleon and Snowball hold differing views on the windmill, food production, and defense. When the animals listen to the two, they have trouble deciding which of them is right, and tend to believe whichever is speaking at the time. (p. 826)

2. _____ Napoleon wears two medals, "Animal Hero, First Class," and "Animal Hero, Second Class," that he has awarded to himself. (p. 836)

3. _____ Squealer explains Napoleon's decision to end the democratic Sunday-morning meetings by saying that he is concerned that the animals, left to make their own decisions, might make mistakes. (p. 828)

4. _____ After a night of violent winds, the animals discover that the windmill has been destroyed. Napoleon quickly blames the destruction on Snowball. (p. 833)

5. _____ When Squealer argues that Snowball was a traitor from the beginning, even in his plans for defense, Boxer at first states that he does not believe it, but when told that this is Napoleon's view, he says that it must be true. (p. 836)

a. the tendency of finding a scapegoat

b. the characteristic of vanity and conceit

c. the tendency of adopting a condescending or patronizing attitude

d. the characteristic of being fickle or easily swayed

e. the characteristic of blind allegiance

Applying Skills

Use the blanks provided to complete the following activities.

1. A new play opens that criticizes the politics of war. Describe how attitudes about war might be satirized in the drama.

_____

_____

_____

_____

_____

_____

2. On the blanks provided, create a short dialogue between two characters in which greed, vanity, or some other human weakness is satirized.

_____

_____

_____

_____

_____

_____

_____

Predicting Outcomes

Writers often provide clues to hint at events that will occur later in the story. This is known as **foreshadowing**. At times, readers can predict what will happen later in a story by other means, such as predicting the way certain characters will likely respond to events in the story and by carefully tracking the development of the **plot**, the related events that make up a story.

Understanding Outcomes

Each of the following statements represents a possible outcome for the animals' rebellion. Inside the box following each statement, write at least one reason why that outcome might come about, using evidence from the text. For number 4, make a prediction of your own and give reasons to support it.

1. The animals will rebel against Napoleon and establish a better life.

2. The humans will finally recapture the farm.

3. Napoleon will change his ways and become a more compassionate leader.

4. _____

_____

```
┌─────────────────────────────────────────────────────────┐
│                                                         │
│                                                         │
│                                                         │
│                                                         │
│                                                         │
│                                                         │
│                                                         │
│                                                         │
└─────────────────────────────────────────────────────────┘
```

Applying Skills

Assume that you are an opinion researcher interviewing the animals on Animal Farm. In the spaces below, write each animal's opinion of (**a**) what has happened on the farm since the rebellion; and (**b**) what he or she wishes would happen next. Write your answers in first person, using the animal's own words.

1. Snowball

   a. _____

   b. _____

_____

2. Squealer

   a. _____

   b. _____

3. Benjamin

   a. _____

   b. _____

Evaluating Theme

One of the main **themes**, or central ideas, of *Animal Farm* is the effects of tyranny. By comparing the expression of this theme in the novel with what you know about the effects of tyranny on people in real life, you can judge, or evaluate, the validity of the theme.

Understanding A Story's Theme

The events below happen in Chapter X of *Animal Farm*. As you look over the events, think what you know about dictators such as Stalin (Soviet Russia) and Hitler (Nazi Germany). On the blanks provided, explain how the event in *Animal Farm* is like life under a dictatorship.

1. There is no longer any talk about animals retiring.

_____

_____

_____

2. The new horses cannot learn much of the alphabet. They accept everything they are told about the Rebellion and the principles of Animalism.

_____

_____

_____

3. The animals no longer talk about such luxuries as electric lights and water in the stalls. Napoleon has decreed these niceties contrary to the spirit of Animalism.

_____

_____

_____

4. The farm has prospered without making individual animals much better off—with the exception of the pigs and the dogs.

_____

_____

_____

5. The single remaining Commandment asserts that all animals are equal, but that some are more equal than others.

_____

_____

_____

6. The custom of addressing each other as "Comrade" is abolished, the green flag with the white hoof and horn is replaced with a plain green flag, and the name "Animal Farm" is replaced with "The Manor Farm."

_____

_____

_____

Applying Skills

Below are summaries of observations from Chapter X of _Animal Farm_. In your own words, explain what theme is revealed in each observation.

1. The lives of the animals had not really changed: they still worked long hours, often experienced hunger, slept on the straw. They were cold in the winter and were bothered by flies in the summer. (p. 851)

_____

_____

_____

2. When the animals heard the sound of the gun and saw the flag fluttering on the flagpole, they were filled with a sense of pride. (p. 852)

_____

_____

_____

3. Neighboring farmers were invited to inspect the farm, and when the social gathering of humans and pigs turned into a shouting match, the other animals peered into the window of the farmhouse and found it impossible to tell the pigs from the humans. (p. 854)

_____

_____

_____

Workbook: Elements of Literature, Third Course

HRW material copyrighted under notice appearing earlier in this work.

197

Workbook: Elements of Literature, Third Course

198

HRW material copyrighted under notice appearing earlier in this work.

Workbook: Elements of Literature, Third Course

HRW material copyrighted under notice appearing earlier in this work.

199